Radiation, Radioactivity, and Insects

AMERICAN INSTITUTE OF BIOLOGICAL SCIENCES

and

U. S. ATOMIC ENERGY COMMISSION

MONOGRAPH SERIES ON

RADIATION BIOLOGY

FRANK FREMONT-SMITH, *Series Director*
AMERICAN INSTITUTE OF BIOLOGICAL SCIENCES

ADVISORY COMMITTEE

MONOGRAPH TITLES AND AUTHORS

RADIATION, RADIOACTIVITY, AND INSECTS
    R. D. O'BRIEN, *Cornell University*
    L. S. WOLFE, *Montreal Neurological Institute*

RADIATION, ISOTOPES, AND BONE
    F. C. McLEAN, *University of Chicago*
    A. M. BUDY, *University of Chicago*

RADIATION AND THE IMMUNE MECHANISMS (in press)
    W. H. TALIAFERRO, *Argonne National Laboratory*
    L. G. TALIAFERRO, *Argonne National Laboratory*
    B. N. JARASLOW, *Argonne National Laboratory*

(IN PREPARATION)

HUMAN RADIOBIOLOGY
    V. P. BOND, *Brookhaven National Laboratory*
    T. M. FLIEDNER, *Brookhaven National Laboratory*
    J. D. ARCHAMBEAU, *Brookhaven National Laboratory*

TRANSPLANT IMMUNITY AND RADIATION
    J. F. LOUTIT, *Radiobiological Research Unit, Harwell*
    H. S. MICKLEM, *Pasteur Institute*

PHYSICAL ASPECTS OF RADIOISOTOPES IN THE HUMAN BODY
    F. W. SPIERS, *University of Leeds*

LIGHT: PHYSICAL AND BIOLOGICAL
    W. D. McELROY, *Johns Hopkins University*
    H. H. SELIGER, *Johns Hopkins University*

SPACE RADIATION BIOLOGY
    C. A. TOBIAS, *Donner Laboratory*
    P. TODD, *Donner Laboratory*

MUTAGENESIS
    I. I. OSTER, *Institute for Cancer Research*

Radiation, Radioactivity, and Insects

R. D. O'BRIEN

Department of Entomology
Cornell University
Ithaca, New York

L. S. WOLFE

Department of Neurochemistry
Montreal Neurological Institute
Montreal, Canada

Prepared under the direction of the American Institute of Biological Sciences for the Division of Technical Information, United States Atomic Energy Commission

ACADEMIC PRESS ● New York and London

ACADEMIC PRESS INC.
111 Fifth Avenue, New York, New York 10003

United Kingdom Edition published by
ACADEMIC PRESS INC. (LONDON) LTD.
Berkeley Square House, London W.1

LIBRARY OF CONGRESS CATALOG CARD NUMBER: 63-23198

PRINTED IN THE UNITED STATES OF AMERICA

To Ann and Jeanne

FOREWORD

This monograph is one in a series developed through the cooperative efforts of the American Institute of Biological Sciences and the U. S. Atomic Energy Commission's Division of Technical Information. The goal in this undertaking has been to direct attention to biologists' increasing utilization of radiation and radioisotopes. Their importance as tools for studying living systems cannot be overestimated. Indeed, their application by biologists has an added significance, representing as it does the new, closer association between the physical and biological sciences.

The association places stringent demands on both disciplines: Each must seek to understand the methods, systems, and philosophies of the other science if radiation biology is to fulfill its promise of great contributions to our knowledge of both the normal and the abnormal organism. Hopefully, the information contained in each publication will guide students and scientists to areas where further research is indicated.

The American Institute of Biological Sciences is most pleased to have had a part in developing this Monograph Series.

JOHN R. OLIVE
Executive Director
American Institute of Biological Sciences

October, 1963

PREFACE

This book is intended for two audiences. One is made up of entomologists and other biologists who want to know the way in which research with radiation and radioisotopes has advanced our understanding of insects, and what entomological problems of their own could be profitably attacked with such techniques. For members of this audience, an appendix has been added which gives a brief introduction to concepts, techniques, and units of measure, so that even if they have no contact with work that uses radiation or radioactivity the book should be comprehensible.

The second audience comprises those knowledgeable in work with irradiation and radioisotopes who would like a comprehensive account of what has been done with insects, and perhaps would like to know for what kinds of problems the insect is a suitable organism. For this second audience, Chapter 1 was written as an introduction to the special features of insects—structural, functional, and behavioral. Insects sometimes are used because they are convenient to rear and treat in large numbers, as in genetic studies on *Drosophila*, and sometimes as organisms with adaptations of special interest, as in cases where metamorphosis can be accurately induced by giving a blood meal.

In view of the fact we are writing for two audiences, we have tried to use language that any scientist would understand, and we have in mind the undergraduate science student as representative of the minimum level of training we anticipate in our readers.

We have seldom attempted to insert material published after the appropriate chapter was written because of the patchwork consequences of such attempts. We have not discussed the genetic effects of radiation upon insects, because this will form a large portion of another monograph in this series concerned with genetic effects on organisms in general. With these exceptions, the book is intended to give a rather complete account of both the academic and utilitarian radiation work that has been applied to insects; and also of the diverse uses of radioisotopes in entomology, both for labeling of insects and for elucidation of biochemical, physiological, and toxicological mechanisms.

The insect names used are those approved by the Entomological Society of America. This has often led us to use names different from those used by the original authors. The reader should therefore not be puzzled if we tell him that Smith worked with *Bracon hebetor*, although Smith himself talks of *Habrobracon juglandis.* All such synonyms are given in the glossary, along with the brief names which we have generally used for much-discussed organisms, such as *Drosophila* for *Drosophila melanogaster.* However, when an insect is first mentioned in any chapter, its full name is given. Occasionally the full name will also appear in a table, when consistency within the table demands it. Our taxonomic adviser, Dr. W. L. Brown of Cornell University, has suggested that we omit the parenthetical mention of authorities for insect names, except in the glossary where there occur a few cases in which confusion is possible.

We acknowledge our indebtedness to the extensive bibliography of Mr. H. Custodio (Philippine Bureau of Plant Industry) in his M.S. thesis from Cornell (1961) entitled "A review of the literature on the use of radioisotopes in entomological research and radiation effects for pest control."

Our reviewers were Dr. L. E. Chadwick (University of Illinois) and Dr. P. A. Dahm (Iowa State University), to whom we are extremely grateful for the scrupulousness of their review and the helpfulness of their suggestions. Since final decisions were left to us, they are in no way responsible for errors or omissions.

R. D. O'BRIEN

L. S. WOLFE

October, 1963

CONTENTS

GLOSSARY

CoA	Coenzyme A
IDP	Inosine diphosphate
ITP	Inosine triphosphate
NAD	Nicotine-adenine dinucleotide (formerly DPN)
NADH$_2$	Reduced form of NAD (formerly DPNH)
NADP	Nicotine-adenine dinucleotide phosphate (formerly TPN)
Aedes	*Aedes aegypti* (L): yellow fever mosquito
Anagasta	*Anagasta* (= *Ephestia*) *kühniella* (Zell): Mediterranean flour moth
Blatella	*Blatella germanica* (L): German cockroach
Bracon	*Bracon hebetor*, Say [= *Habrobracon juglandis* (Auct.)]: a parasitic wasp
Bombyx	*Bombyx mori* (L): a silkworm
Calliphora	*Calliphora erythrocephala* (Meig.): blow fly
Callitroga	*Callitroga hominovorax* (Coq.): screw-worm fly
Chortophaga	*Chortophaga viridifasciata* (De G.): green meadow locust
Culex	*Culex tarsalis* Coq: a mosquito
Dahlbominus	*Dahlbominus fuscipennis* (Zetterstedt): a parasitic hymenopteron
Dermestes	*Dermestes maculatus* (= *vulpinus*) De G.: hide beetle
Drosophila	*Drosophila melanogaster* (Meig.): domestic fruit fly
Galleria	*Galleria mellonella* (L.): greater wax moth
Hyalophora	*Hyalophora* (= *Platysamia*) *cecropia* (L.): cecropia moth
Leptinotarsa	*Leptinotarsa decemlineata* (Say): Colorado potato beetle
Locusta	*Locusta migratoria* L.: migratory locust
Melanoplus	*Melanoplus differentialis* (Thos.): differential grasshopper
Metatetranychus	*Metatetranychus ulmi* (Koch): European red mite
Musca	*Musca domestica* L.: house fly
Myzus	*Myzus persicae* (Sulz.): green peach aphid
Oncopeltus	*Oncopeltus fasciatus* (Dall.): large milkweed bug
Periplaneta	*Periplaneta americana* (L.): American cockroach
Phoenicia	*Phoenicia* (= *Lucilia*) *sericata* (Meig.): a green bottle fly
Phormia	*Phormia regina* (Meig.): black blow fly
Rhodnius	*Rhodnius prolixus* (Ståhl): an assassin bug
Schistocerca	*Schistocerca gregaria* (Forskål): desert locust
Sitophilus	*Sitophilus granarius* (L.) (= *Calandra granaria*): granary weevil
Tenebrio	*Tenebrio molitor* (L.): yellow mealworm
Tribolium	*Tribolium confusum* Duv.: confused flour beetle

TERMS USED FOR RADIATION AND RADIOACTIVITY

Alpha (α) particle. A particle emitted from a few radioisotopes—e.g., promethium[147]. It consists of two protons and two neutrons and is identical with the helium nucleus. It has extremely low penetrating power.

Beta (β) particle. A particle emitted from numerous radioisotopes—e.g., C[14]. It is an electron. Its penetrating power depends on its energy (which in turn depends on its source) and is usually low.

Curie (c). A quantity of radioactivity, measured by the number of disintegrations in a given time. One curie produces 2.22×10^{12} disintegrations per minute.

Gamma (γ) ray. An electromagnetic radiation emitted from certain radioisotopes—e.g., I[131]. A relatively deeply penetrating emanation.

Kilovolt (kvp). The crest value of the electrical potential wave in a cathode ray tube used to generate x-rays.

Millicurie (mc). One thousandth of a curie.

Million electron volts (Mev). A unit of energy commonly applied to α, β, γ, and X radiations. For any given radiation, high Mev implies high penetration.

Rad. See "roentgen."

Rep. See "roentgen."

Roentgen (r). An exposure dose of x or γ rays. One roentgen will deposit 83.8 ergs of energy in 1 g of dry air at standard conditions. As essentially equivalent unit, though now historical, is the rep. "roentgen equivalent physical", which is an energy deposition ϕ of 93 ergs in 1 g of soft tissue. Another unit, applied to all radiation is the rad, "radiation absorbed dose." The rad, by definition, is the amount of radiation which will deposit 100 ergs per gram in any material.

CHAPTER 1

Insects

Before specific aspects of the effect of radiation on insects and the use of radioisotopes in entomology are considered, a few general remarks on some of the distinctive features of the anatomy and physiology of insects will be given to orient readers who are not entomologists.

1. Importance and Dominance of Insects in the Animal Kingdom

The phylum Arthropoda is unequaled in the animal kingdom in the number and variety of species it contains and in the diversity of life histories and behavior. It contains 80% of all animal species. The class Insecta is the largest and most successful group of arthropods, and this has been so since Carboniferous times, long before the emergence of man. Insects are small, highly organized, essentially land arthropods in which the body is divided into three parts: head, with the mouthparts and principal sense organs; thorax, with locomotor organs, legs, and wings; and abdomen, with the digestive, reproductive, and excretory organs. Most insects have six legs and are often classified as Hexapoda.

Almost a million species of insects have been described, and several times this number probably await classification. Estimates of total numbers of individuals soon reach incomprehensible figures. Many honey beehives contain 40 to 50 thousand individuals, and ant colonies contain about half a million. On a single tomato plant, 24,688 aphids have been counted. An acre of agricultural land may contain roughly 4 million insects. One square yard of river bed in a rill section at the outlet of lakes in the forests of the southern margin of the Canadian shield is capable of producing half a million black flies. Put another way, despite their small size the combined bulk of insects is about equal to that of all other land animals.

To the layman, insects are either pests such as cockroaches, bedbugs, houseflies, biting flies, ants, wasps, etc., or often beautiful creatures such as dragonflies, butterflies, moths, and beetles. However, the majority of insects are of minute size, scarcely visible to the naked eye. Myriads of microscopic soil collembolans may appear like black soot on the surface of irrigation ditches following heavy rain. The actual number of pest insect species is surprisingly small; certainly no greater than 10,000, only 500 of which

1

are of major importance. Again, these pest insects primarily affect agricultural crops and produce; less than a hundred species are involved in disease transmission in man. In spite of this, the amount of damage caused to crops, products, livestock, and health by insects annually in the United States alone is in the billions of dollars. The appearance in Europe of the grape phylloxera, *Phylloxera vitifoliae*, brought from North America in 1863, had by 1870 cost France alone 10,000 million francs, twice the indemnity exacted from France by Bismarck in the Prussian War. In 1955 Kenya was invaded by a moderate-sized swarm of desert locusts estimated to contain 1500 million insects spread over eight square miles. Each locust eats about its own weight in green vegetation daily, and, since this swarm weighed about 3000 tons, the resulting denudation of the land was catastrophic. It is difficult to exaggerate the economic consequences to man of a handful of the major pest insects.

Not only are insects unique in the great variety of species but also in the number of forms within individual species. Many larvae and pupal forms bear no obvious resemblance to adult forms. An important part of the systematist's and field naturalist's work is involved in connecting the great variety of described larval forms to the correct adult forms. Certain aphids have amazingly complex life histories, and one species, *Phylloxera quercus*, is known to have 21 forms.

All stages in the evolution of animal behavior are found in insects, and this is closely associated with form differentiation or polymorphism. Three broad levels in this process can be seen. In the first level are those insects that behave individualistically and often sustain a heavy loss of their numbers because of it; in the second level, care of the young by the mother has developed; and in the third level, the young offspring, usually female, assist and cooperate with others to form the family-like society characteristic of the social insects such as termites, wasps, bees, and ants. In the most advanced form of insect society the female is the most important member, and the only function of the males is fertilization. Further, the workers dominate and operate the society. The queen becomes the egg producer and also the means by which organization is maintained. This is achieved through the elaboration of chemical substances, called pheromones, which are disseminated throughout the colony and inhibit ovary development and queen rearing. Queen substance secreted by the mandibular glands of the queen bee contains such a material, which has been characterized chemically as 9-oxodec-2-enoic acid. The efficiency of insect communities such as those of ants and bees is due in large measure to the following factors: (1) the division of labor between the queen and workers and among the workers; (2) the attraction workers have for each other and the attraction of the queen for the workers; (3) the development of a method of communication between workers to enable detailed information about food sources and other important matters to be given to all; (4) the development of a method of distinguishing members of one's own colony from intruders and the establishment of a system of nest defenses; and (5) the development of a control system of ovary development and queen rearing which enables replacement of an unsatisfactory queen by a new young one and which, during favorable conditions, leads to reproduction and swarming. The behavior patterns in these remarkable, truly cooperative societies are in many ways in a more advanced stage of behavioral evolution than human societies.

The identification of chemical factors which control insect behavior is a rapidly advancing and exciting field. It has been known for many years that in certain insects sex attraction is elicited by characteristic odors produced by the female. For example, the virgin female American cockroach, *Periplaneta americana*, emits a powerful attractant which causes intense excitement and characteristic wing-raising behavior in the males. The substance causing this activity has now been chemically characterized as 2,2-dimethyl-3-isopropylidenecyclopropyl propionate.[1] A response is elicited from males by amounts below 10^{-14} µg. The gregarious male desert locust, *Schistocerca gregaria*, which is bright yellow in color when mature, secretes a volatile, fat-soluble substance from the surface of its cuticle. This substance is transmitted to young locusts by olfaction through the antennae or by body contact under crowded conditions and accelerates their maturation. The presence of this substance is indicated by a characteristic vibration reaction of the antennae, palpi, and hind femora in the immature locusts.[2]

The evolution and diversification of insects has been very extensive. This is due to their great fecundity, rapid development, and small size, which enable large populations to build up in any one year and to colonize a great number of microenvironments. Adaptations have arisen for survival in every type of environment on this planet, from the arctic wastes of Ellesmere Island to the extraordinary aridity of the Arizona and Atacama deserts. Two factors account for the success of insects. The first is the development of wings, which permits entry to a great variety of new environments. This great evolutionary innovation necessitated considerable advances in the development of sense organs, particularly those for vision and olfaction. The nervous system, in a parallel fashion, became progressively more elaborate, with more and more concentration toward the anterior end (cephalic dominance). However, the so-called brain which is thus formed does not exert as comprehensive a control as does the vertebrate brain; for instance, many insects can survive and perform complex activities after decapitation. The conservatism in the number of neurones required for these reactions at first sight appears remarkable. But insect behavior is predominantly based on habituation and stereotyped instinctive patterns and lacks the modifiability based on the experiential memory and learning of mammals.

The second factor in insect evolution upon which their success to a large measure depends is the development of complete metamorphosis. By this is meant the splitting up and specialization of the life history of the insect into three periods: (1) the larval period of feeding and growth; (2) the prepupal and pupal period of differentiation; and (3) the adult or imaginal period of mating, migration, and reproduction. The three great but antagonistic phases of development—growth, differentiation, and reproduction—are completely separated. The larva, pupa, and adult differ completely in form and thus may utilize a variety of environments appropriate for each stage. Each form has been subject independently to adaptive changes. The evolution of complete metamorphosis is intimately associated with the development of wings which are restricted to the adult stage of intense locomotory and reproductive activity. An indication of the value of metamorphosis is seen when the number of species of insects with complete metamorphosis is compared with those without metamorphosis or with an incomplete one. Eighty-five per cent of all insect species have complete metamorphosis, about 13% have incomplete metamorphosis, and the remaining 2% show no true metamorphosis.

2. Classification of Insects

The classification of insects into subclasses is based on either structural or functional principles. On a structural basis the subclasses are termed (1) Apterygota, primitive wingless insects; (2) Exopterygota, insects in which the wings develop as external wing pads; and (3) Endopterygota, insects in which the wings develop internally in peripodal sacs. On a functional basis the following subclasses are recognized: (1) Ametabola, insects without metamorphosis; (2) Prometabola, insects which pass through four stages of development, egg, aquatic nymph, subimago (sexually immature winged form), and imago (adult); (3) Hemimetabola, insects which pass through a partial metamorphosis from an immature, nymphal stage to adult but with no subimago or true pupa; (4) Holometabola, insects with a complete and exceedingly complex metamorphosis from larva through prepupal and pupal forms to the adult. Table 1.1 lists the orders of insects, common names, and the approximate number of species within each order. Most insects are given generic and specific names only, although some insects which show many geographical variations are named trinomially.

TABLE 1.1

SIMPLE CLASSIFICATION OF INSECTS INTO MAJOR GROUPS

Subclasses	Orders	Vernacular names	Approximate no. of species
Ametabola	Collembola	spring-tails	1,250
	Diplura	two-pronged bristletails	—
	Thysanura	three-pronged bristletails	325
	Protura	—(minute soil insects with primitive abdomen)	62
Prometabola	Ephemeroptera	May flies	1,270
Hemimetabola	Odonata	dragonflies, damselflies (demoiselles)	5,000
	Orthoptera	cockroaches, grasshoppers, crickets, katydids, mantids, etc.	21,000
	Plectoptera	stone-flies	1,260
	Dermaptera	earwigs	1,050
	Isoptera	termites	16,000
	Zoraptera	—(minute colonial insects frequently associated with termite nests)	12
	Embioptera	—(small semisocial insects living in silken tunnels)	100
	Corrodentia	psocids, book lice	875
	Mallophaga	biting lice	2,500
	Thysanoptera	thrips	2,500
	Hemiptera	cicadas, leaf hoppers, aphids, scale insects, water and plant bugs, bed bugs, stink bugs, etc.	57,500
	Anoplura	sucking lice	280
Holometabola	Coleoptera	beetles	250,000
	Strepsiptera	stylops	200
	Neuroptera	ant lions, alder flies, lace-wings, mantispids, etc.	4,350
	Mecoptera	scorpion-flies	310
	Trichoptera	caddis flies	3,600
	Lepidoptera	moths and butterflies	120,000
	Diptera	true flies, mosquitoes, midges, gnats, warble flies, etc.	78,000
	Siphonaptera	fleas	900
	Hymenoptera	sawflies, wasps, bees, ants, ichneumon flies	230,000

3. Anatomy

The anatomical design of insects is very different from that of chordates. Basically, they are bilaterally symmetrical, segmented animals, covered by an exoskeleton and with a dorsal heart and ventral nervous system. In the evolution of insects, the body segments and exoskeleton have been modified

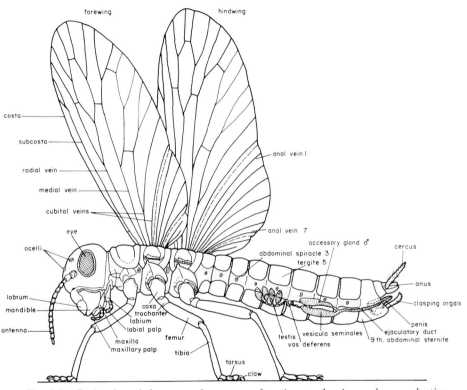

FIG. 1.1.   Basic plan of the external anatomy of an insect, showing male reproductive system. (Adapted from H. Weber, *Grundriss der Insektenkunde*, Gustav Fischer, Stuttgart, 1949.)

in many ways. The ancestors of insects are believed to have had segmented bodies with a pair of appendages to each segment. Modern insects have discarded most of these appendages and have modified three thoracic pairs for locomotion, some anterior ones to serve as mouthparts, and the terminal abdominal segments as external sexual organs. The insect head superficially appears unsegmented. However, a careful study of the development of the head of primitive insects reveals its segmented nature. Typically, each body

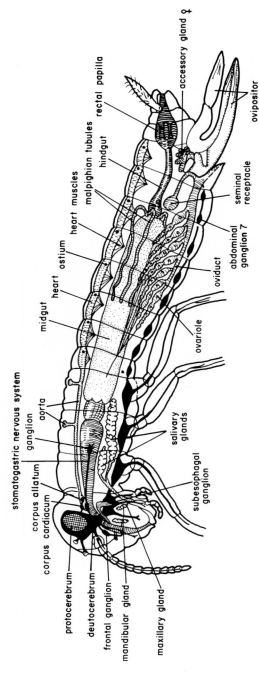

FIG. 1.2. Basic plan of the internal anatomy of an insect, showing female reproductive system. (Adapted from H. Weber, *Grundriss der Insektenkunde*, Gustav Fischer, Stuttgart, 1949.)

segment has a pair of ganglia. But varying degrees of fusion of successive ganglia occur. The insect "brain" consists of a fusion of three parts: the protocerebrum, deutocerebrum, and tritocerebrum represent the ganglia of the optic, antennary, and intercalary segments, respectively. The subesophageal ganglion represents the coalescence of the mandibular, maxillary, and labial segments.

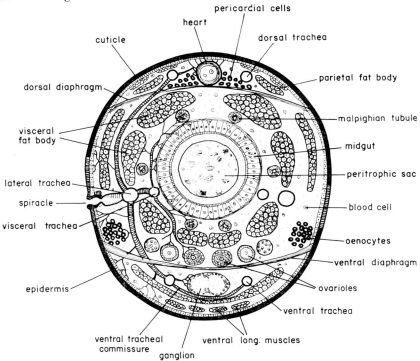

Fig. 1.3.   Cross section of the midabdominal region of an insect to show the distribution of the internal organs. (Adapted from H. Weber, *Grundriss der Insektenkunde*, Gustav Fischer, Stuttgart, 1949.)

The thorax is always composed of three segments. The number of segments present in the abdomen varies. The primitive number is 11, and these are all present in the primitive bristletails (Thysanura). In the higher insect orders, modification of the abdominal segments has progressed to such a degree that the primitive pattern can be seen only during embryonic development. The eighth, ninth, and sometimes the tenth segments are modified into the copulatory and egg-laying organs of the adult insect.

The exoskeleton, on physical principles, limits insects to a small size. Few insects weigh more than a gram. A disadvantage of a rigid exoskeleton is that during growth it must be shed regularly, and a new one must be formed. The entire process is called "molting," and the actual shedding of the old exoskeleton is called "ecdysis." The separate stages in growth interrupted by molting are termed "instars." The number of times molting occurs varies with the species. It may be as low as three, or over twenty. Because the linings of the respiratory tubes or tracheae are derived from the epidermal cells, they must also be shed during growth and are pulled out through the spiracles. The whole molting cycle presents some of the most important and challenging problems of insect physiology. An advantage of the exoskeleton to insects is that it can provide a water-impermeable covering. In certain aquatic insects it has been modified to entrap air and thus enable prolonged periods of submersion (plastron respiration).

The basic external and internal anatomical plan of insects is illustrated in Figs. 1.1, 1.2, and 1.3. It is clearly impossible to discuss the modifications of each element of this plan in various species. The bibliography should be consulted for sources of further information.

4. Embryonic Development

The eggs of insects are enclosed by two envelopes: an outer chorion containing a scleroprotein, chorionin, and an inner vitelline membrane. In some insects another serosal cuticle is formed beneath the vitelline membrane. The chorion is a multilayered structure which may be thin and flexible, or rigid. It is modified in many ways to serve the needs of respiration. Eggs which are laid in exposed places are highly resistant to desiccation. A waterproof waxy layer is deposited on the inside of the chorion before the egg is laid. On the other hand, eggs laid in moist surroundings (damp soil, stems of plants) are often modified for the absorption of water—e.g., the hydropyle of eggs of the grasshopper, *Melanoplus differentialis*. Fertilization takes place by the entry of sperm or sperms (polyspermy is common) through micropyles located at the anterior end of the egg.

The egg consists of yolk and a central nucleus embedded in a small island of cytoplasm, with fine strands spreading through the yolk which condense at the periphery to form a cortical layer, the periplasm. Following fertilization, which usually takes place before the time of laying, the fusion nucleus divides a number of times by synchronous mitotic divisions, and then the nuclei divide independently. At each division of the nucleus, the cytoplasmic island surrounding it cleaves as well, but the daughter nuclei still remain connected with each other and to the periplasm. Two types of cleavage nuclei are formed: those destined for the prospective vitellophages (yolk nuclei) and those taking part in the formation of the embryo proper. As the cleavage nuclei divide, they migrate toward the periphery, leaving behind the vitellophages. This peripheral movement is always from a clearly defined region of the egg called the "cleavage center." At the periphery, the nuclei arrange themselves into a single, clearly defined cell layer, the blastoderm. The beautiful studies of Seidel on the embryogenesis of the dragonfly, *Platycnemis pennipes*, have shown, by using spot irradiation with ultraviolet light to destroy particular cells, that the cleavage nuclei are totipotent at least until the 128-cell stage. That is, the egg is capable of formation of a complete embryo, even if the egg material is reduced by experimental means.

The first visible differentiation of the embryo is the formation of the germ band by aggregation of the blastoderm cells first in the region of the future prothorax and then spreading anteriorly and posteriorly. Although the nuclei contain the genetic determinants of hereditary characteristics, the form and organization of the embryo is controlled by the cytoplasm. But the constitution of this cytoplasm reflects the earlier action of genes. The initiation of embryonic organization in all insects is controlled through the interaction of three different centers: the cleavage center, the activation center, and the differentiation center. The cleavage center has already been mentioned. The activation center is located at the posterior pole of the egg and interacts with the cleavage nuclei to produce a specific substance which diffuses from the center to influence the peripheral zone of the egg. If the posterior pole of the egg is destroyed by excision or burning with ultraviolet light in the early cleavage stages, no germ band is formed. In later stages of development, larger portions of the egg have to be destroyed to prevent embryo formation. Thus, in the first few hours of development, the activating principle spreads over a larger and larger area of the egg. Around the middle of the future germ band in the cortical periplasm there is a differentiation center which becomes active under the influence of the activation center. This center subsequently organizes the differentiation of the germ band. At the differentiation center, visible differentiation occurs first and is greatest at any time subsequently. The second maxillary and first thoracic segments are the first to be delineated in the germ band, and from here differentiation of the segments proceeds anteriorly and posteriorly.

The median portion of the germ band invaginates to form a ventral gastrulation groove which closes over. The invaginated cells form a layer which becomes the inner mesodermal layer of the germ band. Invaginations appear at the anterior and posterior ends of the germ band and mark the anlagen of the stomadeum and proctodeum, the future foregut and hindgut, respectively. These anlagen become connected by a band of endodermal cells which originate from the inner layer, the future midgut. Thus the germ band has at this stage a three-layered structure from which all the organs arise. During organ separation and differentiation, the margin of the embryo grows around the yolk and closes dorsally.

Experimental studies on the determination of organ formation and differentiation have shown two general types of insect eggs. In one type, termed regulation or indeterminate eggs, of which the dragonfly *Platycnemis pennipes* is an example, the relative amount of cytoplasm is small, and the germ band is short. The embryonic parts destined for special purposes can, under certain conditions, be used for others. Experimental splitting of the future germ band results in the formation of twin embryos. In the other type, termed mosaic or determinate eggs, of which the Mediterranean flour moth, *Anagasta kühniella*, and the blowfly, *Calliphora erythrocephala*, are examples, the amount of cytoplasm is relatively large, and the germ band is long and slender, often showing visible differentiation. The embryonic parts of these eggs are determined before fertilization, and removal or destruction of egg parts before the first nuclear division results in partial development. There are many transitional types of eggs between the regulation and mosaic types. For example, the egg of the honey bee is of an incompletely determinate type. Removal of egg parts in the very early stages of development still permits formation of dwarf embryos.

The form of the insect which develops in the egg is the larval form of the particular insect species. In holometabolous insects, i.e., those with complete metamorphosis, the egg also contains groups of cells from which many of the structures of the adult insect originate. These groups of cells are called imaginal discs and represent the anlagen of the adult organs. They are carried through the larval stages to the pupa, when they are activated and differentiate into the distinctive adult organs. Experiments using a fine beam of ultraviolet light to injure the eggs of such insects have shown that determination of the imaginal regions takes place just after the larval characters are determined. Thus, in the fruit fly, *Drosophila melanogaster*, and Muscidae the first few hours after egg laying are regulative with respect to imaginal characters, but irradiation of eggs 7 hours or more after oviposition produces localized defects in the adult epidermis without visible effects on larval development. Dipteran eggs therefore have two waves of determination, a larval one terminated at fertilization and an imaginal one at the early germ-band stage. For a detailed account of the whole subject of embryogenesis, determination, and postembryonic development, the chapters by Bodenstein in Roeder's book on *Insect Physiology* should be consulted.[3]

5. Physiology and Biochemistry

Biochemical, biophysical, and physiological processes dominate the modern entomologist's thinking. Only a brief glimpse of this rapidly expanding field will be given in this chapter. Detailed accounts can be found from the references in the Bibliography.

5.1. THE INTEGUMENT

The insect is covered by a continuous single layer of epidermal cells which deposit on their outer surfaces a complex, multilayered cuticle and are separated from the body cavity by a thin basement membrane. The cuticle can be flexible to allow movement or rigid to serve as an exoskeleton. Into it the muscles are attached by noncontractile fibers termed tonofibrillae. Through it penetrate the ducts of the dermal glands which secrete either cement or waxy materials onto the outermost surface of the cuticle (tectocuticle) and the specialized sense organs and setae of various types. On the cuticle surface a great variety of hairs, scales, and sculpturings may be formed. The cuticle is divided into two main parts, an outer epicuticle and an inner laminated procuticle. The procuticle contains chitin, an unbranched polymer of N-acetylglucosamine units in α-glycosidic linkage. It is weakly combined with a protein, arthropodin. The procuticle is differentiated into two regions: an inner, soft endocuticle and an outer exocuticle which in general contains a protein, sclerotin, that is hardened and darkened by a tanning mechanism which involves the oxidation of o-dihydroxyphenols to their corresponding quinones. The process is called sclerotization, and an amber or black cuticle is produced. Black pigments are due to melanin (polymerized indoles) derived from oxidized polyphenols. The exocuticles of some insects (e.g., stick insects) are hard but not sclerotized. Insoluble cuticular proteins contain about 0.5% sulfur, and hardening may be produced in certain cuticles through the formation of disulfide linkages from the sulfhydryl groups of sulfur-containing amino acids.

Delicate cytoplasmic extensions of the epidermis project through the procuticle, and around these the pore canals are formed. These canals transport enzymes and epicuticle precursors from the epidermis to the epicuticle that overlies the exocuticle. The cuticle is thus a truly living tissue. The epicuticle is a complex, nonchitinous structure about 1 μ in thickness. It contains a lipoprotein into which various substances such as polyphenols, enzymes, waxes, and protective coverings of cement, wax, oil, or lac are deposited in an orderly fashion. The innermost layer of epicuticular wax is oriented as a monolayer. The physical properties of these waxes vary among insects. They are of fundamental physiological importance in the control of water loss through the cuticle. Removal of lipids and waxes from the cuticle surface by abrasive dusts, solvents, or detergents causes a great increase in the rate of evaporation of water from the cuticle surface. Increasing the temperature above a critical level also changes the physical properties of wax monolayers and results in increased transpiration rates. Several levels of resistance to desiccation conferred by epicuticular lipids occur: (1) high water resistance due to oriented layers of fluid or solid wax, (2) moderate water resistance produced by impregnation of the cuticular protein with unoriented wax molecules, and (3) low resistance to the passage of water shown by the lipoprotein. Besides protecting against water loss, the cuticles of some insects can actively absorb water from humid though unsaturated air. The asymmetry of the oriented wax layers may in part account for this phenomenon.

The epidermal cells cytologically appear quite unremarkable, but they are capable of an amazing sequence of metabolic activities at each molt. These activities are timed and controlled by a complex neurohumoral mechanism. At each molt the epidermal cells either increase in number by mitotic divisions (e.g., the silkworm, *Bombyx mori;* the assassin bug, *Rhodnius prolixus*) or by increase in cell size, no mitoses occurring (e.g., Diptera, suborder Cyclorrhapha). Somatic polyploidy occurs in larvae of the latter. The difference in the behavior of the epidermal cells at molting is important in connection with the effects of radiation on larval insects discussed in Chapter 2.

5.2. ENDOCRINE SYSTEMS

The functional plan of the neuroendocrine system of insects is in many superficial ways similar to the hypothalamic-neurohypophyseal system of vertebrates. Within the insect brain are groups of nerve cells which accumulate in their cell bodies neurosecretory material. This material passes down the axons in clearly defined tracts to small paired endocrine glands, the corpora cardiaca and corpora allata, which lie in or on the wall of the aorta. From these glands hormones are released into the hemolymph which then affect specific physiological processes either directly or through the control of further hormonal secretions from other nonnervous glandular tissues. Neurosecretory cells have been found in the pars intercerebralis of the protocerebrum, the lateral regions of the protocerebrum, the tritocerebrum, the subesophageal, thoracic, and abdominal ganglia of the ventral nerve chain, and in the ganglia of the stomatogastric nervous system. The neuroendocrine control of growth, molting, metamorphosis, and reproduction has been intensely studied for the past 30 years, but every year new specific physiological processes are discovered to have a neurohumoral basis. The basic anatomical plan of the neuroendocrine system is shown in Fig. 1.4.

The growth of insects is discontinuous. Increase in size occurs each time the cuticle is shed. A consequence of this is that a change of form can only occur at molting, and so metamorphosis and molting are intimately associated. The studies of Fukuda, Wigglesworth, Williams, Bodenstein, and others in establishing the basic mechanisms of hormonal control of molting

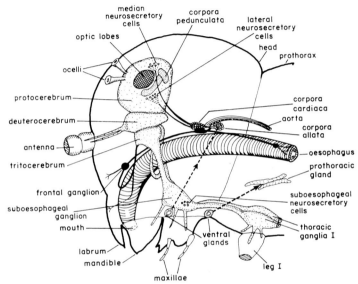

Fig. 1.4. General features of the central nervous system of a hemimetabolous insect which show the location of the neurosecretory cells and endocrine glands. The corpora allata and prothoracic glands are derived from the ventral glands as shown by the dotted arrows. The ventral glands persist in certain primitive insects. (Adapted from H. Weber, *Grundriss der Insektenkunde*, Gustav Fischer, Stuttgart, 1949, and P. M. Jenkin, *Animal Hormones, A Comparative Survey*, Pt. I, Pergamon Press, London, 1962.)

and metamorphosis by ligation, parabiotic, and implantation experiments are reviewed by Wigglesworth (see Bibliography). Only a brief summary can be given here, together with more recent work on the chemical identification of the hormones involved. The endocrine tissues involved in molting and metamorphosis are the neurosecretory cells of the pars intercerebralis of the brain, the corpora cardiaca, the corpora allata, and the prothoracic glands. Molting is initiated from the median neurosecretory neurones of the brain, which probably activate the corpora cardiaca to liberate a hormone into the blood, which then activates the prothoracic gland to secrete another hormone that acts directly on epidermal cells and certain other tissues. The latter hormone has been called the growth, differentiation, or molting hormone. It induces enlargement, multiplication, and reorganization of the epidermal cells in the premolt period. The character of the molt, whether from larva to larva or larva to pupa, depends on the concentration of another hormone in the hemolymph. This hormone, termed the "juvenile hormone," or "neotenin," whose secretion is regulated by the brain, arises from the corpora allata. It suppresses the progressive differentiation of larval stages and blocks metamorphosis. When larval growth is complete, the endocrine activity of the corpora allata declines, the titer of the juvenile hormone gradually decreases to zero, and differentiation from larva through pupa to adult occurs.

Considerable advances have been made recently in the difficult tasks of assay, purification, and characterization of insect hormones. Butenandt and Karlson in 1954 isolated a crystalline substance, ecdysone, in milligram amounts from large quantities of *Bombyx* pupae.[4] It is a 2β-unsaturated ketone of molecular weight 300, but the chemical structure is uncertain. Ecdysone stimulates puparium formation in the ligated larval abdomen of *Calliphora*; induces pupation in *Anagasta, Galleria,* and *Hyalophora*; initiates development in brainless diapause pupae of *Hyalophora* and in diapause larvae; induces molting in termite larvae or decapitated *Rhodnius* nymphs; and induces sexual cycles in cockroach symbionts (unicellular organisms in the roach which undergo sexual cycles synchronous with molting in the host).[5] The biological activity of ecdysone is in these respects the same as that of the prothoracic gland hormone. The bioassay method utilizes the initiation of puparium formation and pupation in the *Calliphora*.[5] Ecdysone governs the hardening and darkening of the cuticle and stimulates the metabolism of tyrosine through dopa, dopamine to N-acetyldopamine, the principal sclerotizing agent. The primary site of action of ecdysone, however, is at a more fundamental level. There is increasing experimental support for a primary action of ecdysone on the nucleus of specific tissues, notably the epidermal cells. Ecdysone causes enlargement of the nucleus in epidermal cells, an increase in the ribonucleic acid content, an increase in protein synthesis, and swelling of the mitochondria. It also causes the "puffing" phenomenon—i.e., enlargement of the chromosomal bands due to accumulation of ribonucleic acid—in the larval polytene salivary gland chromosomes of the midge *Chironomus*.[5] Recent ideas indicate that ecdysone acts directly on the genes and induces messenger ribonucleic acid synthesis that directs and controls protein synthesis in the cytoplasm of the epidermal cells. Although each body form of an insect is controlled genetically, the balance of specific hormones that act at the gene level appears to induce the biochemical events which result in the transformation of these forms.

The extraction and isolation of the juvenile hormone has been fraught with difficulties. Although the juvenile hormone must be absent for transformation from the pupa to adult to occur, the endocrine activity of the corpora allata recovers in the adult. Ether extracts of the abdomens of male cecropia moths are rich in juvenile hormone activity.[6,7] Bioassay of the extracts is based on its juvenilizing action on fifth-stage *Rhodnius* larvae, the pupae of the cecropia moth, or the pupae of the yellow mealworm, *Tenebrio molitor*. Juvenile hormone activity has been found in many insect tissues; in other invertebrate tissues; in bacteria, yeasts, and some higher plants; and in many mammalian tissues, particularly the calf thymus and adrenal cortex, and the human placenta.[6,7] Recently, a juvenile hormone principle has been isolated from the excreta of *Tenebrio* and shown to be an acyclic sesquiterpene farnesol (Fig. 1.5) and its aldehyde farnesal.[8,9]

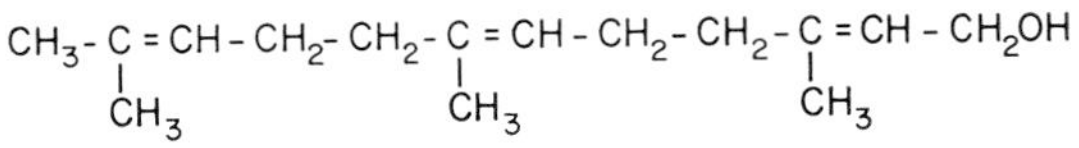

$$CH_3-C=CH-CH_2-CH_2-C=CH-CH_2-CH_2-C=CH-CH_2OH$$
$$\quad\; |\qquad\qquad\qquad\quad |\qquad\qquad\qquad\quad |$$
$$\quad CH_3\qquad\qquad\qquad\; CH_3\qquad\qquad\qquad CH_3$$

FIG. 1.5. Structure of farnesol I.

Synthetic farensol has powerful juvenile hormone activity.[10] When applied to the cuticle of fifth-stage larvae of *Rhodnius*, it leads to the formation of giant sixth-stage larvae, the same effect that is produced by implanting corpora allata. Similarly, smearing farnesol on adults induces molting with the formation of a new cuticle, partially of the larval type, just as does parabiosis with molting fifth-stage larvae or implantation of active corpora allata.[10] However, it should be noted that the unit activity of farnesol is far less than that of partially purified extracts of cecropia moths, and, consequently, farnesol may not be the true juvenile hormone.

The corpora allata, inactive during the pupal period, become active again in the adult under the stimulus of the pars intercerebralis of the brain. In the adult the corpora allata produce a secretion that is necessary for the deposition of yolk in the eggs (vitellogenesis) and the secretory function of the accessory glands in the male. Are several hormones produced by the corpus allatum? The question is still unsettled, but recent evidence suggests that there may be only one hormone which has different effects at different periods of development. For example, the deposition of yolk in the eggs of *Rhodnius* adults can be produced by joining decapitated females in parabiosis with fourth-stage larvae, by implantation of corpora allata from fifth-stag larvae, or by smearing decapitated adult females with farnesol.[10]

So far, only the hormonal control of growth, metamorphosis, and reproduction has been considered. A number of other functions in insects are regulated by hormones. Embryonic diapause (i.e., arrested growth) in

Bombyx is controlled by secretions from the subesophageal ganglion (diapause egg inducer) and the corpora allata (nondiapause egg inducer). The brain elicits or inhibits these secretions, depending on the external conditions of temperature and photoperiod to which the mother was exposed during larval or early pupal life.[11] Pupal diapause, characterized by a cessation of development, low respiratory rate, and increased resistance to cold, has been thoroughly analyzed in *Hyalophora*.[6] Chilling diapausing pupae for a period and returning them to higher temperatures activates the brain, which in turn activates secretion of the prothoracic-gland hormone. The respiratory rate increases, epidermal mitoses begin, and development resumes. Apparently the initiation of development commences after the resynthesis of cytochrome c, which disappears in diapause; the reappearance of acetylcholinesterase; and the restoration of electrical and neurosecretory activity in the brain.[12] Adult diapause in the Colorado potato beetle, *Leptinotarsa decemlineata*, is caused by a deficiency in secretion of the corpora allata, which leads to the changes in behavior, the arrest of oögenesis, and the low respiratory rate. Implanted active corpora allata or juvenile hormone extracts restore normal adult development.[13]

The morphological color change in the locust, *Locusta migratoria*, from the green, relatively sedentary, solitary form to the dark, swarming, gregarious form is controlled by a corpus allatum hormone, probably the juvenile hormone. Injection of blood, corpus allatum extracts, or implanting corpora allata into gregarious locusts changes the color to that characteristic of the solitary form. The adaptive physiological color changes of phasmids such as the walking stick insect, *Carausius morosus*, depend on secretions from the subesophageal ganglion. The pigment aggregations in the epidermal cells show diurnal rhythms. Removal of the brain (tritocerebrum in this case) or sectioning the subesophageal connectives stops the rhythm.[12] A similar control of diurnal activity rhythms occurs in the cockroach, *Periplaneta*.[14]

Another important advance in the study of insect hormones has been the discovery of a peptide hormone in the corpora cardiaca of the cockroach, which causes striking histological and histochemical changes in the pericardial cells and leads to the liberation of an indolealkylamine related to serotonin which accelerates the contractions of the heart.[15]

A fascinating aspect of insect hormone action is the discovery of chemical substances, termed pheromones or ectohormones, which are produced by one individual and are spread by contact to others, affecting their behavior and development.[16] The aliphatic acid present in queen substance, which inhibits ovary development and alters the behavior of workers, has already been mentioned. A pheromone also affects caste differentiation in termites by inhibiting sexual development.[17] Removal of sexual forms from a colony induces molting in certain larvae and the production of neotenic (juvenile) sexual forms. The neurosecretory cells of the brain, as well as the corpus allatum and thoracic glands, become activated. Extracts of the heads of these sexual forms stimulate the development of all the castes. A pheromone is also involved in the swarming of locusts. It has been known for a long time that overcrowding leads to the transformation of the solitary to the gregarious form. A substance secreted by the whole body of mature males stimulates the maturing of the gregarious females. The pheromone activates the brain corpora allata axes to produce a hormone which profoundly influences the protein metabolism of the female and the rate of deposition of yolk in the growing eggs. The solitary female is subject to less stimulation by the male pheromone, there is less stimulation of the neurosecretory cells, and egg growth is slower.

5.3. Nutrition and Intermediary Metabolism

Insects eat almost every kind of organic material. The adaptations of feeding mechanisms and digestive processes are exceedingly diverse. The digestive enzymes produced by the salivary glands and the midgut are adapted to the natural food habits. Symbiotic microorganisms in the gut may aid digestion of certain substances such as cellulose or may contribute a number of vitamins. Insect requirements for oxygen; water; energy-providing foods such as carbohydrates, fats, and proteins; for minerals; accessory growth factors; and vitamins are fundamentally similar to those of other animals. The principal metabolic pathways by which energy is made available to the insect through the metabolism of foodstuffs and the storage of the energy in high energy compounds such as adenosine triphosphate are similar to those found in all living cells (see Chapter 5). There are differences in details which depend on the particular adaptation of the insect and the developmental stage. Insects are capable of synthesizing a wide range of chemical substances. This is usually done in special glands. Silks, waxes, lac, venoms, stinks, scents, pigments, and a variety of urticating substances are some of these.

There are, however, some important differences from mammals. Most insects require cholesterol in the food and are incapable of synthesizing sterols (see Chapter 5). Neither isotopically labeled acetate or mevalonate, the key precursors for cholesterol synthesis, are incorporated into insect lipids. This inability likely arises from the absence of the enzymes necessary for the conversions from farnesyl pyrophosphate to squalene and cholesterol. Insects apparently do have the ability to synthesize isoprene units, since they produce a number of terpenoid derivatives (carotenoids, farnesol).

Flight muscles of Diptera and Hymenoptera are capable of contracting at higher frequencies than any other known muscle and for long periods of time. In them there is no synchrony between muscle contraction and each nerve impulse. They stretch and contract several times to each muscle spike potential. The reason for this is complex and is based in part on the mechanical properties of the muscle and the manner of insertion into the thoracic walls to which the wings are articulated. The liberation of energy and the consumption of oxygen and carbohydrate increase enormously when these flight muscles go from rest to activity. Glycolysis in the flight muscle cells differs in two ways from that in the muscles of higher animals.

(1) Lactic dehydrogenase is virtually absent in flight muscle. Consequently, when the reoxidation of $NADH_2$ to NAD cannot be carried out by the cytochrome system—e.g., because of inadequate oxygen—the flight muscle does not couple $NADH_2$ oxidation to the pyruvate-lactate reduction. Instead, it couples it with the reduction of dihydroxyacetone phosphate to α-glycerophosphate, making use of the enzyme α-glycerophosphate dehydrogenase, which is of high activity in flight muscle. Therefore, under anaerobic conditions, α-glycerophosphate accumulates instead of lactate. When the oxygen supply becomes adequate again, the accumulated α-glycerophosphate is utilized very effectively by direct oxidation by the sarcosomes (flight muscle mitochondria). It is this oxidation which accounts for the very high increase in oxygen uptake which occurs when the flight muscle passes from the resting to the active state.[18,19]

(2) Most of the energy for flight activity is derived from the nonreducing disaccharide, trehalose. Trehalose is present in considerable amounts in the blood and fat body of many insects. Although glycogen is used as a carbohydrate source during continuous flight, the amount of carbohydrate used considerably exceeds the glycogen depleted. The importance of trehalose in insect carbohydrate metabolism was only discovered in the past few years. Its rate of synthesis is very rapid. The intensity of flight activity appears to be determined by the rate of trehalose utilization by the flight muscles and the rate of synthesis of it in the fat body.[20]

Insect physiology should not be regarded as a separate compartment of knowledge, but rather as one part of comparative physiology. Consequently, wherever possible in the following chapters similarities with and differences from other animals, particularly mammals, are given.

6. The Advantages of Insects as Experimental Animals

In many ways, insects, despite their small size, are ideal experimental animals. The choice of a particular species of insect for experimentation is important. The success of the beautiful experiments of Wigglesworth which demonstrated the endocrine basis of molting and metamorphosis depended to some extent on the choice of the bug, *Rhodnius*. The growth phases of this insect are related to each blood meal and so can be accurately controlled. In the studies of Williams and his associates on the juvenile hormone and pupal diapause, the large sphingid moth *Hyalophora* proved an ideal experimental animal. Modern genetics is to a large extent based on experiments using the fruit fly, *Drosophila*. Some of the virtues of insects for experimentation are listed below.

(1) Large populations can be reared under controlled conditions easily, inexpensively, and in a small space. They can be readily transported.

(2) Their short life histories enable short-term and long-term effects of any experimental procedure to be assessed quickly. This is a particularly valuable feature for studies of the effects of ionizing radiations.

(3) Insects withstand surgical procedures well. With practiced technique, extirpations, implantations, and parabiotic unions can be readily performed and the results can be obtained in a fraction of the time required for such experiments in mammals.

(4) Many insects are easily handled and can be quickly and harmlessly anesthetized with carbon dioxide. They survive under a wide range of environmental conditions and so enable long-term physiological experiments to be conducted.

(5) The technical ease of manipulation of insects makes them favorable objects for fundamental biochemical studies, and for these studies they have found favor comparable to that found for certain microorganisms.

(6) In many insects, the small size is an advantage.

BIBLIOGRAPHY

Annual Review of Entomology, Annual Review, Inc., New York, 1956-1962.

J. Busvine, *Insects and Hygiene*, Methuen and Co. Ltd., London, 1951.

F. L. Campbell (Ed.), Physiology of Insect Development, *Development Biology Conference*, University of Chicago Press, Chicago, 1959.

J. H. Comstock, *An Introduction to Entomology*, Cornell University Press, Ithaca, New York, 1925.

E. M. Du Porte, *Manual of Insect Morphology*, Reinhold, New York, 1959.

Encyclopaedia Britannica, Insect, Vol. 12, 1959, and Year Books 1959-62.

M. Florkin and H. S. Mason (Eds.), *Comparative Biochemistry*, 2 Vols., Academic Press, New York, 1960.

General and Comparative Endocrinology, Suppl. 1, Progress in Comparative Endocrinology, 1962.

D. J. Gilmour, *The Biochemistry of Insects*, Academic Press, New York, 1961.

P. Grassé (Ed.), *Traité de Zoologie*, Vol. 9, 10 (Pt. I and II), Masson, Paris, 1949, 1951.

A. D. Imms, Social Behavior of Insects, *Methuen Monographs on Biological Subjects*, Methuen and Co. Ltd., London, 1947.

A. D. Imms, *A General Textbook of Entomology*, Methuen and Co. Ltd., London, 1957.
O. A. Johannsen and F. H. Butt, *The Embryology of Insects and Myriopods*, McGraw-Hill, New York, 1941.
L. Levenbook (Ed.), Biochemistry of Insects, *Proc. 4th Intern. Congr. Biochem.*, *12*, Pergamon Press, London, 1959.
C. L. Prosser and F. A. Brown (Eds.), *Comparative Animal Physiology*, W. B. Saunders Co., Philadelphia, 1961.
A. G. Richards, *The Integument of Arthropods*, Minneapolis University Press, Minnesota, 1951.
K. D. Roeder, *Insect Physiology*, John Wiley and Sons, New York, 1953.
B. T. Scheer, *Recent Advances in Invertebrate Physiology*, University of Oregon Press, Eugene, 1957.
H. Weber, *Grundriss der Insektenkunde*, Gustav Fischer, Stuttgart, 1949.
V. B. Wigglesworth, *The Principles of Insect Physiology*, E. P. Dutton and Co. Inc., New York, 1950.
V. B. Wigglesworth, *The Physiology of Insect Metamorphosis*, Cambridge University Press, Cambridge, England, 1954.
V. B. Wigglesworth, *The Control of Growth and Form*, Cornell University Press, Ithaca, New York, 1959.

REFERENCES

1. M. Jacobson, M. Beroza, and R. T. Namamoto, Isolation and Identification of the Sex Attractant of the American Cockroach, *Science*, **139**: 48 (1963).
2. W. Loher, The Chemical Acceleration of the Maturation Process and Its Hormonal Control in the Male of the Desert Locust, *Proc. Roy. Soc. B*, **153**: 380 (1961).
3. D. Bodenstein, Embryonic Development, in *Insect Physiology* (Ed. K. D. Roeder), John Wiley and Sons, Inc., New York, p. 780, 1953.
4. A. Butenandt and P. Karlson, Über die Isolierung eines Metamorphosehormons der Insekten in kristallisierter Form, *Z. Naturforsch.*, **96**: 389 (1954).
5. P. Karlson, On the Chemistry and Mode of Action of Insect Hormones, *Gen. Comp. Endocrinol*, Suppl. 1, p. 1, 1962.
6. C. M. Williams, The Juvenile Hormone—I, *Biol. Bull.*, **116**: 323 (1959).
7. C. M. Williams, The Juvenile Hormone, Symp. 10, *Trans. 1st Intern. Congr. Endocrinol.*, Copenhagen, p. 189, 1960.
8. P. Karlson and P. Schmialek, Nachweis der Exkretion von Juvenilhormon, *Z. Naturforsch.*, **14b**: 821 (1959).
9. P. Schmialek, Die Identifizierung zweier in Tenebriokot und in Hefe vorkommender Substanzen mit Juvenilhormonwirkung, *Z. Naturforsch.*, **16b**: 461 (1961).
10. V. B. Wigglesworth, Some Observations on the Juvenile Hormone Effect of Farnesol in *Rhodnius prolixus* Stal (Hemiptera), *J. Insect Physiol.*, **7**: 73 (1961).
11. S. Morohoshi, Hormonal Studies on the Diapause and Non-diapause Eggs of the Silkworm, *Bombyx mori* L. *J. Insect Physiol.*, **3**: 28 (1959).
12. B. T. Scheer, The Neuroendocrine System of Arthropods, *Vitamins Hormones*, **18**: 141 (1960).
13. J. De Wilde and J. A. De Boer, Physiology of Diapause in the Adult Colorado Beetle. II. Diapause as a Case of Pseudo-allatectomy, *J. Insect Physiol.*, **6**: 152 (1961).
14. J. E. Harker, Endocrine and Nervous Factors in Insect Circadian Rhythms, in *Biological Clocks*, Cold Spring Harbor Symp. Quant. Biol., **25**: 279 (1960).

15. K. G. Davey, The Mode of Action of the Heart Accelerating Factor from the Corpus Cardiacum of Insects, *Gen. Comp. Endocrinol.*, **1**: 24 (1961).
16. P. Karlson and M. Luscher, Pheromones: a New Term for a Class of Biologically Active Substances, *Nature (London)* **183**: 55 (1959).
17. M. Luscher, Über die Entstehung der Soldaten bei Termiten, *Rev. Suisse Zool.*, **65**: 373 (1958).
18. E. Bueding and E. Farber, Comparative Biochemistry of Glycolysis, in *Comp. Biochem.* (Eds. M. Florkin and H. S. Masson), Vol. 1, Academic Press, New York, 1960.
19. B. Sacktor, Biochemical Basis of Flight Muscle Activity, *Proc. 4th Intern. Congr. Biochem.*, **12**: 138 (1958).
20. J. S. Clegg and D. R. Evans, The Physiology of Blood Trehalose and Its Function During Flight in the Blowfly, *J. Exptl. Biol.*, **38**: 771 (1961).

CHAPTER 2

Nongenetic Effects of Radiation

Insects have long been favored for radiation studies. Some advantages of the egg of the Mediterranean fruit fly, *Drosophila melanogaster*, as a subject for studying the somatic effects of radiation were described in 1935 by Packard[1]: ". . . the flies can be easily obtained and reared, and they lay eggs throughout the year in large quantities. The eggs are so small that . . . the entire egg is uniformly irradiated. Finally, the proportion of eggs that

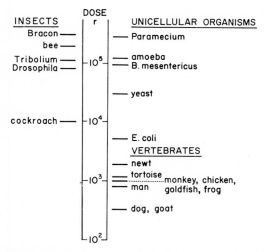

FIG. 2.1 LD_{50} for adults (in roentgens, log scale) of vertebrates, insects, and unicellular organisms. (Data from various sources.[22,51,83,84,87])

survive . . . a definite dose . . . is remarkably constant. . . ." These advantages are shared to some extent by numerous insect species. Other advantages in special cases, such as controllable, simultaneous mitosis and reliable variations in genome number, will be described below.

It is rather widely known that insects are insensitive to radiation when compared to vertebrates. Figure 2.1 demonstrates the sorts of doses of radiation needed to kill insects and to affect other organisms. However, broad generalizations about "effective doses" are seen to have only limited meaning when one considers, even for a single insect such as the wasp

23

Bracon hebetor, the very large difference between the sterilizing dose, 5000 r, and the lethal dose, 300,000 r. The same insect serves also to illustrate the enormous variation in sensitivity with age; the lethal dose is 100 r for embryos in the cleavage stage, 100,000 r for old pupae, and 300,000 r for adults. Figure 2.2 shows the approximate doses required to affect insects in various ways. The large species variation which it demonstrates is a further caution against sweeping statements.

Nevertheless, it remains true that adult insects are at least 100 times less sensitive to the lethal effects of radiation than are vertebrates, and

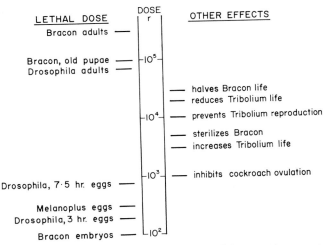

Fig. 2.2. Effect of radiations (in roentgens, log scale) upon insects; to show importance of age, stage, and effect measured. (Data from various sources. [63,65,82,84-86,88, 89])

this phenomenon must be explained. The most generally accepted explanation is based on two facts: (1) a generalization which was formulated in 1906 as the Bergonie-Tribondeau "law"—the sensitivity of cells to irradiation is in direct proportion to their reproductive activity and inversely proportional to their degree of differentiation;[2] (2) a special feature of insects— after they hatch from the egg, very little cell division occurs during larval life. Cell division and differentiation of tissues occur instead during embryonic development in the egg, so that, in larval life, growth occurs primarily by enlargement of cell volume without an increase in cell number. There are other short bursts of mitotic activity: just before molting and (where a pupal form occurs) in the later stages of pupation.

It follows that dividing insect cells are as sensitive as dividing vertebrate cells, but the peculiarly static quality of the adult insect's cell life makes it insensitive to radiation. However, certain cells do divide in the adult—the cells of the gonads—and one finds that these dividing cells are in fact very sensitive to radiation, so that quite low doses can sterilize the insect or cause the production of genetically deranged gametes. It is this that explains the large difference quoted above between sterilizing and lethal doses. However, the explanation is not complete, for, when developing gonadial tissues are irradiated, the somatic cells are undamaged by doses that sterilize the insect.[3] Therefore, quite apart from developmental rate, the germ cells show added sensitivity. It may be that the molecular damage is similar, but that the requirement for undamaged chromosomes is more stringent in the case of germ cells.

Since the adult insect owes its radioresistance to its paucity of dividing cells, one would expect to find in juvenile forms a much greater sensitivity. This is indeed the case, and some striking examples of the changes of sensitivity with age have been found. Thus, for eggs of the locust, *Locusta migratoria*, the LD_{50} for X-rays increased from 136 r for 1-day-old eggs to 6900 r for those 6 days old—a 61-fold increase.[4]

Henshaw[5,6] has examined the age variation in sensitivity to X-rays of *Drosophila* eggs. The sensitivity changed remarkably in a few hours, as Fig. 2.3 demonstrates. Calculations from the figure show that the LD_{50} increased from 304 r at 1 hour to 1170 r at 3 hours. Maximum sensitivity (i.e., in Fig. 2.3, minimum minutes for a given survival) occurred at cleavage and blastulation, with a peak of insensitivity at gastrulation and just after. The variations correlated well with mitotic activity; high activity was associated with high sensitivity. In an even more precise study, Packard[1] has shown marked increases in the early minutes after laying: from 0 to 100 minutes the sensitivity increased twofold and then declined sharply in agreement with Fig. 2.3. Presumably, mitotic rate was maximal at 100 minutes. However, although mitosis is undoubtedly a period of special radiosensitivity, nuclear damage can occur without mitosis if the dose is sufficiently high.[7]

Figure 2.3 suggests that sensitivity can be neatly correlated with microscopic appearance. However, this is only true as long as appearance reflects the dynamic state of the organism: two apparently identical stages may differ markedly in sensitivity. In 1935 it was shown[8] that, when eggs of the differential grasshopper, *Melanoplus differentialis*, were developing continuously, their sensitivity to X-rays diminished progressively. However, when a diapause stage intervened, the eggs were very resistant to damage. For instance, during diapause they survived 1000 r, which would stop the development of prediapause eggs immediately and would stop that of postdiapause eggs after 20 days. Similarly, diapausing larvae of the mud-dauber wasp,

Sceliphron caementarium, were about 50% more resistant to X-rays than nondiapausing larvae.[9]

Such studies show that, as well as stage of development, the rate of development is important; this might account for the irregular variations in sensitivity reported for eggs of the blowfly, *Calliphora erythrocephala*.[10] Other studies[7] have shown that irradiated eggs of *Melanoplus* were completely unaffected by X-rays while held at 0°C; if so held for only from 4 to 10 days after a variety of doses and then brought to 25°C, they became damaged to the same extent as eggs not so held, as judged by pycnosis of the nuclei* and

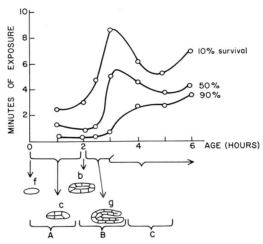

Fig. 2.3. Effect on *Drosophila* eggs of X-irradiation at 234 r per minute: f, fertilization; c, cleavage; b, blastulation; g, gastrulation. At A, mitotic activity is high; at B, mitosis decreases, differentiation begins; at C, mitosis and differentiation increase. (Redrawn, with additions, from Henshaw and Henshaw.[5])

respiratory inhibition. However, if they were held at 0°C for 25 days after irradiation, less damage occurred when the eggs were later returned to room temperature. Clearly, some form of repair process occurred at 0°C.

So far we have considered primarily the change in sensitivity of eggs. Even after hatching, very marked changes in sensitivity occur with age. For *Drosophila*, Villee[11] reported that larvae were relatively sensitive to 6925 r of X-rays, but that after the puparium was formed irradiation of the latter led to only minor malformations in the adult. Within the various larval ages, there appeared to be an early period of relative insensitivity (68–71 hours)

---

* Condensation and shrinkage to a structureless clump of intensely staining chromatin.

and a later one (about 90 hours) for which no explanation was available. Villee described in detail the various adult monsters produced in different strains by larval irradiation with various X-ray doses, of which 4165 r seemed most productive. Typical deformations were duplication of body parts and abnormal developments such as leglike antennae and formation of palps in the eye (Fig. 2.4). A very extensive discussion of morphological abnormalities in *Drosophila* after larval irradiation has been given by Waddington.[12] Effects have also been described for the beetle *Onthophagus texanus*.[13]

In *Bracon*, the normal life span of the female adult is 25–29 days. A dose of 5000 r of X-rays given to adults reduced their life span to 21 days, but a dose of only 3000 r given to larvae reduced the life span of subsequent

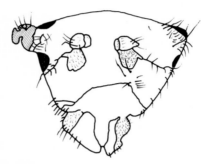

Fig. 2.4. Anterior view of head of adult *Drosophila*, irradiated as a 102-hour larva with 4165 r of X-rays. Note extra palp in left eye. (Redrawn from Villee.[11])

adults to 6 days.[14] Figure 2.5 shows actual data from which the comparative sensitivity, as judged by dose to reduce life 50%, is seen to vary fivefold between larvae and adults. Another study on X-irradiation of this insect[15] demonstrated the sharp decrease in sensitivity with age and also the growing divergence of the lethal and sterilizing dose, which at first are nearly identical. The implication is that, in young, rapidly differentiating tissues, somatic and genetic tissues are equally sensitive; but that somatic tissues lose their sensitivity more rapidly with age.

Further evidence for the association of radiosensitivity with larval differentiation is the finding[16] that, in X-irradiated *Drosophila* larvae, the organs most affected (as judged by cell degeneration) are those which are most rapidly dividing and differentiating at the time of irradiation.

When insects pass from one instar to another by going through a molting process, there is a brief period of intense mitotic activity. If the insect is irradiated prior to molting, visible damage may not show up until molting occurs. This delayed effect has been called "latent radiation damage" by Baldwin and Salthouse, who have examined the effect in the blood-sucking bug, *Rhodnius prolixus*.[17,18,19] *Rhodnius* only molts after a blood meal. The sequence of events is: (1) the blood meal leads to distension of abdomen; (2) a "stretching stimulus" stimulates the brain via the nervous system; (3) the brain produces a hormone which activates the thoracic gland; (4) the thoracic gland secretes molting hormone; (5) molting occurs. The first observable aspect of (5) is cell division in the epidermis, and it begins about 5 days after (1). Consequently, one can control the time of onset of the mitosis associated with cell division by controlling the time of feeding. When

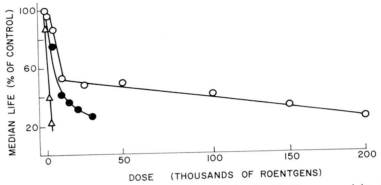

FIG. 2.5. Longevity of adult *Bracon* females irradiated with X-rays as adults (open circles), pupae (solid circles), or larvae (open triangles). (Plotted from data of Clark.[13])

molting occurs, the result of prior irradiation is seen as a burn in the new cuticle, as shown in Fig. 2.6. With this elegant procedure, one can vary at will the time between irradiation and visible effect.

The first study with *Rhodnius* involved 50,000 r of X-rays applied to a spot on the abdomen. Even with a latent period of 2 months, burns appeared at molting. The effect was quite abrupt and unlike the gradual appearance of symptoms typical in a mammalian response. This abruptness was attributable to the virtually simultaneous division of all the epidermal cells which occurred in response to the molting hormone.

When *Rhodnius* was irradiated just before feeding, the cell enlargement which immediately followed the blood meal was quite normal, and "oxidase enzymes" were quite unaffected. At the 5th day after feeding, mitosis began and was usually successful through prophase and metaphase, but then block occurred, and the irradiated cells were destroyed, showing large blobs of ag-

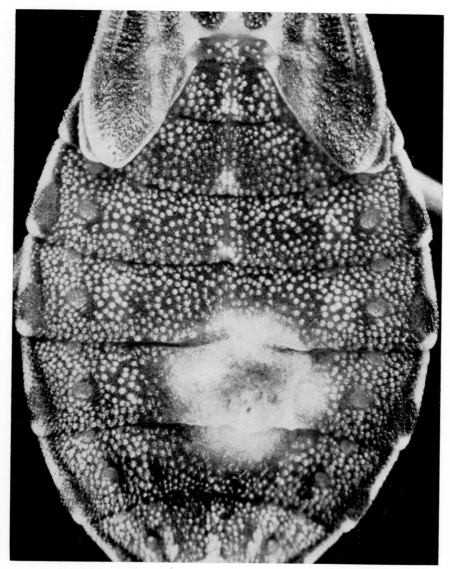

FIG. 2.6. Photograph of abdominal tergite of *Rhodnius prolixus* irradiated as fourth-instar nymph, which shows burn after molting to fifth instar. (Photograph kindly supplied by Dr. Baldwin, from Baldwin and Salthouse.[17])

gregated chromatin internally. Just as with thermal burns, the peripheral, unaffected cells responded to this destruction after a few days and migrated inward to repair the damage. The repair was not perfect, however; for instance, epicuticle (outer layer) was not formed. Furthermore, in subsequent molts the burn persisted. One of the consequences of the blocked mitosis and subsequent repair process was a delay of between 7 and 10 days in the molting process.

In further studies the period between irradiation and feeding was varied.[18] With increased periods, *Rhodnius* seemed to recover from some of the effects of the radiation, so that the delay in molting was not so severe. However, the diameter of the burn was unaffected (Table 2.1). These findings implied

TABLE 2.1

EFFECT OF INTERVAL BETWEEN IRRADIATION AND FEEDING ON RADIATION EFFECT IN *Rhodnius*[a]

Number of days between irradiation and feeding	Effects	
	Days between feeding and molting	Diameter of burn (mm)
0	26	1.5
14	21	1.6
21	18	1.2
28	16	1.8
No irradiation	14	0

[a] Adapted from Baldwin and Salthouse.[18]

that no recovery occurred in the cells directly in the burn, since no reduction of burned area occurred. The return to near normal of the feed-to-molt interval was attributed to recovery of the peripheral cells responsible for repair, which must therefore have been partially damaged by the irradiation.

In order to study this lesser degree of damage, Baldwin[19] then used a lesser radiation dose (9000 r) applied to the whole body, but with head and abdomen shielded, a process which was observed to permit normal feed-to-molt interval (absence of shielding lengthened the interval). He then observed the effects of varying the interval between irradiating and feeding. The following phenomena induced in the epidermal cells by irradiation were all observed to be most intense when the irradiation-feeding interval was zero, and least intense when the interval was long (intervals of up to 4 weeks were employed): (1) a delay in the time for maximal number of mitotic cells to develop, and a reduction in the maximum number; (2) a great increase in the percentage of dividing cells at any time which were in metaphase, which suggests that it was this phase which was blocked by prior irradiation; (3) a reduction in the total number of cells on any one day after feeding; (4) a delay of up to 4 days in the time required to complete the molt.

The precise stage which suffered most radiation damage was shown to be the metaphase.[20] At doses which prevented molting, division proceeded normally until metaphase and then ceased. That this cessation was the cause of inhibited molting was further suggested by the fact that, when similar doses were given with the insect held in nitrogen rather than air, inhibition of molting and of the metaphase process were comparably reduced.

This fine series of studies utilized a special feature of a special insect, i.e., the synchronous mitosis of a population of cells, to pinpoint the place and time of radiation damage. The conclusions were that damage was not evident until mitosis began and was most prominent at the end of the metaphase; that, while severe irradiation permitted no recovery, smaller doses permitted considerable spontaneous recovery to occur during the resting stage; and that, since recovery was improved by delaying the onset of mitosis, the recovery was progressive throughout the 4-week interval studied. Baldwin[19] was careful to point out, however, that some of these conclusions could be peculiar to the Hemiptera, whose mitotic process shows minor peculiarities.

French workers[21] have recently studied the influence of timing on interference with molting of *Locusta*. They found that, if the insects were irradiated just before molting, then that particular molt succeeded, but further molts were prevented. However, if the irradiation preceded a molt by a sufficient time, then that molt was blocked. This implies a sort of obligate latency—a time for the lesion to develop fully. It is a rather novel finding with considerable implications.

Let us consider briefly the quantitative relationship between dose and effect.

Within a population of any one organism, one finds a variation in susceptibility to toxic agents. The variation is usually normally distributed so that if one plots "log dose" against "mortality" one gets a sigmoid curve. In order to avoid this inconveniently shaped curve, one can plot "probit of mortality" instead of "mortality," and then a straight line results.* If the responses of longevity to a toxic agent were also normally distributed, one would expect similar relationships to hold when measuring longevity instead of mortality.

Figure 2.5 makes it clear that this type of relationship does not hold for longevity of X-irradiated *Bracon* adults. A substantially similar curve was reported[22] for longevity of *Periplaneta* adults irradiated with electrons:

---

* For present purposes, the probit can be considered as a mathematical device—a figure which can be looked up in a table and used in order to obtain a straight line instead of a sigmoid response.

there was a drastic drop in survival time from 25 down to 7 days when the dose increased from 6000 to 10,000 rads; between 10,000 and 50,000 rads it only dropped to 5 days. One interpretation of such curves is that there was a heterogenous response of the population, so that (in Fig. 2.5) the first 50% of the population were killed within a narrow dose range; the second 50%

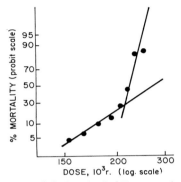

Fig. 2.7.   Effect of X-rays on adult female *Dahlbominus fuscipennis*. (Redrawn from Baldwin.[23])

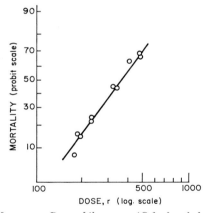

Fig. 2.8.   Effect of X-rays on *Drosophila* eggs. (Calculated from data of Packard.[1])

were less susceptible, and also their susceptibilities were more scattered. Possibly the first 50% were homozygous with respect to a hypothetical susceptibility factor, and the second half were heterozygous. Alternatively, the population might be of mixed ages, with a consequent heterogeneous response.

However, it is by no means certain that curves such as Fig. 2.5 do measure a quantal response, and it may therefore be inaccurate to apply the above interpretation. Instead, one might argue that there was a uniform population with two mechanisms of response, one involving an easily damaged "target" which, on destruction, halved their mean life, and a second "target" which was much harder to destroy completely.

With X-irradiated *Dahlbominus fuscipennis* adults,[23] the curve of log-dose *versus* probit-effect also showed a sharp break (Fig. 2.7), but in this case 25% responded in one fashion, being of high sensitivity and wide scatter (i.e., the curve had a flat slope), and 75% were less sensitive but more uniform in response.

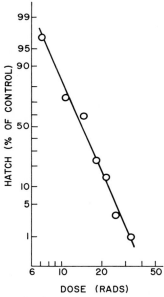

FIG. 2.9.   Effect of X-rays on hatch of *Bracon* eggs. Hatch is on probit scale, dose on log scale. (Calculated from data of Amy.[26])

By contrast, the relation of log dose to probit effect in *Drosophila* was almost linear, both for per cent mortality of X-irradiated eggs[62] as shown in Fig. 2.8 and for life expectancy of cobalt-60 gamma-irradiated adults.[24] The same was true for hatch of X-irradiated *Bracon* eggs (Fig. 2.9).

We will now consider some of the factors of importance in determining response to radiation.

1. Radiation Conditions

In most studies, radiation dosage is accepted as the major parameter when dealing with any one kind of radiation. In at least one instance,[11] X-irradiation rate has been shown to be extremely important, higher rates being more effective. When *Drosophila* larvae of a particular strain were given 6925 r at a rate of 5540 per minute, 57% died after pupating, whereas, when given 7000 r at 78 r per minute, only 39% died after pupating. In another study[25] on *Drosophila* egg irradiation, 5 r per minute had little effect, but 4690 r per minute was extremely potent.

In spite of the considerations of rate described above, the commonly used irradiation rates do not vary greatly and can be taken as essentially equiactive.[1] Voltage is also not of much importance, at any rate in the commonly used range between 12 and 700 kvp.[1]

The evidence suggests that all forms of ionizing radiation operate in substantially the same way and produce the same results. There are, of course,

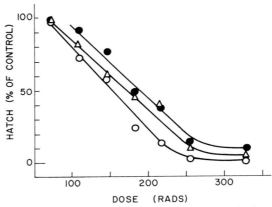

FIG. 2.10.   Comparison of effects of gamma rays (solid circles), beta rays (open triangles), and X-rays (open circles) on the hatch of irradiated *Bracon* eggs. (Plotted from data of Amy.[26])

variations in penetration and ability to "deposit energy," but these are also seen within any one form of radiation. One comparison that was made[26] involved using beta (from P[32]), gamma (from Co[60]), and X-rays (125 kvp) against haploid eggs of *Bracon*. The effects of equienergetic doses of the three radiations were substantially similar; although gamma rays were most and X-rays least effective, the differences were mostly not statistically significant (Fig. 2.10).

A number of studies with alpha particles have been reported. The short range of such particles (e.g., 39 μ for polonium alpha particles in tissues) has special virtues but imposes special difficulties. A full discussion of the technical problems and their solutions has been given by Rogers.[27] A comparison of alpha with other types of radiation was made with cultures of embryos of the green meadow locust *Chortophaga viridifasciata*. The effects of 56 rads upon mitosis of neuroblasts showed that, with respect to total mitotic activity, alpha particles were most potent, X-rays less potent, and beta particles least potent.[27]

A given dose is usually more effective when administered all at once than when split up into sessions with intervals between them ("fractionated"). The effectiveness decreases with increasing intervals. For instance, when granary weevil, *Sitophilus granarius*, adults were irradiated with a single dose of 5666 rep of Co[60], survival was reduced from 97 days to 5 days. When the same dose was given in five daily fractions, survival was completely unaffected. In the sterilization effect, fractionation was somewhat less important in these same adults. But in larval irradiation, it was again most important—a dose (4012 rep) which completely sterilized when given all at once, or in five fractions separated by 10-minute intervals, had only minor effects when given in five daily fractions.[28]

Similar studies[22] on survival time of irradiated cockroaches showed that a 2000 rad dose was almost twice as effective given at once than when given as five fractions at $1\frac{1}{2}$-hour intervals.

These studies all imply that some repair process can occur which obviates a part of the effect of a small radiation dose. Whiting[29] found that when damage was strictly chromosomal it was not reduced by fractionation, but when cytoplasmic injury occurred, the effect was reduced or prevented by fractionation. Her experimental approach is reported below (p. 47). If this is true, it suggests that effects reported above are due in part to cytoplasmic injury.

2. Sex and Genome Number

Male insects are more sensitive to lethal effects of radiation than female. For instance, in American cockroaches irradiated with 10,000 rads of 2 Mev electrons, 8-week-old females survived about 14 days, 8-week-old males only 8 days. The difference was less with younger insects.[30] *Dahlbominus* males were twice as sensitive as females to X-rays, as judged by survival time[23]; but this might be associated with the haploidy of the males in this species (see below).

With regard to differential sensitivity of the sexes to sterilization, two opposite conclusions are reported. For newly emerged adult khapra beetles (*Trogoderma granarium*), sterilization of all males was not achieved by the highest dose, viz., 15,000 r of Co[60] gamma rays, whereas 5000 r sterilized all females.[30] By contrast, when pupae of the screw-worm (*Callitroga hominivorax*) were gamma irradiated, 2500 r sterilized all the males, but 4000 r failed to sterilize all the females.[31]

It is therefore apparent that the picture of relative sensitivity of the sexes depends in part upon what response is measured. This is well illustrated by an experiment in which a massive dose of 60,000 r of X-rays was given to *Drosophila* adults, resulting in a median lethal time of about 2 weeks, the males being the more sensitive sex. Yet in most of the other responses examined the male was less sensitive. For example, growth of males was unaffected, and that of females was delayed, so that maximum size was reached in 7 days instead of the usual 2 days. Phosphorus turnover in males was unaffected, and that of females was slowed to one-half. Average food uptake was reduced by one-third in males and by one-half in females. However, 40% of the males were totally inhibited from feeding, and only 10% of the females were so affected. Oxygen utilization responded identically in both sexes: it was unaffected at 1 day after irradiation and 26% inhibited at 6 days.[32]

The genome number, that is, the number of sets of chromosomes per cell, has been studied, particularly by Clark and his associates, as a factor which influences radiation sensitivity. In some insects, the males are usually produced from unfertilized eggs, and the nuclei of their genetic cells are haploid. The females are produced from fertilized eggs, and their genetic cells are diploid. This is the phenomenon of haplodiploidy. White[33] points out that whether the somatic cells contain half as many chromosomes in such males is unknown. It happens that all insects so far examined show endopolyploidy; that is, their somatic cells are usually polyploid, with 2, 4, 16, etc., up to 2048 sets of chromosomes. Consequently, the number of chromosomes in the somatic cells of a haploid male need not necessarily be one half of that in a diploid female; whether it is or not has never been determined. The insects showing haplodiploidy are: all the Hymenoptera (bees, wasps, ants, etc.), a few Homoptera, one Coleopteron, and possibly several Thysanoptera.[33]

In the wasp *Bracon*, most males are haploid, all females are diploid, and the males are more radiation-sensitive.[34] Is the sensitivity difference due to sex or genome number? Fortunately, a few males of *Bracon* emerge from fertilized eggs and are therefore diploids, and it was shown that adult diploids, whether male or female, were equally sensitive, and both were less sensitive than adult haploid males.[35] This relation holds also for other stages than adult; in fact, with early pupae of *Bracon*, the diploids are only one-third as sensitive as the haploids.[36]

Unfortunately, it is difficult to get many diploid males of *Bracon hebetor*, the most-used species. In 1961, work was reported[37] on a new species as yet unnamed which is structurally identical with *Bracon hebetor* but will not breed with it. This species produces adequate numbers of both haploid and diploid males.

A comparison was made of the life-shortening effects of X-rays upon diploid and haploid males of the new species. A distinct difference was found between the median life spans of haploid and diploid adult males after irradiation of larvae, pupae, or adults. The difference was greater for irradiation of pupae (10,000 r reduced the span of haploids 77%, of diploids 24%) than of adults (10,000 r reduced the span of haploids 34%, of diploids 16%). This difference between haploid and diploid males was greater than that between diploid males and females. Some implications of this study are: (1) that the life-shortening mechanism involves the genes; (2) that differences in genome number are more important than differences in gene kind; and (3) since irradiation of adults shortens their life span, and the body (somatic) cells of adult insects do not divide, the damage is not due to a disruption of cell reproduction but to disruption of the ability of the nucleus to control the functioning of the cell, quite apart from cell division.

Genome number alone apparently does not control all sex differences in *Bracon*. Haploids are more resistant than diploids during cleavage in the egg stage, equally resistant after cleavage, and less resistant during larval, prepupal, and pupal stages.[38]

3. Age

Baxter and Tuttle[24] found for X-irradiated *Drosophila* adults that $D = kT/E$ where D is dose, T is survival time, E is the life expectancy of the controls, and k is a constant. In other words, the survival after irradiation depends upon age; old insects, whose normal life expectancy is short, will die sooner after a given dose than young insects. Wharton and Wharton[22] found that, for adult cockroaches irradiated with 10,000 rads of electrons, older insects were more affected than younger. But, whereas Baxter and Tuttle found with *Drosophila* that, for a given dose, T/E was constant, Wharton and Wharton found that T/E decreased steadily with age, falling from 0.543 for 2-week-old insects down to 0.278 for 25-week-old insects. It follows that old insects were not only more sensitive than young, but also they were proportionately more sensitive.

This difference in findings is a very crucial one, for it bears on the whole question of the relation between aging and radiation. Such a relation is suggested by the fact that mild irradiation decreases life expectancy, and in vertebrates it hastens the onset of some diseases associated with old age. Consequently, it has been suggested that such irradiation accelerates some process which occurs normally.[39] One possibility is the occurrence of deleterious somatic mutations, i.e., unfavorable alterations in the chromosomes of the body tissues. If such is the case, a study of the mechanism of radiation damage may throw light not only on this process but upon the supremely important phenomenon of senescence.

If aging had no effect upon intrinsic radiation sensitivity, then one would find that a given dose had the same effect at all ages; e.g., a certain dose might halve the life span. This is what Baxter and Tuttle found: T/E was constant for any dose. It conforms with the theoretical relations worked out by Blair for mammals.[40] If, on the contrary, aging and radiation were interrelated, T/E should decrease with age, as the Whartons found. Their findings conformed with the theoretical relations of Sacher[41] and Davidson[42] and with other experiments on mice.[41,43]

This is not the place to argue the pros and cons of the dispute on aging. All that can be done is to indicate what the dispute is about and to describe some of the evidence. Insects will probably continue to play an important part in such studies because of their conveniently short life spans and the possibility of rearing large numbers, which permits statistically excellent studies.

A different approach to aging theory comes from a study[37] which showed that in a wasp of the *Bracon* genus the life spans of haploid and diploid adult males were identical (median span, 62 days). This constituted evidence against the deleterious-somatic-mutation theory of aging, for a corollary of that theory would seem to be that two sets of chromosomes should give a better survival chance than one, since in the diploid one set could be destroyed without effect. Furthermore, the effects of X-irradiation on life span of haploid and diploid males were different (see above, p. 37), so the radiation effect did not parallel the aging effect.

4. Nutritional Status

In a new *Bracon* species (p. 36), it was observed[37] that the life-shortening effect of X-irradiation of larvae was much less if the female adults were fed honey than if they were fed their normal diet of larvae of the Mediterranean flour moth, *Anagasta kühniella*. Thus, 2000 r shortened the life of the subsequent adults by 78% if *Anagasta* were given, but by only 27% if honey was given. The life span of the unirradiated insects was also very different: 40 days with *Anagasta* and 92 days with honey.* It is curious that the reduction of life, expressed in days, is rather similar both for controls and irradiated insects—25 days with honey, 31 days with *Anagasta*. It seems at

---

* This effect may be connected with the fact that the honey-fed females lay no eggs: in *Drosophila*, egg laying shortens life.[44]

first paradoxical that a diet (honey) which is deficient as judged by its ability to support the normal activity of egg laying is better than a sufficient diet as far as radiation protection is concerned. But, clearly, matters other than simply nutritional ones are concerned here; it seems likely that the life-shortening effect of egg laying is particularly effective on the irradiated insect.

5. Oxygen

Oxygen at high tensions is toxic to insects, as it is to the many other animals which have been examined. For instance, oxygen reduced viability of adult *Drosophila azteca*[45] and delayed embryonic development of *Drosophila melanogaster*.[46] In *Bracon*, only the prepupae and the white pupae were sensitive to 1 atm of oxygen; earlier and later stages were unaffected. The effects seen were prevention of emergence in some cases and wing and antennal abnormalities in others.[47] In *Anagasta*, the Mediterranean flour moth, 1 atm of oxygen allowed pupal development, but the adults could not emerge.[48]

It is a familiar observation in radiobiology that radiation damage is reduced at low oxygen tensions. Such finds have been made with insects. For instance, when *Rhodnius* was irradiated locally with X-rays, retardation of molting and size of burn were much greater when the irradiation was in air than when it was in nitrogen.[49] To delay molting to 22 days after a blood meal, a dose of 70,000 r was required in air, but 175,000 r in nitrogen. To produce a 0.5-mm burn took 80,000 r in air but 140,000 r in nitrogen.* These effects were paralleled by the degree of inhibition of the metaphase; a dose could be selected which would totally inhibit metaphase in air but only prolong it in nitrogen.[20]

A Russian report[50] of the quantitative aspects of oxygen influence showed that, with *Sitophilus* irradiated with gamma rays, increasing the oxygen concentration from 0 to 15% progressively increased the mortality, but further increases had no effect.

A possible explanation for the above facts would be that oxygen poisoning and radiation damage operate by the same mechanism. There is some evidence in favor of this possibility. Substances that protect against radiation often protect against oxygen poisoning.[51] When larvae in cocoons or pupae of *Bracon* were irradiated,[52] the effect as judged by interference with emergence from cocoons was three times greater in air than in nitrogen. However, oxygen exclusion was not the only factor of importance in determining the effect of various gas mixtures: irradiation in hydrogen had more effect than irradiation in nitrogen or carbon dioxide.

---

* See p. 28 for details of such experiments.

Other evidence that oxygen excess does not have the same effect as X-rays on *Bracon* was: (1) female pupae were more resistant than males to X-rays, but less resistant to oxygen; (2) the larva-in-cocoon stage was more resistant than pupae to oxygen, but less resistant to X-rays; (3) oxygen (at 2 atm) inhibited oxygen consumption strongly and promptly, while comparably damaging X-ray doses had no such effect. The *Bracon* data are therefore evidence against a common mechanism for oxygen poisoning and radiation damage.[52]

A similar conclusion was drawn for *Anagasta* and the yellow mealworm *Tenebrio molitor*.[48] In these insects the larvae were more sensitive to oxygen than were the pupae, but the reverse was true for sensitivity to X-rays.

6. Temperature

Baldwin has used the hymenopterous parasite *Dahlbominus* to show some dramatic effects of heat upon radiation sensitivity, or of radiation upon heat

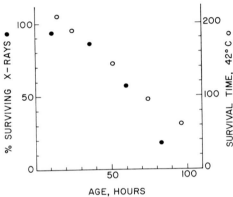

FIG. 2.11. Comparison for *Dahlbominus fuscipennis* adults of per cent survival from 225,000 r of X-rays with survival time in minutes during exposure to 42°C. (Plotted from data of Baldwin.[23])

sensitivity—it is not easy to distinguish between these two. For instance,[53] with a fixed dose of 200,000 r of X-rays, the mortality at temperatures between 10 and 25°C was approximately 30%, but at 35°C it was 100%. Small differences were noted if the heat treatment, which lasted 35 minutes, was given before or during irradiation. However, if heating was given after irradiation, mortalities were considerably fewer, e.g., 75% at 35°C.

Recovery from this heat sensitivity was examined after irradiation with 80,000 r. Recovery was highly temperature dependent, being 10 times faster at 32 than at 12°C. Food and oxygen did not affect recovery. To give some actual figures: exposure to 43°C for 60 minutes killed no control insects but killed 99% of insects irradiated just before heating. If a 2-hour recovery period at 32°C was permitted between heating and irradiating, only 22% were killed. If a similar period at 12°C was permitted, 96% were killed.[54]

These findings might suggest a common mechanism in the effects of heat and radiation. Supporting evidence is that the sensitivity to both increased with age, and to a strikingly similar extent, as Fig. 2.11 shows. Furthermore, the males were twice as sensitive as the females both to irradiation and to heat.[23] However, Baldwin[53] feels that, because the sequence of heat and irradiation is important, heat and X-rays cannot have equivalent effects.

7. Other Effects of Radiation

From what has been said so far it is evident that the major effects of radiation which have been measured are lethality and the shortening of life. Burning and delayed molting have also been mentioned. Lethality and life shortening are of course interrelated, for, if a sufficiently long period intervenes before lethality is measured, a life-shortening effect is recorded as a lethality. In practice, however, one can frequently distinguish between extremely rapid killing (by very large doses of radiation which probably act by a gross denaturation of protein) and delayed death. We shall consider later whether this delayed death is due to cytoplasmic or nuclear damage.

An important effect of radiation is sterility, of both males and females. In considering sterilization of female insects, one must distinguish between effects upon egg production and upon hatch of the eggs that are laid.

When female *Bracon* were irradiated with X-rays,[55] a dose of 4858 r was needed for permanent inhibition of egg laying and 3312 r for temporary inhibition. Of the eggs that were laid, hatch was affected by radiation. Figure 2.12 shows an unexpected two-cycle effect of sterility followed by recovery. This two-cycle effect has not been seen in other X-ray studies[56] or in beta sterilization using P^{32} radiation.[55] Figure 2.12 also shows that 16 days after irradiation the irradiated females laid eggs which hatched better than controls. This last effect might perhaps be connected with the ability of certain X-ray doses to prolong the life of starved insects, probably by inducing lethargy (see p. 44).

An extremely important effect of radiation is interference with the developmental process. In some cases this may not be readily separated from a simpler lethal effect, for example, in the case of reduction of egg hatch. The effect can be studied more easily with lower doses which delay development instead of terminating it. It was noted in 1932 that the irradiation of *Drosophila* larvae with X-rays delayed pupation.[57] In 1950 Whiting showed that a dose of 40,000 r of X-rays prevented pupation of the flour moth

Anagasta, many specimens of which continued to live in the larval form for up to 40 days, i.e., 37 days after the controls had pupated.[58]

In 1956 the delay in pupation was examined in detail by Bourgin *et al.*[16] with *Drosophila*. Two kinds of effect were observed: (1) Immediate—rapidly dividing cells, such as those of brain and testis, degenerated. Recovery was common, but at various rates, and this may account for malformations such as those discussed on p. 27 and shown in Fig. 2.4. (2) Latent—these make their appearance when pupation is normally due. The irradiated larvae seem to show what Bourgin *et al.* called an additional stage between the larval and

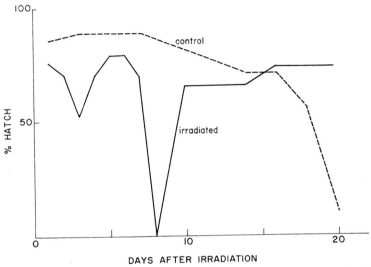

FIG. 2.12.   Effect of 2650 r of X-rays given to female *Bracon* adults upon hatchability of their eggs. (Redrawn from Grosch and Sullivan.[55])

prepupal stages; the larva lost weight, the ring gland stopped growing, and cuticle and fat-body growth were greatly slowed. They interpreted their observations as showing that there are normally two control mechanisms, one which terminates the larval stage and another which initiates prepupation. Only the second is damaged by radiation. Local irradiation work tentatively located the site of this damage as the ring gland. The authors therefore suggested that of the two control mechanisms (probably hormonal), the second originates in the ring gland and the first in some other radiation-insensitive area. This fine piece of work is an example of the way in which radiobiological techniques can contribute to fundamental physiological problems which bear no apparent relation to radiobiology.

There are at least two ways in which development could be retarded or stopped: by direct modification of the developing tissues or indirectly by modification of the hormonal mechanism which governs development. An ingenious technique of combined irradiation and tissue culture was used by Horikawa and Sugahara[59] to elucidate these effects. They irradiated third-instar larvae of *Drosophila* with X-rays at doses of from 500 to 25,000 r and removed various imaginal discs* and larval organs along with brain preparations to provide appropriate hormones. They found that most of the imaginal discs were relatively radiation resistant, but that the brain preparations were particularly sensitive. For example, 500 r applied to the eye discs but not to the brain preparations had no effect; when this dose was applied to the brain preparation but not to the eye discs, differentiation of the discs was eliminated. It seems, therefore, that, in this case at least, interference is indirect rather than direct.

After irradiation of *Bracon* eggs by beta, gamma, or X-rays, Amy[26] noted that visible developmental interference occurred mainly in early stages, so that animals which avoided embryonic death were not much harmed. Thus, the percentage yield of pupae from larvae was affected only by high radiation doses, and the percentage yield of adults from pupae was not affected at all. Such findings are to be expected from the considerations discussed earlier in this chapter. Nevertheless, the incidence of pupae without cocoons was much changed; normally, 7% occur thus, and this was increased up to 66% by high doses. Thus, subtle changes undoubtedly existed even in those pupae which were normal as judged by emergence, and this is confirmed by studies on longevity (p. 27) which show it to be a good index of mild radiation damage.

A life prolongation was reported as long ago as 1917 by Davey[60,61] with low doses of X-rays against adults of the confused flour beetle *Tribolium confusum*. The median life expectancy, normally 40 days, could be extended to 75 days by small daily doses; high doses, of course, reduced the expectancy. Life prolongation of honey-fed *Bracon* females has also been reported when the honey contained between 13 and 271 μc of P^{32} per gram. Higher doses shortened life.[62]

A more thorough investigation of the life-prolongation effect was made in 1957 by Cork,[63] also with the use of *Tribolium*. In an extensive study using over 5000 insects, he found a distinct prolongation caused by 100 r daily or by a single dose of 300 r, using 0.66 Mev gamma rays. Figure 2.13 shows results for single doses and demonstrates further interesting facts. Although 11,000 r killed 40% quite rapidly, the survivors then outlived the controls on

---

* Clusters of undifferentiated embryonic cells, which later give rise to adult tissues.

the average. At 15,000 r, the last 12% to survive lived almost as long as the last 12% of surviving controls, and it took the same time (400 days) for 87% of the controls and of the irradiated to die. In short, low doses protected all the insects and high doses protected the strongest (most radio-resistant) individuals.

A different kind of beneficial effect of small doses of radiation has been reported[64] for the flour mite *Tyroglyphus farinae*, for which egg laying and hatching were greatly increased by 5×10^3 or by 10^4 rads of gamma rays. Higher levels, such as 2×10^4 rads or more, had the reverse effect.

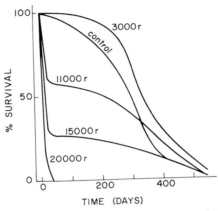

FIG. 2.13. Effect upon longevity of *Tribolium confusum* adults of single doses of gamma radiation from Cs[137]. (Redrawn from Cork.[63]) The actual points, here omitted, were shown in the original and were very numerous—about 60 per line.

Anorexia (lose of appetite) is a typical consequence of irradiation in insects as well as mammals. The effect has been described by Grosch[65]: "Strikingly characteristic is the lack of interest in food shown by these wasps, even though it is present in abundance. In fact each wasp is found day after day standing at the same place in approximately the same position."

This anorexia has given rise to the question as to what extent radiation damage is due to starvation. It is certainly true that irradiation reduces food intake. For instance, the daily food intake of male cockroaches was reduced from its normal level of 14.4 mg down to 1.03 mg by 10,000 rads of 2-Mev electrons, to 0.64 mg by 15,000 rads, and to 0.03 mg by 20,000 rads.[22]

Furthermore, feeding commonly increases postirradiation survival. Table 2.2 shows that in female *Bracon* wasps this protective effect held except at high doses; at doses over 100,000 rads (of X-rays), no protection was found. A similar effect has been observed in male American cockroaches but not in females.[22] This odd sex effect was probably due to the large fat stores in the females, for, if the insects were starved before irradiation, thus depleting their stores, postirradiation survival was reduced in both sexes.

The data of Table 2.2 also show that suitable doses of radiation actually prolonged the life of starved insects but not of fed insects. This was almost certainly due to the lethargy induced by radiation, so that energy consumption was diminished.[22] At higher doses this prolongation disappeared. No prolongation was seen in starved cockroaches irradiated with 10,000 rads of 2-Mev electrons.[22]

Effects on feeding behavior have also been observed[66] for the red flour beetle *Tribolium castaneum*. Sufficient doses of electrons caused a temporary cessation of feeding; e.g., 27,400 rads delayed feeding for 2 days. After resumption of feeding, the intake rate depended on the radiation dose.

TABLE 2.2

EFFECT OF FOOD AVAILABILITY ON LIFE SPAN AFTER IRRADIATION OF FEMALE *Bracon* WASPS[a]

X-ray dose (rads)	Life span (days)	
	Food available	No food
0	20.9	7.2
25,000	11.5	6.7
50,000	12.3	8.9
102,000	11.1	11.3
180,000	7.3	7.4

[a] Data from Grosch.[65]

Respiratory effects in insects were first examined with radium in 1928.[67] More extensive studies[68] with X-rays on eggs of *Melanoplus* showed respiratory inhibition which at low doses (300 to 900 r) was transient. At higher doses (1000 to 2000 r) the same respiratory effect was seen, but the eggs failed to hatch. At very high doses (6000 r) the eggs died promptly. However, Tashmisian,[7] working with the same species some 15 years later, found substantial stimulation of respiration by 25,000 r (e.g., up to 48%), with inhibition at higher levels (e.g., 69% inhibition by 200,000 r).

With another grasshopper species, the green meadow locust, *Chortophaga viridifasciata*, Tipton and Amand[69] found that the only significant effect of X-irradiation on respiration was inhibition. From 1000 up to 7000 r the effects were negligible, but from 10,000 to 40,000 r a progressively increasing inhibition was seen, the maximum being 50%.

Enzymic studies have shown effects following similar irradiations of *Melanoplus*.[70] An unidentified oxidase (hydroquinone as substrate, sensitive to cyanide, but not to copper reagents) was first rapidly depressed by irradiation, then recovered, and was finally greatly stimulated. Both effects were greatest at the lowest dose, viz., 25,000 r: this produced a prompt 20% inhibition and, by 15 days, a 175% activation. Meanwhile, —SH groups were unaffected at first and greatly inhibited at 15 days. The significance of the effects is obscure.

An odd feature of egg development of *Bracon* following lethal X-irradiation has been described by Von Borstel.[71] He used X-rays on females and examined histochemically the development of the eggs which (as is usual in this insect when well fed) were retained in the female's body. He found that meiosis and a series of cleavages occurred, but the nuclei so formed did not contain DNA, as judged by Feulgen staining. The notion of a nucleus without DNA is strange indeed, and the formation of a modified DNA, unreactive to the Feulgen reagent, presents a possible explanation.

Wharton and Wharton[72] consider that they have evidence in insects of effects upon cell constituents other than nucleic acids. They examined the effect of irradiation of starved adult male cockroaches with 10,000 rads of 2-Mev electrons. This was about the LD_{50}. The findings were that water consumption was greatly increased (up to fourfold); fecal pH was lowered (from 7.1 to 6.7 at 6 days), and nitrogen excretion was increased (about doubled at 6 days); uric acid—which accounted for only about 3.5% of the total nitrogen—was increased rather similarly; and inorganic phosphorus excretion was unaffected until 6 days and then progressively depressed, being about one-third at 15 days. The authors felt that these effects were not attributable to nucleic acid damage but rather to increases in cellular permeability. The data, however, offer little evidence on the site of damage.

Clark[14] has noted in *Bracon* that death is associated with numerous urate bodies in the abdomen. He suggests that destruction of the ability to excrete toxic materials might be a factor in radiation death of insects.

A behavioral disturbance of interest has been briefly reported.[73] Doses of less than 25 r given to ants led to disturbed and speeded motion, apparently in a reversible way. When irradiated and unirradiated areas were available, the ants accumulated in the unirradiated area, since they moved rapidly out of the irradiated and were more "content" in the unirradiated area.

Most studies on radiation effects have been directed to individual survival. Effects upon whole populations have been reported[74] for a Collembola* species, *Proisotoma minuta*, following irradiation by Co^{60} gamma rays, with doses from 3000 to 7000 r. The authors found that, even with control populations, there was a lag before vigorous population growth took place; in 6 days, the mean population of controls grew from 26 to 40, but in the next 6

---

* Small, primitive, wingless insects.

days, it increased to 120. Radiation prolonged the lag but had no effect upon the rate of increase achieved eventually.

These results are of interest but cannot be analyzed in any detail without knowing more about the characteristics of such populations. Presumably, whether one has a lag or not depends upon the numbers and the environmental conditions. Genetic factors may be of paramount importance in such cases.

The effect of gamma radiation (from Co^{60}) upon populations of the beetle, *Trogoderma sternale*, was followed.[75] A dose of 4000 r exterminated the colony in 2 months. In this case the effect was attributed to lowered vitality, morphological deformities, and a failure of coincident emergence of males and females. All these factors reduced reproduction rates.

8. The Mechanism of Radiation Damage

There are many questions about the mechanism of radiation damage, and very few have been satisfactorily answered. One of the simplest is whether the main damage is primarily in the nucleus or in the cytoplasm.

The egg of *Bracon* has been used to answer this question. The nucleus of the newly laid egg is located at the anterior end of the convex surface. By localized irradiation with alpha particles, which have poor penetrating power and therefore have a short range within the egg, one can choose to irradiate separately either nucleus or cytoplasm.

Alpha-particle irradiation of nuclei of newly laid *Bracon* eggs reduced hatch, the reduction being exponentially related to the dose. This conformed with expectation, if a single hit on a hypothetical target was assumed to suffice for inactivation. The area of the target was calculated as 4.71 μ^2, which corresponded to a diameter of 2.41 μ for a sphere. The diameter of the egg nucleus is 2.8 μ at oviposition and increases up to 5.7 μ in 5 minutes. It therefore seems probable that the target is the nucleus in the 2.8 μ stage, and that one hit destroys it.[76] When the cytoplasm was irradiated, by contrast, the hatch reduction was sigmoidally related to the dose. To obtain 50% kill, 16×10^6 alpha particles were needed per egg.[77] Cytoplasmic killing was thus 16 million times more difficult than nuclear killing.

Similar findings for ultraviolet radiation have been made.[78] If the *Bracon* egg is irradiated on its convex side (where the nucleus is), a given dose is from 3 to 10 times more effective than when it is irradiated on the opposite side, where only cytoplasmic damage can occur.

An ingenious method of distinguishing nuclear and cytoplasmic damage in *Bracon* eggs was used by Whiting.[29] As already pointed out, normal, unfertilized eggs of this insect develop into males, for the eggs are haploid.

Such eggs owe all their chromosomes to the female, and are called "gyno-genetic." Another way of producing effectively haploid eggs is to fertilize, with normal sperm, eggs which have been irradiated severely enough to destroy the chromosome function. The irradiation is carried out on the gravid female. These fertilized eggs are also haploid and so develop into males, but in this case all the chromosomes come from the male, and the egg is called "androgenetic."

Whiting irradiated the gravid females with various doses of X-rays, then crossed them with unirradiated males, and examined the sex ratio of the progeny as a function of dose. She found that the ratio rose from about 0.01 (males : females) in controls to about 0.1 at 15,000 r and slowly declined again at increasing doses, being zero at 55,000 r. The control males probably represented the few males that do develop from diploid eggs in the species. The extra males produced by irradiation were presumably all androgenetic haploids. These androgenetic males were normal, healthy, and fertile—much more so than gynogenetic males.

Whiting interprets her data as showing that up to 15,000 r only nuclear effects occur. The cytoplasm of the egg is unaffected and can support normal development, guided by the "implanted" male nucleus. At higher doses, the cytoplasm is affected, and production of androgenetic males becomes increasingly difficult, for the altered cytoplasm cannot support development even with an unirradiated nucleus.

A quite different approach comes from the study of variation of sensitivity at different nuclear stages. It has already been pointed out that the insensitivity of adult insects and the marked variations of juvenile sensitivities with time point to an association of mitotic activity with sensitivity. Furthermore, there is considerable variation within the mitotic stages. In eggs of the grasshopper *Chortophaga* it was found[27] that midprophase cells were severely and immediately affected by 56 rads of alpha rays or X-rays, whereas late prophase cells showed absolutely no immediate effect. When small doses of alpha particles were used, and the midprophase stages were examined at five different times after onset, statistical analysis favored the hypothesis that a single hit served to disrupt mitosis. The radiosensitivity was found to decrease progressively, although chromosomal optical cross section increased throughout midprophase. It follows from this study that the nucleus is the critical target, and that its dynamic condition, rather than the size of its chromosomes, determines its sensitivity.

Tissue cultures of insect material have been used to explore the precise way in which radiation interferes with mitosis.[79] *Chortophaga* neuroblasts in hanging drop preparations were irradiated with X-rays, with the use of doses of from 64 to 4096 r. The effect of this treatment upon various stages in mitosis was analyzed. It was found that the earlier the stage at which radiation was given, the greater the effect of any dose. The most evident effect was a kind of "stickiness" of the chromosomes which caused them to clump in metaphase or caused failure of the sister chromatids to separate normally at anaphase. There was usually a delay between radiation and "stickiness," perhaps due to delayed depolymerization of deoxyribonucleic acid.

The above experiments all suggest that the nucleus is the prime target except at high doses and that its precise condition determines the severity of the effects. But in what way does the damaged target in the nucleus (presumably the chromosomes) express its damage?

Henshaw[6] pointed out in 1935 that, after an X-ray dose which is eventually lethal to *Drosophila* eggs, mitosis continues unmolested, but differentiation ceases, so that one may produce a solid mass of undifferentiated cells. In this case, the lesion is at a level concerned with cell specialization. A more detailed account of effects of alpha, beta, and X-radiation on *Bracon* eggs came to essentially the same conclusion.[26] The nuclei were much affected, as shown by a threefold enlargement, but considerable cell division took place. Differentiation, however, was severely inhibited.

These conclusions offer an interesting parallel with neoplastic growth.

9. Endogenous Irradiation

Most of the studies so far described have dealt with exogenous radiation. Some studies on artificially produced endogenous radiation are also available for insects which have been fed radioisotopes. With P^{32} and *Drosophila* larvae, an LD_{50} of 3.3 μc per milliliter of medium was reported.[80] Also, the ratio of females to males was increased, presumably due to the greater sensitivity of the males.[80]

In such studies, most of the effects are due to internal beta radiation, but calculations[81] suggest an important contribution by the conversion of phosphorus into sulfur which accompanies the decay of P^{32}. Clearly, such a change occurring in a P^{32} atom incorporated into the cell structure will have an adverse effect.

With *Bracon* fed on honey containing P^{32}, much greater apparent radioresistance was found: 200 μc per gram of medium stopped egg production, and lower levels reduced production and viability.[62] However, what is of more interest is the actual dose ingested, and in later studies this was determined. For instance, a comparison was made of the sterilizing effects of various beta emitters.[82] Phosphorus-32 proved most effective; ingestion of 0.25 μc gave permanent sterility. Strontium-89 was next best, requiring 0.5 μc for permanent sterility. Sulfur-35 was far less effective—1.5 μc gave only temporary sterility—and Ca^{45} was almost without effect at the low dose of 0.15 µc, which was all that could be obtained. These differences were attributed to a combination of two factors: (1) Half-life—the ratio for $P^{32} : Sr^{89} : S^{35} : Ca^{45}$ is 14 : 53 : 87 : 152. The shorter-lived isotopes would decay rapidly, giving a smaller total dose and, also, 1 µc of a short-lived isotope represents fewer molecules. (2) Energy—the ratio of the energies is 1.7 : 1.5 : 0.17 : 0.25. The more energetic radiation would be more penetrating.

REFERENCES

1. C. Packard, The Relationship Between Age and Radiosensitivity of *Drosophila* Eggs, *Radiology*, **25**: 223 (1935).
2. J. Bergonie and L. Tribondeau, Interpretation de Quelque Resultats de la Radiotherapie et Essai de Fixation d'une Technique 'Rationelle,' *Compt. Rend.*, **143**: 983 (1906).
3. J. E. Erdman, Analyses of the Differential Radiosensitivity of Developing Reproductive Tissues in *Habrobracon juglandis* (Ashmead) to Ionizing Radiation, *Intern. J. Radiation Biol.*, **3**: 183 (1961).
4. G. Colombo, Different Sensitivities to X-irradiation with Respect to the Stage of Development of the Embryos of *Locusta migratoria migratoriodes* (R. and F.), *Atti. Accad. Nazl. Lincei, Rend., Classe Sci. Fis., Mat. Nat.*, **26**: 583 (1959).
5. P. S. Henshaw and C. T. Henshaw, Changes in Susceptibility of *Drosophila* Eggs to X-rays. I. A Correlation of Changes in Radiosensitivity with Stages in Development, *Radiology*, **21**: 239 (1933).
6. P. S. Henshaw, Changes in Sensitivity of *Drosophila* Eggs to X-rays. II. Correlation of Biological Sensitivity and Radiosensitivity, *Radiology*, **24**: 438 (1935).
7. T. N. Tahmisian, The Effect of X-radiation on the Metabolic Processes of the Resting Cell, *J. Exptl. Zool.*, **112**: 449 (1949).
8. T. C. Evans, Variations in Susceptibility to X-rays of *Melanoplus differentialis* Eggs During Development, *Physiol. Zool.*, **8**: 521 (1935).
9. J. H. Bodine and T. C. Evans, Respiration and Development of Individual Mud-dauber Wasp Larvae Following X-irradiation, *Physiol. Zool.*, **7**: 550 (1934).
10. C. M. Scott, Action of X-rays on Eggs of *Calliphora*, *Proc. Roy. Soc. (London)*, *Ser. B.*, **115**: 100 (1934).
11. C. A. Villee, Some Effects of X-rays on Development in *Drosophila*, *J. Exptl. Zool.*, **101**: 261 (1946).
12. C. H. Waddington, Some Developmental Effects of X-rays in *Drosophila*, *J. Exptl. Biol.*, **19**: 101 (1942).
13. H. F. Howden, Investigations on Sterility and Deformities of *Onthophagus* (Coleoptera, Scarabaeidae) Induced by Gamma Radiation, *Ann. Entomol. Soc. Am.*, **50**: 1 (1957).
14. A. M. Clark, Some Effects of X-irradiation on Longevity in *Habrobracon* Females, *Radiation Res.*, **15**: 515 (1961).
15. H. E. Erdman, Divergence Between Lethal Doses and Sterilizing Doses of X-rays with Progressive Development in *Habrobracon* Females, *Nature*, **186**: 254 (1960).
16. R. C. Bourgin, R. Krumins, and H. Quastler, Radiation Induced Delay of Pupation in *Drosophila*, *Radiation Res.*, **5**: 657 (1956).

17. W. F. Baldwin and T. N. Salthouse, Latent Radiation Damage and Synchronous Cell Division in the Epidermis of an Insect. I. Non-reversible Effects Leading to Local Radiation Burns, *Radiation Res.*, **10**: 387 (1959).

18. W. F. Baldwin and T. N. Salthouse, Latent Radiation Damage and Synchronous Cell Division in the Epidermis of an Insect. II. Reversible Effects in Burn Repair, *Radiation Res.*, **10**: 397 (1959).

19. W. F. Baldwin, Latent Radiation Damage and Synchronous Cell Division in the Epidermis of an Insect. III. Spontaneous Reversal of Effects Leading to Delay During Mitosis, *Radiation Res.*, **14**: 426 (1961).

20. W. F. Baldwin and T. N. Salthouse, Effect of O_2 Deficiency on Radiation Induced Mitotic Damage in Synchronously Dividing Cells, *Can. J. Zool.*, **37**: 1061 (1959).

21. P. Joly and G. Biellman, Effects of Irradiation on *Locusta migratoria* (L.), *Compt. Rend.*, **247**: 243 (1958).

22. D. R. A. Wharton and M. L. Wharton, The Effect of Radiation on the Longevity of the Cockroach, *Periplaneta americana*, as Affected by Dose, Age, Sex and Food Intake, *Radiation Res.*, **11**: 600 (1959).

23. W. F. Baldwin, Similarities in Killing by Heat and by X-radiation in the Insect *Dahlbominus fuscipennis* (Zett.), *Radiation Res.*, **5**: 46 (1956).

24. R. C. Baxter and L. W. Tuttle, Life-span Shortening in Irradiated *Drosophila*, *Radiation Res.*, **7**: 303 (1957).

25. R. Sievert and A. Forseberg, Time Factor in Biological Action of X-rays; Investigations on Drosophila Eggs, *Acta Radiol.*, **12**: 535 (1939).

26. R. L. Amy, A Comparative Study of β Rays, γ Rays and X-rays on Development in *Habrobracon*, *Radiation Res.*, **3**: 166 (1955).

27. R. W. Rogers, Particle Dosimetry and the Inhibition of Mitosis in the Grasshopper Neuroblast by Low Dosage α Irradiation, *Radiation Res.*, **3**: 18 (1955).

28. D. J. Jefferies and P. B. Cornwell, Lethal and Sterilizing Effects of Single and Fractionated Doses of Gamma Radiation on *Calandra granaria* L, *Nature*, **182**: 402 (1958).

29. A. R. Whiting, Androgenesis, a Differentiator of Cytoplasmic Injury Induced by X-rays in *Habrobracon* Eggs, *Biol. Bull.*, **97**: 210 (1949).

30. G. C. Carney, Differential Response of Male and Female Adults of *Trogoderma granarium* (Everts) towards Sterilizing Doses of Radiation, *Nature*, **183**: 338 (1959).

31. R. C. Bushland and D. E. Hopkins, Sterilization of Screw-worm Flies with X-rays and Gamma-rays, *J. Econ. Entomol.*, **46**: 648 (1953).

32. R. C. King and L. P. Wilson, Studies of the Radiation Syndrome in *Drosophila melanogaster*, *Radiation Res.*, **2**: 544 (1955).

33. M. J. D. White, Animal Cytology and Evolution, 2nd ed., 454 pp., Cambridge University Press, England, 1954.

34. A. R. Whiting and C. H. Bostian, The Effects of X-radiation of Larvae in *Habrobracon*, *Genetics*, **16**: 659 (1931).

35. A. M. Clark and E. M. Kelly, Differential Radiosensitivity of Haploid and Diploid Prepupae of *Habrobracon*, *Cancer Res.*, **10**: 348 (1950).

36. A. M. Clark and C. J. Mitchell, Radiosensitivity of Haploid and Diploid *Habrobracon* During Pupal Development, *J. Exptl. Zool.*, **117**: 489 (1951).

37. A. M. Clark and M. A. Rubin, The Modification by X-irradiation of the Life Span of Haploids and Diploids of the Wasp, *Habrobracon* sp., *Radiation Res.*, **15**: 244 (1961).

38. A. M. Clark and C. J. Mitchell, Effect of X-rays upon Haploid and Diploid Embryos of *Habrobracon*, *Biol. Bull.*, **103**: 170 (1952).

39. B. L. Strehler, Origin and Comparison of the Effects of Time and High-energy Radiations on Living Systems, *Quart. Rev. Biol.*, **34**: 117 (1959).

40. H. A. Blair, A Formulation of the Relation Between Radiation Dose and Shortening of Life Span, *Proc. 1st. Intern. Congr. Peaceful Uses Atomic Energy*, **11**: 118 (1956).

41. G. A. Sacher, Dependence of Acute Radiosensitivity on Age in Adult Female Mice, *Science*, **125**: 1039 (1957).

42. H. O. Davidson, quoted in D. R. A. Wharton and M. L. Wharton, The Effect of Radiation on the Longevity of the Cockroach, *Periplaneta americana*, as affected by Dose, Age, Sex and Food Intake, *Radiation Res.*, **11**: 600 (1959).

43. H. I. Kohn and R. F. Kallman, Age, Growth and the LD_{50} of X-rays, *Science*, **124**: 1078 (1956).

44. J. M. Smith, Rate of Aging in *Drosophila subobscura*, *Ciba Found. Symp.*, Life Span of Animals, pp. 269-281, 1959.

45. C. M. Williams and H. K. Beecher, Sensitivity of *Drosophila* to Poisoning by O_2, *Am. J. Physiol.*, **140**: 566 (1944).

46. B. Glass and H. L. Plaine, The Role of O_2 Concentration in Determining the Effectiveness of X-rays on the Action of a Specific Gene in *Drosophila melanogaster*, *Proc. Nat. Acad. Sci.*, **38**: 697 (1952).

47. A. M. Clark and E. B. Herr, The Sensitivity of Habrobracon During Development to O_2, *Biol. Bull.*, **107**: 329 (1954).

48. A. M. Clark and F. J. Cristofalo, Some Effects of O_2 on the Insects, *Anagasta kuehniella* and *Tenebrio molitor*, *U. S. Atomic Energy Comm.*, TID 6052, 1961.

49. W. F. Baldwin and T. N. Salthouse, O_2 Deficiency and Radiation Damage in the Insect *Rhodnius*, *Nature*, **183**: 974 (1959).

50. G. V. Sumarkov, The Dynamic Radiation Injury in *Calandra granaria* Under Various Irradiation Conditions, *Biophysics U.S.S.R.* (Engl. transl.), **3**: 359 (1958).

51. Z. M. Bacq and P. Alexander, *Fundamentals of Radiobiology*, 555 pp., Pergamon Press, New York, 1961.

52. A. M. Clark and E. B. Herr, The Effect of Certain Gases on the Radiosensitivity of *Habrobracon* during Development, *Radiation Res.*, **2**: 538 (1955).

53. W. F. Baldwin and C. A. Narraway, Interaction of Heat and X-rays in Killing a Chalcid, *Nature*, **179**: 971 (1957).

54. W. F. Baldwin, Recovery from X-ray Induced Sensitivity to Heat in an Insect, *Radiation Res.*, **8**: 17 (1958).

55. D. S. Grosch and R. L. Sullivan, The Quantitative Aspects of Permanent Sterility Induced in Female Habrobracon by X-rays and β Radiation, *Radiation Res.*, **1**: 294 (1954).

56. A. R. Whiting, Sensitivity to X-rays of Different Meiotic Stages in Unlaid Eggs of Habrobracon, *J. Exptl. Zool.*, **83**: 249 (1940).

57. R. Hussey, W. Thompson, R. Tennant, and N. Campbell, Effects of Radiations on Biological Systems. I. Influence of High-frequency X-irradiation on Duration of Prepupal Period of Drosophila, *J. Gen. Physiol.*, **16**: 207 (1932).

58. A. R. Whiting, Failure of Pupation of *Ephestia* Larvae Following Exposure to X-rays, *Anat. Record*, **108**: 609 (1950).

59. M. Horikawa and T. Sugahara, Studies on the Effects of Radiation on Living Cells

in Tissue Culture. I. Radiosensitivity of Various Imaginal Discs and Organs in Larvae of *Drosophila melanogaster*, *Radiation Res.*, **12**: 266 (1960).

60. W. P. Davey, The Effect of X-rays on the Length of Life of *Tribolium confusum*, *J. Exptl. Zool.*, **22**: 573 (1917).

61. W. P. Davey, Prolongation of Life of *Tribolium confusum* Apparently Due to Small Doses of X-rays, *J. Exptl. Zool.*, **28**: 447 (1919).

62. D. S. Grosch and R. L. Sullivan, The Effect of Ingested Radiophosphorus on Egg Production and Embryo Survival in the Wasp *Habrobracon*, *Biol. Bull.*, **102**: 128 (1952).

63. J. M. Cork, Gamma-radiation and Longevity of the Flour-beetle, *Radiation Res.*, **7**: 551 (1957).

64. C. Melville, An Apparent Beneficial Effect of Radiation on the Flour Mite, *Nature*, **181**: 1403 (1958).

65. D. S. Grosch, Induced Lethargy and the Radiation Control of Insects, *J. Econ. Entomol.*, **49**: 629 (1956).

66. W. I. Rogers and J. D. Hilchey, Studies on the Post-irradiation Feeding Activity of *Tribolium castaneum* (Tenebrionidae: Coleoptera), *Ann. Entomol. Soc. Am.*, **53**: 584 (1960).

67. R. Blumenthal and M. D. Williams, Effects of Radium on the O_2 Consumption of Grasshopper Eggs, *Anat. Record*, **41**: 45 (1928).

68. T. C. Evans, Respiration and Visible Development of Individual Grasshopper Eggs Following X-irradiation, *Physiol. Zool.*, **7**: 556 (1934).

69. S. R. Tipton and G. S. Amand, The Effect of X-rays on the Respiratory Metabolism of Eggs and Embryos of the Grasshopper *Chortophaga viridifasciata*, *Physiol. Zool.*, **27**: 311 (1954).

70. T. N. Tahmisian and D. M. Adamson, Oxidase Increase in *Melanoplus differentialis* Eggs Caused by X-irradiation, *J. Exptl. Zool.*, **115**: 379 (1950).

71. R. C. Von Borstel, Feulgen-negative Nuclear Division in *Habrobracon* Eggs after Lethal Exposure to X-rays or Nitrogen Mustard, *Nature*, **175**: 342 (1955).

72. D. R. A. Wharton and M. L. Wharton, Effects of Radiation on Nitrogen and Phosphorus Excretion by the Cockroach, *Periplaneta americana* L., *Radiation Res.*, **14**: 432 (1961).

73. O. Hug, Biological Effects of Small Radiation Doses, *Intern. Atomic Energy Assoc. Bull.*, **1**: 7 (1959).

74. S. I. Auerbach, D. A. Crossley, and M. D. Engelman, Effects of Radiation on Collembola Population Growth, *Science*, **126**: 614 (1957).

75. H. F. Howden and S. L. Auerbach, Some Effects of Gamma Radiation on *Trogoderma sternale* (Jayne), *Ann. Entomol. Soc. Am.*, **51**: 48 (1958).

76. R. W. Rogers and R. C. Von Borstel, Particle Bombardment of the *Habrobracon* Egg. I. Sensitivity of the Nucleus, *Radiation Res.*, **7**: 484 (1957).

77. R. C. Von Borstel and R. W. Rogers, Particle Bombardment of the *Habrobracon* Egg. II. Response of the Cytoplasm, *Radiation Res.*, **8**: 248 (1958).

78. R. C. Von Borstel and H. Moser, Differential UV Irradiation of the *Habrobracon* Egg Nucleus and Cytoplasm, in *Progress in Radiobiology*, J. S. Mitchell, B. E. Holmes, and C. L. Smith (Eds.), pp. 211-215, Oliver and Boyd, Edinburgh, 1956.

79. J. G. Carlson and N. G. Harrington, X-ray Induced "Stickiness" of the Chromosomes of the *Chortophaga* Neuroblast in Relation to Dose and Mitotic Stage at Treatment, *Radiation Res.*, **2**: 84 (1955).

80. T. J. Arnason, R. L. Irwin, and J. W. T. Spinks, Some Effects of P^{32} on the Development of *Drosophila, Can. J. Res.*, **27D**: 186 (1949).

81. R. C. King, Studies with Radiophosphorus in *Drosophila*. III. The Lethal Effect of P^{32} Treatment upon Developing Flies, *J. Exptl. Zool.*, **126**: 323 (1954).

82. D. S. Grosch, R. L. Sullivan, and L. E. LaChance, The Comparative Effectiveness of 4 β-emitting Isotopes Fed to *Habrobracon* Females on Production and Hatchability of Eggs, *Radiation Res.*, **5**: 281 (1956).

83. G. Courtois and J. Lecomte, The Resistance to a γ Irradiation of the Worker Bee, *Ann. Abeille*, **4**: 285 (1959).

84. G. Heidenthal, The Occurrence of X-ray Induced Dominant Lethal Mutations in *Habrobracon, Genetics*, **30**: 197 (1945).

85. V. H. Baker, O. Taboada, and D. E. Wiant, Lethal Effect of Electrons on Insects Which Infest Wheat Flour and Beans. Part I, *Agr. Eng.*, **34**: 755 (1953).

86. A. M. Clark, The Relation of Genome Number to Radiosensitivity in *Habrobracon, Am. Natural.*, **41**: 111 (1957).

87. C. C. Hassett and D. W. Jenkins, Uses of Fission Products for Insect Control, *Nucleonics*, **10**: 42 (1952).

88. R. L. Sullivan and D. S. Grosch, The Radiation Tolerance of an Adult Wasp, *Nucleonics*, **11**: 21 (1953).

89. M. L. Wharton and D. R. A. Wharton, The Production of Sex Attractant Substance and of Oothecae by the Normal and Irradiated American Cockroach, *Periplaneta americana* L, *J. Insect Physiol.*, **1**: 229 (1957).

CHAPTER 3

Tagging

Radioisotopes are commonly used to mark particular molecules or atoms, as, for instance, when one uses glucose-C^{14} to study glucose absorption or Na^{24} to measure sodium movements. An alternative is to use them merely as markers for some vehicle which cannot itself be rendered radioactive but which can carry a radioactive substance. This latter alternative is the one considered in this chapter, as applied to the tagging of insects or their food-stuffs in order to follow dispersal, measure population densities, or examine behavior.

Tagging has been used most often to determine the extent and direction of dispersion of insects. Insects are either trapped or reared, labeled with a radioisotope, and released at one or a few centers. Fairly extensive trapping is conducted thereafter, and the numbers of tagged specimens found at various locations give the desired information.

What are the advantages of tagging with radioisotopes rather than with conventional markers such as pigments or dyes? Pigments often rub off or become localized around halteres.[1] Molting or pupating will eliminate an external label, but internal tagging with a radioisotope avoids this problem. It is tedious to examine large batches of collected insects for a few colored ones, whereas a quick check with a Geiger counter can reveal at once if radioactive flies are present. Another consideration is that one can combine radioisotope tagging with dyes, and so double label. As described below, this permits releases from two places (or at different times) and can add greatly to the scope of a study. Finally, one can follow isotopically labeled insects that are out of sight (e.g., underground) and thus get information available in no other way.

However, contrary arguments have been presented by experienced workers. Kettlewell[2] argued that for locust research isotopic labeling had no advantage over orthodox pigment labeling, because ". . . untrained workers can see and record these, whereas radioactive locusts demand highly skilled technicians using special apparatus." This view would seem to exaggerate the skills required and neglect the rapidity of checking and the relative permanence (especially while the insects are molting) of isotope techniques. In this locust work, Kettlewell reports that with P^{32} one could detect labeled insects at a distance of 10 in. for a period of 2 weeks.

The question of which radioisotope to use has all too seldom been studied experimentally. Major factors are safety, availability, ease of application and detection, damage to the insect, half-life of the isotope, and economy. A comparative study by Rings and Layne[3] compared P^{32}, Co^{60}, Sr^{89}, Zn^{65}, and I^{131} as tracers for the plum curculio, *Conotrachelus nenuphar*. Inorganic salts of these elements were fed either in water or via peach-tree twigs. Iodine-131 was ineffective, perhaps owing to its short half-life of 8 days. Cobalt-60 was most persistent (half-life 5.3 years) and proved most effective. However, its gamma emission implied some hazard, and it was not distributed well in plants. Strontium-89 had a convenient half-life (55 days), and its strong beta emission made detection easy, but as a "bone seeker" it was a trifle hazardous to use. Zinc-65 was poor in this particular experiment because of its low specific activity. Phosphorus-32 represented the ideal with respect to safety, activity, and ease of detection, and its only drawback was its short half-life of 14 days. And, indeed, the most popular radioisotope for tagging is P^{32}.

Where prolonged observations must be made, the short half-life of P^{32} is a disadvantage. In 10 weeks the activity would be only 3% of the starting level. This problem arose in a study[4] of the boll weevil, *Anthonomus grandis*, in which observations were required over a 5-month period. An effective procedure was to dip the insects in a solution of $Co^{60}Cl_2$, at a concentration of 5 μc/ml. Dipped weevils averaged 710 counts/minute each, a value which could be increased, by adding detergent, to 4690 counts/minute. The same need of a long half-life dictated the use of Co^{60} for tagging the white-pine weevil *Pissodes strobi;* in this case the isotope was "spotted" onto the insect by using an acetone solution of Co^{60} (NO_3) and cellulose acetate.[5]

Other workers needing a persistent label have recommended Ce^{144}. It has a half-life of 282 days; it appears to bind to tissues (in an unknown way) and is therefore retained well in the body; and it has a short-lived daughter, Pr^{144}, half-life 18 minutes, which emits an energetic beta particle of 2.97 Mev, which can be easily detected. Cerium-144 has been used[6] with fleas, mosquitoes, ticks, cockroaches, and other insects, which are tagged by bathing in a water solution (10 μc/ml) or by applying aqueous solutions (1 μl of 1 μc/ml) externally. Count rates between 90 and 7500 counts/minute per insect were described.

Toxicity to the insect is a serious problem. Not only does it reduce the number of labeled individuals, but it may lead to serious errors in interpretation of results. It is a requirement for these techniques that the labeled insect behave precisely as the unlabeled. Toxicity may be associated with particular isotopes. For instance, Ca^{45} and I^{131} were very toxic when fed to adult houseflies at 1 μc per milliliter of milk, whereas P^{32} was satisfactory.[7] In other cases, particular techniques may be satisfactory where a minor variation may fail: dipping lone star ticks (*Amblyomma americanum*) in a solution of $NaH_2P^{32}O_4$ at 10 µc/ml was successful, but, if a wetting agent was included, labeling was less and mortalities were high.[8] However, other workers with houseflies and fleshflies found a wetting agent was necessary and gave no mortalities with P^{32} at 5 µc/ml; and yet 80% of aphids were killed by such a procedure.[9]

1. Methods

Insects for labeling are often reared for the purpose. It has been pointed out[1] that this procedure commonly involves creating an entirely artificial, high, local population at the release point and may thereby vitiate the results. The alternative is to capture, label, and release insects all at one site.

Rearing procedures most commonly use inorganic P^{32} for a label. Perhaps the earliest example was published in 1949 by Hassett and Jenkins,[10] who reared larvae of the yellow-fever mosquito *Aedes aegypti* in water containing up to 1 µc/ml; higher concentrations were deleterious. Adults with up to 10,000 counts/minute each were produced. A week after this report, Bugher and Taylor[11] proposed essentially the same procedure. Problems were reported in using this method for rice field mosquitoes.[12] A variant was to add the radioisotope to small natural pools of water (at only 0.3 µc/liter) and thereby label the indigenous mosquito population.[13] Counts up to 5100 per adult were obtained. Larval rearing in vats was applied on a very large scale to blackflies[14] by using 0.2 µc of P^{32} per milliliter. By this means, 800,000 larvae were tagged and released, with counts up to 50,000 counts/minute each.* But as only a single labeled insect was recaptured (out of 6000 unlabeled adults trapped), this concentration of P^{32} may have been deleterious.

A detailed study of the conditions affecting mosquito tagging with P^{32} compared stage, age, P^{32} concentration, and so on.[15] Third-instar larvae were optimal, younger larvae were too radiosensitive, and older larvae and pupae absorbed little phosphorus. The maximum concentration in the water was 0.1 µc/ml; mortalities were high above this level. Females took up three times as much as males and averaged 15,858 counts/minute each; they thus concentrated the P^{32} about 75 times over the concentration in the medium.

Larvae of screw-worm flies (*Callitroga americana*) have been reared on a labeled medium, using 0.5 µc of inorganic P^{32} per gram of a ground-meat medium.[16] Similar procedures were successful for the oriental fruit fly *Dacus dorsalis*.[17]

In one of the few cases where the effectiveness of feeding a radioisotope

---

* Estimated from reported value of 500,000 disintegrations per minute.

to adults and to larvae was compared, adult feeding was superior.[18] Larvae of houseflies and secondary screw-worms (*Callitroga macellaria*) fed on a medium with 0.1 μc of P^{32} per gram gave adults averaging 100 counts/minute, wheras feeding adults on milk with 1 μc/ml gave counts of 1100 for males and 2000 for females. Adult feeding is now used widely for various species and has the advantage of permitting labeling of captured insects. Typical procedures involve feeding houseflies on sugar water with 1.7 μc of inorganic P^{32} per milliliter.[19] Gnats have also been so labeled.[20,21]

However, in spite of the success of adult-feeding methods, a comparative study by Donnelly[22] showed that larval feeding of the greenbottle (*Lucilia sericata*) gave far more uniform labeling, with a coefficient of variation of 16%. This contrasted with a 25-fold variation of labeling with adults fed on milk.

Adverse changes in the ovaries of houseflies have been shown as a result of feeding adults for several days on milk containing the enormous dose of 0.23 mc of inorganic P^{32} per gram.[23]

A double label has been used[7] to locate points of release; houseflies were tagged by feeding on milk containing P^{32}, and also by dusting them with one of several dyes. When a radioactive fly was recovered later, it was washed off with acetone onto a filter paper to give colored spot from the dye. By using a different dye for each release point, quite elaborate release-and-recovery experiments were possible.

Another labeling procedure involves submersion. A simple device for submerging quantities of insects in radioactive solutions has been described.[24] In this case, 20% ethanol was suggested to aid wetting of the insects, and NaI^{131}, $Sc^{46}Cl_3$, and $Na_2Ir^{192}Cl_6$ were effective as markers. The technique was used[25] with $Sc^{46}Cl_3$ (a gamma and hard beta emitter with a half-life of 85 days) to show that the white-pine weevil *Pissodes strobi* disperses over areas up to 600 ft from release points—a piece of information of assistance in determining the placement of experimental plots near infested areas.

Some workers have chosen to attach radioactive objects to insects. Pieces of radioactive wire, made of Co^{60} and gold plated to prevent corrosion, have been used[26] to tag the wireworm *Melanotus communis*. The wire, 1 mm long and 0.5 mm in diameter, was stuck to the outside of the wireworm with a plastic cement. The wireworms were released into soil, and their location was subsequently determined by an end-window Geiger tube and rate meter. The procedure was used[27] to show the way in which both horizontal and vertical movements were affected by soil treatments. A repellent effect was commonly noted with all treatments (aldrin, dieldrin, lindane, heptachlor) when wireworms were given a choice between treated and untreated soils. A variant on the above procedure was the use of Ta^{182}. This can be obtained as strips or wires, and 0.05 × 0.16 mm strips have been used[28] to label coccinellid larvae. The strip was glued to the prothorax of the insect. It increased the weight 24%, to 0.192 mg, but apparently had no ill effect on larval movement or molting.

Beetles of the *Agriotes* genus were labeled[29] by gluing under their wing cases sandwiches of 2 mm aluminum discs containing 5 µg of radium. The weight, 2 mg, was said not to hinder the 36-mg insect. (It would be comparable to a 10-lb weight carried by a 180-lb man.) The tagged beetles could be located through 3 in. of soil by use of an end-window counter.

Finally, we should consider indirect methods of labeling, in which a plant or animal is rendered radioactive and used as a food source for insects. Barnes[30] has sprayed foliage with a solution of 50 µc of inorganic P^{32} per milliliter in corn protein hydrolyzate to label the walnut husk fly *Rhagoletis completa*. The flies averaged 8022 counts/minute, and 15% of those captured in the orchard were labeled. This is a way of tagging an indigenous population without even capturing it.

Sulfur labeling has been used[31] in marking Lepidoptera. Food plants were grown in water containing 100 µc of S^{35} per liter and were offered to the larvae. One gathers that counts up to 417 counts/minute were obtained using the moths *Panaxia dominula* and *Arctia caja*. Although S^{35} has a convenient half-life of 87 days, it is a weak beta emitter (0.168 Mev) and therefore a poor choice for tagging. Aphids have been tagged[32] by feeding them on bean plants watered with a solution of inorganic P^{32}. However, a study with locusts[2] showed no advantage in feeding plants grown hydroponically with P^{32} over feeding the insects wheat bran treated with inorganic P^{32}.

Screw-worm flies have been tagged[16] by injecting P^{32} intravenously into goats or sheep, at 0.1 µc per gram body weight, and rearing the screw-worm larvae in wounds on the animals. Counts of 2500 counts/minute per adult fly were obtained in a sheep experiment, and half as much with a cow.

A procedure has been described[33] which permits labeling of spermatozoa and which should be useful in examining copulatory mechanisms, competition between males, and so on. Half-grown larvae of the brown spider beetle *Ptinus hirtellus* were injected with 10 µl of a solution of adenine-8-C^{14}. In *Drosophila*, larvae could be fed on a medium containing the labeled compound. Heavy labeling of particular sperm bundles was observed in the subsequent adults.

Let us now consider briefly the ways in which insects are trapped and examined for radioactivity.

Insects may be caught with baited or light traps. Typical numbers used are 24 in an area of up to 12 miles' radius.[1] It has been pointed out[34] that an artifact often enters into dispersion studies in which the collecting sites per unit area are frequently much more concentrated in central than in distant zones, so that recoveries would seem low in the distant zones, even if distribution were in fact uniform.

Detection methods for tagged flies include trapping, killing, and examining the dead insects or, alternatively, examining living flies at bait stations with a Geiger counter. With this latter method, 10 labeled flies could be found in an inch-thick layer of 50,000 unlabeled flies in less than a minute.[18] However, it was felt that trapping and killing were more efficient in that less counting time had to be spent each day.

Automation of sample counting may permit more extensive studies. A suitable apparatus has been described[35] which utilizes a strip scanner normally used to scan paper-chromatogram strips. The specimens were attached to the strip—for instance, by depositing them in small planchettes—and the results were recorded automatically. Presumably, an automatic planchette counter would do as well. In one case detection was carried out by crushing aphids, each in a numbered square on a glass plate, applying them to a photographic plate, and developing 30 days later. The procedure is obviously inconvenient and slow, but very sensitive. A factor of interest was that the radioactivity was "inherited" for at least two generations.

A fantastically elaborate machine has been built[36] to follow the position and depth of wireworms in soil; it prints out time and position at intervals. The list of components occupies a full printed page. The insect is labeled with 20 µc of Co^{60} (a large dose) and can be followed through 15 in. of soil.

2. Results: Distribution Studies

Unfortunately, the results of these studies do not lend themselves very well to general discussion. They tend to be particular rather than general and are mostly used to answer special problems concerning particular species in particular areas. By contrast, a successful biochemical study has virtually universal validity for that particular species. The results selected for brief discussion here are only expected to illustrate the kinds of problems studied and the sort of results obtained.

Several experiments have been made on dispersion of houseflies and fleshflies to throw light on their potentialities as disease vectors. In one study,[7] a total of over 7000 individuals, which consisted almost entirely of four genera, were released after tagging by feeding adults on milk with P^{32}, and 1.3% were recovered. The study was in an urban area (Savannah, Georgia). It showed that dispersion was rapid, continuous, and undirected, and the majority of the flies moved from 1 to 4 miles. Some traveled 7.6 miles.

A follow-up study[37] was designed to overcome the possibility that the previous results were affected by the artificial release conditions, for the areas would not normally support (or attract) such populations. In the follow-up, flies were trapped, labeled by feeding, and released, all at the same spot. In this case a rural area in Georgia was studied. The results were substantially similar. Some flies moved 5 miles in under 24 hours. The two studies show that houseflies roam constantly within a large area from 8 to 10 miles in diameter. However, an earlier study[38] indicated that over 80% normally remain within a mile of the release point. A constant flux occurs, so that the large numbers at attractive places are not due to an absence of leavers but to a preponderance of arrivals over leavers.

A similar study on a larger scale was made in Arizona[34] when 342,000 tagged houseflies were released, this time from various points of potential attractiveness, such as a hog farm and a poultry ranch. About 1% of them were recovered. There was a suggestion of variation in attractiveness of these sites: for instance, flies released at the poultry ranch dispersed an average of 0.72 miles; those at the hog farm, 1.5 miles. However, statistical evaluation of these data was not possible.

An attempt was made in Arizona[39] to answer the question, "Do flies wander haphazardly, or do they move more directly?" Flies, primarily the housefly, *Musca domestica*, and species of *Phaenicia*, were captured, transported to the site, tagged by feeding on labeled milk, and released in quantity (171,000 simultaneously). For the next two days, individuals that were recovered at each of three stations (15 traps) were marked with specific colors and released again. Seventy traps were used to recover these doubly labeled flies: 155 were found, compared with 7263 radioactive but not dyed. The picture that emerged was of random roaming, by no means in a direct way. The authors suggested an inherent instinct to wander, which maximized the chance transmission of pathogens from infected sources to potential receptors.

A substantially similar conclusion was drawn[40] for the salt-marsh mosquito *Aedes taeniorhyncus* as the result of an extensive study involving release of 1 million tagged adults and trapping of 6.5 million adults.

Another potential disease vector, the American cockroach, has been studied by P[32] tagging to determine its movements within a sewage system.[41] The manholes in Phoenix, Arizona each harbor (on the average) over a hundred cockroaches, and the intrepid investigators captured 6500 insects for tagging. The insects were sprayed with a solution containing (presumably) inorganic P[32], with casein as a sticker. The unexpected finding was that in spite of "overloading" four manholes with about 1600 tagged cockroaches each, only a single tagged specimen was discovered elsewhere in the sewage system. Recovery of the tagged insects from the release points was quite good (906 out of the 6500). The involvement of this insect in disease transmission within sewage systems is therefore negligible.

A study of the movement of *Drosophila melanogaster* and *Drosophila repleta* between pit privies and nearby houses showed extensive interchange, even at distances of 500 feet for *Drosophila melanogaster* and 1000 feet for *Drosophila repleta*, thus underlining the potential role of these insects as disease vectors.[19]

It will be clear from the foregoing that the extent of recovery is an important factor in tagging experiments. An early study[1] in 1951 used three species of flies: 36,000 *Musca*, 1200 black blow flies, *Phormia regina*, and 15,000 *Phaenicia sericata*. An amazing 14% of *Phormia* was recovered in the 24 traps, compared to 5% of *Musca* and 4% of *Phaenicia*. Presumably, these high recoveries were a reflection of the ability of the traps (which were of sugar and decomposed liver) to compete with indigenous attractants. In a later experiment[42] with release of P^{32}-tagged *Musca* and *Phormia*, about 3% were recovered. There was no radical difference between these genera.

In some cases the recoveries have been vanishingly small. Mention was made above of the recovery of one specimen after releasing 800,000 black flies. Another example occurred with aphids[32]: 1600 tagged green peach aphids, *Myzus persicae*, were released on sugar beet plants. Two days later collections began and continued for 3 weeks, but only a single tagged specimen was ever found.

Isotopic techniques designed to indicate whether an insect has fed on a given source have been used in studies of repellency.[43] *Aedes* mosquitoes were fed through artificial membranes on blood to which varying concentrations of the repellent diethyltoluamide had been added. It was found that 0.065% of the repellent in the blood totally stopped feeding. It was also shown by spreading inorganic P^{32} in Carbowax over the membrane that at this concentration of diethyltoluamide mosquitoes did land on the membrane, but they left rapidly without inserting the proboscis. Consequently, contact repellency plays at least some role in the action of this compound.

A somewhat different approach to feeding studies[44] was to label a single plant, a thistle, with the gigantic dose of 1 mc of (presumably) inorganic P^{32} and to examine for radioactivity the many insect visitors to the plant. The study shed light on the territoriality of ants: it was found that no ants (*Formica sanguina puberula*) from a heap 26 ft away were radioactive, whereas *all* those from another heap 16 ft away were labeled, with counts up to 15,000 counts/minute each. All this radioactivity was from honeydew taken from aphids, which themselves had far lower counts (250 counts/minute).

Insects have been used as devices for labeling parasites for which the insect is a vector. Workers in Ceylon[45] reared larvae of mosquitoes, *Armigerea obturbans*, in water containing 1 μc of inorganic P^{32} per milliliter and then let the subsequent adults feed on cows or men infected with microfilaria. The mosquitoes were heavily labeled, giving 7×10^5 counts/minute, and the filaria larvae (*Setaria digitata*) gave 174 counts/minute, enough to permit tracing their passage through host tissues either by counting or radioautographically.

Tagging can be used to determine the density of a population by the capture-recapture method. A known number of insects is captured, labeled, and released, and, after thorough equilibration with the total population, insects are collected. The ratio of total captured insects to labeled captured insects can be used to calculate the total number from the number of labeled

TABLE 3.1

DENSITY OF ANT COLONIES ESTIMATED BY THE CAPTURE-RECAPTURE METHOD[a]

Colony	Number tagged	Number collected		Estimate of density[b]		Difference in estimate
		Sample 1	Sample 2	From sample 1	From sample 2	
1	500	437	46	3174 ± 348	2136 ± 540	49%
2	600	321	134	2147 ± 191	4050 ± 915	89%
3	500	189	153	5278 ± 1152	6417 ± 1709	22%

[a] From Odum and Pontin,[46] with additions.

[b] The density estimates are ± variance. Time between samples 1 and 2 was 5 days for colonies 1 and 2, 2 days for colony 3.

insects initially released. It is surprising that this technique has been used so little with radioisotopes. Although there are problems, such as assuming proper equilibration and avoiding biased recapture, the method represents the only feasible way to estimate total populations when total counting is impracticable.

One study along these lines[46] involved the ant *Lasius flavus*, which was tagged by immersing in a solution of inorganic P^{32}. Table 3.1 shows the data for three of the colonies. By recapturing on two occasions a few days apart, two estimates of the size of each colony were made. As one can see, the agreement of the two estimates was fair, not as good as the variance figures might seem to suggest.

3. Results: Feeding Studies

The experiments described so far have been concerned with locating individual insects. Nonspecific labeling of foodstuffs has also been widely used in order to study feeding as a social function, as in the transfer of food within insect colonies, or as an individual matter, in the study of food or water intake and transfer of plant juices between plants.

There has long been an interest in following the feeding behavior of phytophagous insects and particularly that of disease vectors such as aphids. As long ago as 1935, Miss Hamilton[47] described the use of the α-emitter, polonium, as a tracer in aphid transmission and measured its activity with a gold-leaf electroscope. The insects (*Myzus persicae*) were fed through an excised plant membrane on agar containing polonium and were shown to imbibe 1.38 µl per 100 aphids per day. When these labeled insects were allowed to feed on leaves, a remarkably constant 6.9 ± 0.007% of the imbibed radioactivity was imparted to the leaf. The outsides of the leaves were washed to avoid counting possible excreta.

Miss Hamilton's work was reinvestigated by Australian workers[48] in 1953. Aphids were fed either on leaves from cabbages grown in a P^{32} solution or through a plastic membrane on a sucrose solution labeled with inorganic P^{32}. *Myzus* took up 69 µg of plant material in an hour (35% of its weight); and the cabbage aphid, *Brevicoryne brassicae*, 2.7 µg. These figures were computed from the average radioactivity in leaf tissues and the radioactivity taken up by the insects. When imbibing sucrose, *Myzus* took up only about 3% of its plant value, but *Brevicoryne brassicae* fed as readily as on plants. Clearly then, these artificial systems can be very misleading for some species. Excretion was very varable: up to 7% of the total uptake was excreted in an hour. Finally, it was shown that both species did reinject imbibed material, but only up to 0.5% of the imbibed dose was reinjected in a day—substantially less than the 6.9% shown by Miss Hamilton for *Myzus*. The discrepancy was firmly attributed by the Australians to labeled excreta being absorbed by the plant in Hamilton's study and counted as reinjected.

About the same time, Miss Hamilton published under her married name[49] a revised version of her studies of 18 years earlier. This time the aphids were fed on various plants grown in a soluton containing P^{32}, as in the Australian work. The results agree with the latter. Many observations were made on the time course of P^{32} uptake, and it was clear that for the first hour of feeding the intake was very slow. There was evidence that this was caused by a delay in penetrating to the phloem.

The jassid *Orosius argentatus* is a virus vector of importance in Australia. Transmission of P^{32} from a beet plant grown in a P^{32}-containing medium to other plants was not detected,[50] even though P^{32} uptake and excretion were vigorous; the percentage of the intake excreted in 24 hours fluctuated widely from 19 to 72% and averaged 35%. It was calculated that the insects each ingested about 0.38 µg of plant material per minute, or 2.5% of their own weight in 1 hour.

Transmission of tobacco plant juices by *Myzus* was accomplished[51] by feeding the aphids on tobacco plants grown in soil treated with P^{32}-phosphoric acid. The aphids were then placed on unlabeled plants. Numerous spots of radioactivity were shown after 6 days, and this was not caused by external honeydew or by absorption of honeydew, as shown by independent experiments. Translocation of radioactivity to other leaves of the plant was also found. Similar results have been reported[52] for the two-spotted mite, *Tetranychus telarius*, feeding on beans.

In 1945, Carter[53] fed pineapple mealybugs, *Pseudococcus brevipes*, on labeled agar blocks and found transmission of radioactivity to other agar blocks, as measured by an electroscope. The agar-fed insects also transferred radioactivity to leaves and roots of pineapple plants to which they were later applied. However, contamination by excreta was not rigorously excluded.

As in the case of many sucking insects, the damage done by the tarnished plant bug, *Lygus lineolaris*, to carrots and related crops is very large compared to the extent of feeding, and injection of some toxicant is suspected. In a study of this problem,[54] it was found necessary to label the insects with huge amounts of P^{32} in order to detect injection. By feeding the adults on sucrose containing up to 0.3 mc of inorganic P^{32} per milliliter, counts of up to 613,100 counts/minute per insect were obtained. Mortalities of 58% were found, perhaps due in part to this high activity. Transfer of some of this radioactivity to bean plants was indeed found, but the highest counts found were 61 counts/minute, and only in 10 out of 18 experiments was the count significantly over background. Care was taken to avoid contamination with excrement, but, nevertheless, such small counts make the claim of detection of injection somewhat dubious, since a tiny percentage of the undoubtedly highly radioactive excrement could produce the observed result. In a later study,[55] drops of saliva were collected from the labeled insects, and their radioactivity was assayed: it varied between 66 and 1300 counts/minute per microliter. Individual insects were then fed on plants, and it was calculated that during feeding, which lasted from 20 to 108 minutes, a volume of between 0.038 and 0.251 µl of saliva was transmitted.

The use of P^{32} has made it possible to evaluate the water intake of individual mites.[56] *Tetranychus telarius* was fed on water containing inorganic P^{32} and took in from 1.3 to 4.6 mµl in an hour, which was of the order of 25% of the body weight. The figure gives some picture of the colossal water problems that the mite deals with.

Can some mosquitoes produce viable eggs without a blood meal? Some evidence favored the possibility that certain species of northern mosquitoes might be able to feed satisfactorily on plants. Cut flowers were placed in vials with their ends immersed in water containing inorganic P^{32} (9 μc/ml), and it was shown[57] that *Aedes communis* mosquitoes ingested juices from the plants, for many insects became radioactive, with counts up to 6870 counts/ minute.

The effect upon bean aphids (*Aphis fabae*) of their nurse ants (*Lasius niger*) has been studied by feeding the aphids on beans grown in P^{32}-labeled water.[58] It was shown that ant-attended aphids excreted twice as much honeydew (as measured by excreted P^{32}) as did unattended aphids and presumably consumed twice as much to accomplish this. The evidence therefore supported the notion that ant-attended colonies flourished because of assisted excretion and consumption.

Oertel[59] has shown that drone honey bees are fed by workers. Drones were exposed in a cage with unlabeled sucrose syrup available and separated by a screen from worker bees which had sucrose-C^{14} syrup available. The drones became radioactive as a result of being fed sucrose by the workers.

Sugar syrup mixed with inorganic P^{32} was used[60] to study food transfer in beehives. Six bees were trained to collect from the dish, and the subsequent radioactivity in the 24,500-member colony was observed. Within 4 hours, 19% of all bees, and 62% of the foragers, were radioactive. Within a day, 52% of all bees were tagged, and all the cells of the comb contained radioactivity. The radioactivity in bees was always internal, and food transmission is therefore the vehicle. The academic significance of this rapid spreading is its potential utility for information dissemination; a practical conclusion is that flower contamination by insecticide could rapidly contaminate a whole hive.

Honey transmission in ants was studied using NaI^{131} as a label.[61] A few workers were withdrawn from each nest and given access to the tagged honey for a day, then reintroduced into the nest, and the progress of transmission of radioactivity was examined. The transmission varied widely among species; in the primitive Florida harvester ant, *Pogonomyrmex badius*, less than 10% of adults became labeled in 11 days; in the more specialized imported fire ant, *Solenopsis saevissima*, 65% were labeled in 3 days; and in the highly specialized *Crematogaster lineolata*, more than 90% were labeled in 30 hours. Similar studies[62] with the termite *Calotermes flavicollis* showed rapid transfer; in 35 hours, all insects were labeled.

REFERENCES

1. A. W. Lindquist, W. W. Yates, and R. A. Hoffman, Studies of the Flight Habits of Three Species of Flies Tagged with Radioactive Phosphorous, *J. Econ. Entomol.*, **44**: 397 (1951).
2. H. B. D. Kettlewell, Labelling Locusts with Radioactive Isotopes, *Nature*, **175**: 821 (1955).

3. R. W. Rings and C. W. Layne, Comparative Effectiveness of 5 Radioisotopes as Tracers in Studying Dispersal of *Conotrachelus nenuphar, Ohio J. Sci.,* **54**: 231 (1954).

4. F. H. Babers, C. C. Roan, and R. L. Walker, Tagging Boll Weevils With Radioactive Cobalt, *J. Econ. Entomol.,* **47**: 928 (1954).

5. C. R. Sullivan, Use of Radioactive Cobalt in Tracing the Movements of the White-pine Weevil, *Pissodes strobi* Peck (Coleoptera; Curculionidae), *Can. Entomol.,* **85**: 273 (1953).

6. S. F. Quan, W. V. Hartwell, K. G. Scott, and C. T. Peng, Cerium[44] as a Tag for Arthropods of Medical Importance, *Trans. Roy. Soc. Trop. Med. Hyg.,* **51**: 87 (1957).

7. K. D. Quarterman, W. Mathis, and J. W. Kilpatrick, Urban Fly Dispersal in the Area of Savannah, Georgia, *J. Econ. Entomol.,* **47**: 405 (1954).

8. S. E. Knapp, C. J. Farinacci, C. M. Herbert, and E. L. Saenger, A Method for Labeling the Lone Star Tick (*Amblyomma americanum*) with a Radioactive Indicator (P[32]), *J. Econ. Entomol.,* **49**: 393 (1956).

9. A. R. Roth and R. A. Hoffman, A New Method of Tagging Insects with P[32], *J. Econ. Entomol.,* **45**: 1091 (1952).

10. C. C. Hassett and D. W. Jenkins, Production of Radioactive Mosquitoes, *Science,* **110**: 109 (1949).

11. J. C. Bugher and M. Taylor, Radiophosphorus and Radiostrontium in Mosquitoes. Preliminary Report, *Science,* **110**: 146 (1949).

12. K. D. Quarterman, J. A. Jensen, W. Mathis, and W. W. Smith, Flight Dispersal of Rice Field Mosquitoes in Arkansas, *J. Econ. Entomol.,* **48**: 30 (1955).

13. D. W. Jenkins, A Field Method of Marking Arctic Mosquitoes with Radiophosphorus, *J. Econ. Entomol.,* **42**: 988 (1950).

14. F. J. H. Fredeen, J. W. T. Spinks, J. R. Anderson, A. P. Arnason, and J. G. Rempel, Mass Tagging of Black Flies (Diptera; Simuliidae) with Radiophosphorus, *Can. J. Zool.,* **31**: 1 (1953).

15. C. C. Hassett and D. W. Jenkins, The Uptake and Effect of Radiophosphorus in Mosquitoes, *Physiol. Zool.,* **24**: 257 (1951).

16. R. D. Radeleff, R. C. Bushland, and D. E. Hopkins, Phosphorus-32 Labelling of the Screw-worm Fly, *J. Econ. Entomol.,* **45**: 509 (1952).

17. C. C. Roan, Tagging Oriental Fruit Flies with Radioactive Phosphorus for Field-movement Studies, *J. Econ. Entomol.,* **45**: 826 (1952).

18. J. A. Jensen and R. W. Fay, Tagging of Adult House Flies and Flesh Flies with Radioactive Phosphorus, *Am. J. Trop. Med.,* **31**: 523 (1951).

19. D. Pimentel and R. W. Fay, Dispersion of Radioactively Tagged *Drosophila* from Pit Privies, *J. Econ. Entomol.,* **48**: 19 (1955).

20. R. P. Dow, Dispersal of Adult *Hippelates pusio,* the Eye Gnat, *Ann. Entomol. Soc. Am.,* **52**: 372 (1959).

21. M. S. Mulla and R. B. March, Flight Range, Dispersal Patterns, and Population Density of the Eye Gnat, *Hippelates collusor, Ann. Entomol. Soc. Am.,* **52**: 641 (1959).

22. J. Donnelly, Methods for the Study of Blowfly Populations. III. The Fate and Distribution of P[32] in Blowflies Labeled in the Larval Stage, *Ann. Appl. Biol.,* **46**: 243 (1958).

23. F. H. Babers and C. C. Roan, Distribution of Radioactive Phosphorus in Susceptible and Resistant Houseflies, *J. Econ. Entomol.,* **47**: 973 (1954).

24. J. M. Davis and R. H. Nagel, Technique for Tagging Large Numbers of Live Adult Insects with Radioisotopes, *J. Econ. Entomol.*, **49**: 210 (1956).

25. P. A. Godwin, H. A. Jaynes, and J. M. Davis, The Dispersion of Radioactively Tagged White-pine Weevils in Small Plantations, *J. Econ. Entomol.*, **50**: 264 (1957).

26. W. H. Long and J. H. Lilly, Wireworm Behaviour in Response to Chemical Seed Treatment, *J. Econ. Entomol.*, **51**: 291 (1958).

27. C. F. Fredericksen and J. H. Lilly, Measuring Wireworm Reactions to Soil Insecticides by Tagging with Radioactive Cobalt, *J. Econ. Entomol.*, **48**: 438 (1955).

28. C. J. Banks, The Use of Radioactive Tantalum in Studies of the Behaviour of Small Crawling Insects on Plants, *Brit. J. Animal Behavior*, **3**: 158 (1955).

29. M. V. Brian, On the Ecology of Beetles of the Genus *Agriotes* with Special Reference to *Agriotes obscurus*, *J. Animal Ecol.*, **16**: 210 (1947).

30. M. M. Barnes, Radiotracer Labeling of a Natural Tephritid Population and Flight Range of the Walnut Husk Fly, *Ann. Entomol. Soc. Am.*, **52**: 90 (1959).

31. H. B. D. Kettlewell, Use of Radioactive Tracer in the Study of Insect Populations (Lepidoptera), *Nature*, **170**: 584 (1952).

32. K. Bjorling, D. Lihnell, and F. Ossiannilson, Marking Viruliferous Aphids with Radioactive Phosphorus, *Acta Agr. Scand.*, **1**: 301 (1951).

33. J. Jacob and J. L. Sirlin, Labeling of Insect Spermatozoa by Adenine-C^{14}, *Experientia*, **14**: 402 (1958).

34. H. F. Schoof and R. E. Siverly, Multiple Release Studies on the Dispersion of *Musca domestica* at Phoenix, Arizona, *J. Econ. Entomol.*, **47**: 830 (1954).

35. E. P. Odum, R. P. Martin, and B. C. Loughman, Scanning Systems for the Rapid Determination of Radioactivity in Ecological Materials, *Ecology*, **43**: 171 (1962).

36. B. C. Green and J. W. T. Spinks, Automatic Plotting of the Position of a Moving Radioactively Tagged Object, *Can. J. Technol.*, **33**: 307 (1955).

37. K. D. Quarterman, J. W. Kilpatrick, and W. Mathis, Fly Dispersal in a Rural Area near Savannah, Ga., *J. Econ. Entomol.*, **47**: 413 (1954).

38. H. F. Schoof, R. E. Siverly, and J. A. Jensen, House Fly Dispersion Studies in Metropolitan Areas, *J. Econ. Entomol.*, **45**: 675 (1952).

39. H. F. Schoof and R. E. Siverly, Urban Fly Dispersion Studies with Special Reference to Movement Patterns of *Musca domestica*, *Am. J. Trop. Med. Hyg.*, **3**: 539 (1954).

40. M. W. Provost, The Dispersal of *Aedes taeniorhyncus*. I. Preliminary Studies, *Mosquito News*, **12**: 174 (1952).

41. H. F. Schoof and R. E. Siverly, The Occurrence and Movement of *Periplaneta americana* (L.) within an Urban Sewage System, *Am. J. Trop. Med. Hyg.*, **3**: 367 (1954).

42. W. W. Yates, A. W. Lindquist, and J. S. Butts, Further Studies on Dispersion of Flies Tagged with Radioactive Phosphoric Acid, *J. Econ. Entomol.*, **45**: 547 (1952).

43. M. Bar-Zeev and C. H. Schmidt, Action of a Repellent as Indicated by a Radioactive Tracer, *J. Econ. Entomol.*, **52**: 268 (1959).

44. R. C. Pendleton and A. W. Grundmann, Use of P^{32} in Tracing Some Insect-plant Relationships of Thistle, *Cirsium undulatum*, *Ecology*, **35**: 187 (1954).

45. A. S. Dissanaike, G. A. Dissanaike, W. J. Niles, and R. Surendranathan, Further Studies on Radioactive Mosquitoes and Filarial Larvae Using Autoradiographic Technique, *Exptl. Parasitol.*, **6**: 261 (1957).

46. E. P. Odum and A. J. Pontin, Population Density of the Underground Ant *Lasius flavus* as Determined by Tagging with P^{32}, *Ecology*, **42**: 186 (1961).

47. M. A. Hamilton, Further Experiments on the Artificial Feeding of *Myzus persicae* (Sulz.), *Ann. Appl. Biol.*, **22**: 243 (1935).

48. M. F. Day and H. Irzykiekwiez, Feeding Behavior of the Aphids *Myzus persicae* and *Brevicoryne brassicae*, Studied with Radio-phosphorus, *Austral. J. Biol. Sci.*, **6**: 98 (1953).

49. M. A. Watson and H. L. Nixon, Studies on the Feeding of *Myzus persicae* (Sulz.) on Radioactive Plants, *Ann. Appl. Biol.*, **40**: 537 (1953).

50. M. F. Day and A. McKinnon, A Study of Some Aspects of the Feeding of the Jassid Orosius, *Austral. J. Sci. Res. (B)*, **4**: 125 (1951).

51. F. R. Lawson, G. B. Lucas, and N. S. Hall, Translocation of Radioactive Phosphorus Injected by the Green Peach Aphid into Tobacco Plants, *J. Econ. Entomol.*, **47**: 749 (1954).

52. J. G. Rodriguez, Radiophosphorus in Metabolism Studies in the Two-spotted Spider Mite, *J. Econ. Entomol.*, **47**: 514 (1954).

53. W. Carter, Oral Secretions of the Pineapple Mealybug, *J. Econ. Entomol.*, **38**: 335 (1945).

54. F. Flemion, R. M. Weed, and L. P. Miller, Deposition of P^{32} into Host Tissue through the Oral Secretions of *Lygus oblineatus*, *Contrib. Boyce Thompson Inst.*, **16**: 285 (1951).

55. F. Flemion, L. P. Miller, and R. M. Weed, An Estimate of the Quantity of Oral Secretions Deposited by *Lygus* when Feeding on Bean Tissue, *Contrib. Boyce Thompson Inst.*, **16**: 429 (1952).

56. W. D. McEnroe, The Control of Water Loss by the Two-spotted Spider Mite (*Tetranychus telarius*), *Ann. Entomol. Soc. Am.*, **54**: 883 (1961).

57. A. S. West and D. W. Jenkins, Plant Feeding Habits of Northern Mosquitoes Studied with Radioisotopes, *Mosquito News*, **11**: 217 (1951).

58. C. J. Banks and H. L. Nixon, Effects of the Ant, *Lasius niger* L., on the Feeding and Excretion of the Bean Aphid, *Aphis fabae* Scop., *J. Exptl. Biol.*, **35**: 703 (1958).

59. E. Oertel, R. B. Emerson, and H. E. Wheeler, Transfer of Radioactivity from Worker to Drone Honey Bees After Ingestion of Radioactive Sucrose, *Ann. Entomol. Soc. Am.*, **46**: 596 (1953).

60. H. L. Nixon and C. R. Ribbands, Food Transmission Within the Honeybee Community, *Proc. Roy. Soc. (B)*, **140**: 43 (1952).

61. T. Eisner and E. O. Wilson, Radioactive Tracer Studies of Food Transmission in Ants, *10th Intern. Congr. Entomol., Proc.*, **2**: 509 (1956).

62. J. Alibert, Les Echanges Trophallactiques Chez le Termite a Cou Jaune (*Calotermes flavicollis* Fabr.) Études a l'Aide du Phosphore Radioactif, *Compt. Rend. Acad. Sci.*, **248**: 1040 (1959).

CHAPTER 4

Insect Control by Irradiation

There have been two kinds of practical application of radiation to the problem of insect control. One is direct killing or sterilization by irradiation of the whole pest population. Clearly, this procedure is applicable only to cases such as insects infesting stored products; it will be discussed later. We will consider first the alternative procedure—the sterile male technique.

The procedure involves the rearing, sterilizing, and release of males in sufficient numbers to exceed the natural male population. The sterile males then compete with the indigenous males, and, under appropriate conditions, most of the females will lay sterile eggs. By repeating this process for a few generations, virtually total control may be achieved. Starting with a population of 10^6 males, release of 2×10^6 sterile males for four generations could in theory reduce the total population from 2×10^6 down to a single insect.[1]

The term "sterile male" is something of a misnomer, as Von Borstel has pointed out.[2] What is required in fact is a male which will produce viable sperm which can fertilize an egg but will give an embryo that cannot develop as a result of dominant lethal mutant genes in the sperm. It was once considered helpful if the insect was one whose females copulate only once, as in the screw-worm fly; but it is by no means essential, as the results below on the mosquito demonstrate, and as has been pointed out on theoretical grounds.[3] The reason is, of course, that as long as the sperm from irradiated males can compete with that from indigenous males, then it remains true that by swamping the indigenous population with an x-fold surplus of irradiated males, one can reduce each generation to about $1/x$ of control levels, with or without multiple mating. The production of truly sterile males would be useless in cases where multiple mating can occur, but, fortunately, there is about a 20-fold difference in the dose required for dominant lethal induction and for sterilization.[2]

The technique has been highly successful against one insect, the screw-worm *Callitroga hominivorax*. The remarkable story of its eradication in Curaçao and (until reinfestation occurred) in Florida was admirably recounted by Bushland[4] in 1957 and Weidhaas *et al.* in 1962.[5] All that need be given here is a brief outline and some notes on subsequent history.

There are three basic requirements for such an approach. First, it must be possible to rear insects on a scale large enough to outnumber the native population. Second, there must be a procedure which will induce dominant lethal mutations in the genes of males with almost 100% certainty and yet will not enfeeble the male, either in longevity or in its ability to compete sexually with native males. This is said to be the major difficulty.[6] It is also required that the procedure will render irradiated females incapable of producing fertile eggs, since in practice the separation of sexes in large numbers of insects before irradiation is impracticable, and the females must therefore be made harmless. The procedure must be cheap and operable on a large scale. Third, there must be an appropriate release technique by which the sterile males can be well mixed with the native population.

The screw-worm fly program of the U.S. Department of Agriculture was the result of prolonged research beginning in 1947 which led only slowly to a full-scale program. By 1951 appropriate X-ray sterilization was achieved[7] by pupal irradiation, and in 1953 the more economical Co[60] device was described.[8] It was found that 5000 r applied to late pupae had the desired effect. In this species the females were found to copulate only once, so that fully viable sperm was perhaps not essential. In experiments on caged flies, it was shown that the predicted population lowering occurred.

In 1954 and 1955, screw-worms were eliminated from the island of Curaçao by releasing each week 400 irradiated males per square mile on the 170-square-mile area. This achievement took 22 weeks, and success was total and permanent.

In 1957, the procedure was repeated on a greatly enlarged scale in a 200-square-mile area in eastern Florida. An enlarged Co[60] source of 480 c was installed, and a million flies were reared, sterilized, and released each week for 10 weeks. Eradication was not achieved because of reinfestation from neighboring areas, but 70% of the females mated with sterile males, as judged by production of nonviable eggs.

Subsequently,[5] an even larger project was launched in southeast Florida. A "fly-rearing factory" to produce up to 70 million flies a week was built in an aeroplane hangar. This prodigious effort required gargantuan amounts of food: 40 tons of meat a week, 4500 gallons of blood, 9600 gallons of water, and so on. Total eradication was achieved in 2 years. The whole eradication program in Florida cost $8 million. The depredations of the screw-worm fly before this were estimated at $10 million annually. As Weidhaas comments,[5] this represents quite a good return on the investment.

It is clear that under appropriate conditions one may control screw-worm flies by the sterile male technique. What other species can be so controlled?

An attempt was made in England[9] during 1956 and 1957 to use the technique for control of the blowfly *Lucilia sericata*. The place was Holy Island, with an area of 2 square miles, which at its closest point is 1.2 miles from the mainland. Although an estimated 5:1 preponderance of sterile males was created, the program was a total failure. The cause of the failure could not be located, but the major possibilities were that sterilization was inadequate or that sterilized males failed to inseminate the native females.

The feasibility of using the technique to control three species of fruit flies in Hawaii has been explored.[10] The species were the oriental fruit fly *Dacus dorsalis*, the Mediterranean fruit fly *Ceratitis capitata*, and the melon fly *Dacus cucurbitae*. Doses between 6700 and 8400 r of Co^{60} gamma rays administered to pupae gave good sterilization of both sexes without undue loss in effectiveness of insemination by the males. However, in 30–50 days some fertility returned—a phenomenon not observed in the short-lived screw-worm fly. Multiple mating also occurs in this species. Nevertheless, in caged populations the egg fertility was proportional to the ratio of sterile and normal males present. This disposes of the objection that only single-mating species can be controlled by this technique.[11] It was stated in 1958[12] that as a result of these studies a Co^{60} unit giving 100,000 r/hour had been installed in Hawaii, and methods for mass rearing had been developed. More recent information is not available.

Radiation sterilization for control of the Mediterranean flour moth, *Anagasta kühniella*, in mills has been the subject of a 2-year study in England.[13] First considerations led to optimism: the populations are enclosed, the insect is economically important on a world scale, and current fumigation methods are imperfect. After 2 years, the project was abandoned, primarily because of the inevitability of worsening the situation by releasing large numbers of sterile males for 2 or 3 years before improvement would occur. This need for prolonged treatment was due to the slow development of the insect under some conditions. Anticipated cost was high, and the presence of other cereal insects rendered it necessary to fumigate occasionally in any case. Reinfestation through return of used sacks was also very probable.

The suitability of the technique for the mosquito *Anopheles quadrimaculatus* has been examined and seems quite promising.[14] Pupae of various ages or adults were sterilized by 8865 to 12,900 r of Co^{60} gamma rays. The 48-hour LD_{50} for pupae was 22,000 r, but, even at 12,900 r, deaths were somewhat higher than in controls. However, the main feature was that the sterile insects competed fairly successfully with normal insects for copulation with available females: when 10 irradiated males per normal male were enclosed with normal females, the per cent hatch was 28%, as compared to a theoretical value (for full competition) of 9%.

A brief report[15] in 1957 stated that work had begun on control of the tsetse fly (*Glossina* spp.) in Tanganyika, using pupae irradiated at Harwell, England. However, nothing has been heard of the project since then.

1. Direct Control by Irradiation

The problems involved in insect eradication in foodstuffs by radiation are of three kinds: those concerned with application procedures, those concerned with the effects on the insect, and those concerned with the effects on the product. We will consider first the insect problem, which is primarily a matter of establishing the dose required for a desired effect.

Some of the questions to be considered are: Which stage of the life cycle is involved? Is lethality required or will sterilization suffice? What percentage must be killed? How soon must the effect be produced? What is the optimal kind of radiation? The answers to some of these questions are provided in Chapter 2. For instance, X-rays, gamma rays, and electrons are about equiactive,[16,17] as discussed on p. 34. Several important species are about equal in the sensitivity of adult forms: the confused flour beetle, saw-toothed grain beetle, lesser grain borer,* and cigarette beetle (*Lasioderma serricorne*) had their life expectancies reduced to 1 day by doses of between 1.7×10^5 and 3.0×10^5 rep of gamma rays.[16]

Although prompt killing requires doses in the range of 5×10^5 rep,[16,18] much smaller doses may suffice for delayed effects. Molting of the lesser grain borer is prevented by 5×10^4 rep, and this dose eventually kills all of them.[16] Within 20 days, most stored-products insects are killed by 6.4×10^4 r.[19] These doses are much lower than the levels required for bactericidal action, which are in the range of 5×10^6 rep, but 5×10^5 rep does have some anti-fungal activity.[11] A compromise dose of 10^5 rep was accepted in U.S. Army studies as giving control after a few weeks had elapsed.[16] For cereal infestation by confused flour beetles and granary weevils, a dose of 10^4 rep was adequate to kill eggs and to sterilize adults.[17] For prompt kill of adults, 5×10^5 rep was needed, and 10^5 rep gave over 80% mortality in a week. Such a dose is also miticidal.[11] For the bean weevil *Acanthoscelides obtectus*, 10^4 rep was totally lethal in a week.[20]

The susceptibility of a variety of insects that infest stored cereals is indicated in Table 4.1. It is clear that a dose which gave excellent control 77 days after treatment was often inadequate at 17 days, primarily because the damaging effect was genetic and therefore directed against the progeny rather than the parent. Good control of all 12 species was given by 5×10^5 rep—at least in the long run.

A study on lethality of Co^{60} gamma irradiation to stored-products insects suggested that 10^5 r would cause 100% mortality in 2 months. If rapid action was desired, 151,200 r would kill 100% in 6 days. If, on the contrary,

---

* For scientific names, see Table 4.1.

sterilization was all that was needed, 8400 r was sufficient.[21] The species involved are given in Table 4.2.

Wood-boring insects are difficult to eradicate with insecticides because of their inaccessibility. Preliminary work[22] was done on Co^{60} irradiation of the

TABLE 4.1

MEAN ADULT EMERGENCE OF IMMATURE STAGES IRRADIATED WITH Co60 GAMMA RAYS[a]

	Seventeen days after 2×10^4 rep		Seventy-seven days after 5×10^4 rep	
	Number emerged in controls	Per cent emergence in treated[b]	Number emerged in controls	Per cent emergence in treated[b]
Granary weevil *Sitophilus granarius*	884	0	1522	0
Rice weevil *Sitophilus oryza*	1509	0.4	5004	0
Lesser grain borer *Rhyzopertha dominica*	566	3.4	1250	0
Red flour beetle *Tribolium castaneum*	524	1.5	331	0
Confused flour beetle *Tribolium confusum*	161	38	184	0
Saw-toothed grain beetle *Oryzaephilus surinamensis*	1599	11	116	0
Flat grain beetle *Laemophloeus pusillus*	477	4.2	304	0
Rusty grain beetle *Laemophloeus ferrugineus*	6	100	6	0
Angoumois grain moth *Sitotraga cerealella*	4500	7.3	963	0
Mediterranean flour moth *Anagasta kühniella*	108	2.8	83	0
Almond moth *Ephestia cautella*	27	0	18	0
Khapra beetle *Trogoderma granarium*	38	18	4	0

[a] From data of Cornwell, Crook, and Bull.[35]

[b] Emergence is expressed as a per cent of that in the untreated controls.

powder-post beetle *Lyctus brunneus,* the furniture beetle *Anobium punctatum,* and the death-watch beetle *Xestobium rufoviolosum.* Although fresh eggs of *Anobium* and *Xestobium* were killed by 4000 r, mature eggs needed over 32,000 r. However, with a dose of 800 r, only sterile eggs were laid in all species. Unfortunately, only in *Xestobium* do the adults remain in the timber for many months, so only in this species could one hope 800 r to be useful. This dose given to larvae delays their development, but is not lethal.

Effectiveness of radiation in control of the oriental fruit fly in fruit and vegetables was indicated by a study[23] which showed that young eggs were killed by 4×10^3 r. Proper development of eggs and larvae was prevented by doses of about 1.5×10^4 r. Prompt kill was not feasible, even with doses up to 3×10^5 r.

TABLE 4.2

SPECIES KILLED IN 6 WEEKS BY 10^5 R OF Co[60] GAMMA RAYS[a]

1. Confused flour beetle, *Tribolium confusum*, adult and larva[b]
2. Saw-toothed grain beetle, *Oryzaephilus surinamensis*, adult[b]
3. Lesser grain borer, *Rhyzopertha dominica*, adult
4. Granary weevil, *Sitophilus granarius*, adult
5. Rice weevil, *Sitophilus oryzae*, adult
6. Indian-meal moth, *Plodia interpunctella*, larva[b]
7. Almond moth, *Ephestia cautella*, larva

[a] From Dennis.[21]

[b] Numbers 1, 2, and 6 were killed in 2 months by 151,200 r; the others were not tested for this period.

A rather specialized requirement for sterilization arose when it was desired to make dispersal studies with the white-pine weevil, *Pissodes strobi*, and the investigators did not wish to release normal weevils into a valuable plantation. A dose of 10,000 r was needed to assure that neither males nor females were fertile.[24]

The existence of the fractionation effect, that is to say, the greater efficiency of a single radiation dose than several fractional doses (see Chapter 2), has an important implication for radiation control of insects. The calculated effective dose needs to be applied at once rather than by repeated passes before a weak source. Thus, for the granary weevil *Sitophilus granarius*, five doses of 802 rep daily had little effect, whereas 4012 rep at once gave total control. The longer the lapse between doses, the less effective was treatment.[25]

It is evident that appropriate doses of radiation can kill or sterilize harmful insects—but is irradiation a feasible control method? There are two problems: cost, and the effects on the product.

Irradiation facilities are large and costly. It seems unlikely that they will be useful except at points where large and continuous throughputs are foreseen. It must also be stressed that after irradiation it is essential that storage under insect-proof conditions be arranged. The cost is of course highly dependent on the dose and the quantity processed. The following examples (U.S. currency) include running costs, labor, amortization of equipment, and so on. A gamma irradiator was designed for treating 100-lb sacks of grain or flour, and in 1955 it was estimated[26] that 2.5×10^4 rep treatment would cost 3.73¢ per sack. An appropriate facility could be built for an estimated figure of $38,320.

Some projected estimates of future costs were made in 1959 for English conditions for the irradiation of grain with 10^6 rads, using Co^{60} or Cs^{137} with a pneumatic conveyor tube handling 30 tons an hour.[11] Prices estimated were about 30¢ a ton in 1963 and 6¢ in 1968 for continuous operation. For a 40-hour week, the estimate was quadrupled. For continuous treatment of wheat with an electron accelerator, an estimate in 1954 for United States conditions was 15¢ per ton for 10^5 rep, or 1.5¢ for 10^4 rep.[20,27] Such treatment could not be applied to bagged commodities; 2-Mev electrons penetrate only 0.4 inches into wheat or flour.[20] At the other end of the scale, treatment of 1-oz fruit bars in army rations with cathode rays was estimated in 1954 to cost 8¢ a bar.

Before leaving the question of costs, it is appropriate to consider briefly the dimensions of the loss from stored-products insects. Typical of estimates of annual loss in the U.S.A. are one of $300 million made in 1953[17] and another of $1 billion made in 1952.[19] India is said to lose 1 million tons of stored grain in a year.[28] Internationally, 10% of the world's stored grain is said to be lost to insects.[28]

2. Equipment

It is primarily cost which will decide whether irradiation by gamma rays or electrons is preferable. Cornwell of the United Kingdom[13] (see also discussion at end of Horne and Brownell[29]) expresses considerable scepticism about the promises of lowered prices of gamma emitters and puts his faith in electron accelerators with high throughput, e.g., 200 tons/hour. Brownell of the United States[29] points to mechanical problems in such machines and believes the deep-penetrating powers of gamma rays provide the answer.

Most of the equipment designs published are for gamma irradiation, commonly by Co^{60}. They have in common massive protective shielding and some conveyor system by which the infested material can be moved past a source at a speed the adjustment of which controls the dose received. A major problem is to obtain a sufficiently high dose throughout the commodity without local overdosing. The latter is particularly problematic when the source is very strong or the commodity is brought very close to it, but conditions which minimize this risk often give inefficient utilization of radiation. Thus, a pneumatic conveyor for grain gave little overdosing but very poor utilization (0.5%); a bulk conveyor gave good utilization (40%) but much overdosing (300%); and treatment in containers by a moving-bucket device gave tolerable utilization (25%) and overdosing (25%). Mathematical relations between these factors have been developed.[13] Designs for these facilities are described by American[29] and British[13] workers.

Suggestions have been made for mobile irradiation facilities, installed in rail cars[29] or ships.[30] By this means it is hoped to extend the use of radiation facilities to those who would not need year-round irradiation and to spread the large initial and running costs among many users.

3. Radiation Effects

In considering the effects of irradiation on the product, the major concern is consumer hazard, including problems of toxicity and deficiency. These problems have usually been evaluated with gamma-ray doses designed to kill bacteria, typically 4.8×10^6 rad, and it is probable that if safety is proven with such doses there is no problem with the 2.5×10^3 rad favored for insect control. The current view is that no reliable and repeatable case of the induction of toxic materials by radiation has ever been found, in spite of an extremely extensive and intensive search. Reports of fertility loss in dogs and rupture of the auricle in mice have been effectively disproved.[31,32] However, it is certain that radiation can destroy vitamins, particularly thiamine and pyridoxine, to an extent that varies enormously with dose and foodstuff. In bactericidal treatments, suitable doses (usually millions of rads) have about the same destructive effect as heat treatment suitable for the same purpose.[32] It was this fact that led to many of the early reports of apparent induced toxicants; suitable vitamin supplements must be given if the irradiated food is a large fraction of the diet.

Damage can be done to certain products by doses which are likely to be used. Seed wheat was prevented from correct emergence by 10^5 rep.[17] Navy beans could not germinate after treatment with 10^5 rep and developed very poorly after only 10^4 rep.[20] The administration of 5×10^5 rep to wheat caused a noticeable flavor change in bread prepared from it,[17,18] but this quality change was judged as acceptable.[11] Other small changes caused by such a dose were darkening and changes in gluten property and hence baking properties.[33] If the flour itself was irradiated, off-flavors could be produced with 2×10^4 rad.[18] Spice irradiation at 7.5×10^4 rad was acceptable for the seven tested; at 1.5×10^5 rad, cinnamon flavor was spoiled, but the others were unaffected.[18] Loss of odor and flavor in breakfast cereals was reported following treatment with 6×10^5 rad, a dose which had no effect on cake mixes.[11] Another report stated that 10^5 rep caused no off-flavor in army cereal ration bars or gingerbread mix.[16]

For irradiation of packaged foods, effects of radiation upon the packaging material must be considered. Except that Saran was somewhat darkened,[16] 3×10^6 rep had little effect on most wrapping materials. Induction of radioactivity by irradiation of a product is not a problem at the energy levels of radiation normally used.

Present-day control of stored-products insects is by fumigation. If radiation control is to succeed, it must offer something in cost, effectiveness, or convenience, that fumigation does not have. A comparison of the procedures is given in Table 4.3. From the comparison, it seems that fumigation will continue in favor for a long time to come.

TABLE 4.3

COMPARISON OF FUMIGATION AND IRRADIATION[a]

Fumigation	Irradiation
1. Prompt kill	1. Delayed kill at economic doses
2. Fumigant can be taken to grain	2. Grain has to be brought to irradiation facility
3. Suitable for large or small amounts	3. Economic only for large amounts, preferably at steady rates
4. Appropriate for present grain-handling methods	4. Present handling methods might have to be modified
5. Capital expenditure small	5. Capital expenditure very high
6. No resistance	6. No resistance
7. Residues possible	7. No residues
8. Acceptable cost	8. Costs from 2 to 10 times as much as fumigation

[a] Based on Cornwell and Bull.[13]

An unusual use of direct radiation is reported from Russia.[34] Silkworm cocoons have to be killed prior to silk removal, and the classic procedure involves heating at 80°C. This produces some damage to the silk, an effect which could be avoided if Co^{60} gamma rays were used in place of heating. Doses of between 10^5 and 3.4×10^5 rep were needed, depending on age, season, and source. An extensive study of the effects of radiation on the silk properties was reported, and no adverse effects were found at such doses. An unlooked-for side effect was that irradiated cocoons could be stored in damp places without becoming moldy or putrefied.

REFERENCES

1. E. F. Knipling, Possibilities of Insect Control or Eradication Through the Use of Sexually Sterile Males, *J. Econ. Entomol.*, **48**: 459 (1955).
2. R. C. Von Borstel, Population Control by Release of Irradiated Males, *Science*, **131**: 878 (1960).
3. R. C. Von Borstel and A. A. Buzzati-Traverso, On the Role of Lethal Mutants in

the Control of Populations, in *Radioisotopes and Radiation in Entomology*, p. 273, Intern. Atomic Energy Agency, Vienna, 1962.

4. R. C. Bushland, Male Sterilization for the Control of Insects, *Advan. Pest Control Res.*, **3**: 1 (1957).

5. D. E. Weidhaas, C. H. Schmidt, and W. F. Chamberlain, Research on Radiation in Insect Control, in *Radioisotopes and Radiation in Entomology*, p. 257, Intern. Atomic Energy Agency, Vienna, 1962.

6. E. F. Knipling, Use of Insects for Their Own Destruction, *J. Econ. Entomol.*, **53**: 415 (1960).

7. R. C. Bushland and D. E. Hopkins, Experiments with Screw-worm Flies Sterilized by X-rays, *J. Econ. Entomol.*, **44**: 725 (1951).

8. R. C. Bushland and D. E. Hopkins, Sterilization of Screw-worm Flies with X-rays and Gamma-rays, *J. Econ. Entomol.*, **46**: 648 (1953).

9. J. Macleod and J. Donnelly, Failure to Reduce an Isolated Blowfly Population by the Sterile Males Method, *Entomol. Exptl. Appl.*, **4**: 101 (1961).

10. L. F. Steiner and L. P. Christenson, Potential Usefulness of the Sterile Fly Release Method in Fruit Fly Eradication Program, *Hawaiian Acad. Sci. Proc. 31st. Ann. Meeting, Honolulu*, p. 17, 1956.

11. P. B. Cornwell, The Disinfestation of Foods, Particularly Grain, *Intern. J. Appl. Radiation Isotopes*, **16**: 188 (1959).

12. L. D. Christenson, Recent Progress in the Development of Procedures for Eradicating or Controlling Tropical Fruit-flies, *Proc. 10th Intern. Congr. Entomol., Montreal*, **3**: 11 (1958).

13. P. B. Cornwell, Insect Control by Gamma-irradiation: an Appraisal of the Possibilities and Problems Involved, *J. Sci. Food Agr.*, **11**: 754 (1960).

14. A. N. Davis, J. B. Gahan, D. E. Weidhaas, and C. N. Smith, Exploratory Studies on Gamma Radiation for the Sterilization and Control of *Anopheles quadrimaculatus*, *J. Econ. Entomol.*, **52**: 868 (1959).

15. J. Ray, Will Atomic Radiation Control Africa's Tsetse Fly?, *Foreign Agr.*, **21**: 15 (1957).

16. B. E. Proctor, E. Lockhart, S. A. Goldblith, A. V. Grundy, G. E. Tripp, M. Karel, and R. C. Brogle, The Use of Ionizing Radiations in Eradication of Insects in Packaged Military Rations, *Food Tech.*, **8**: 536 (1954).

17. V. H. Baker, O. Taboada, and D. E. Wiant, Lethal Effects of Electrons on Insects Infesting Wheat and Flour—Part I, *Agr. Eng.*, **34**: 755 (1953).

18. H. F. Kraybill, The Effects of Ionizing Radiation on Insects, *Intern. J. Appl. Radiation Isotopes*, **16**: 187 (1959).

19. C. C. Hassett and D. W. Jenkins, Use of Fission Products for Insect Control, *Nucleonics*, **10** (12): 42 (1952).

20. V. H. Baker, O. Taboada, and D. E. Wiant, Lethal Effects of Electrons on Insects Which Infest Wheat, Flour and Beans. Part II, *Agr. Eng.*, **35**: 407 (1954).

21. N. M. Dennis, The Effect of Gamma-ray Irradiation on Certain Species of Stored-products Insects, *J. Econ. Entomol.*, **54**: 211 (1961).

22. J. D. Bletchley and R. C. Fisher, Use of Gamma Radiation for the Destruction of Wood-boring Insects, *Nature*, **179**: 670 (1957).

23. C. W. Balock and L. D. Christenson, Effect of Gamma Rays from Cobalt-60 on Immature Stages of the Oriental Fruit Fly (*Dacus dorsalis* Hendel) and Possible Application to Commodity Treatment Problems, *Hawaiian Acad. Sci., 31st. Ann. Meeting, Honolulu, Proc.*, p. 18, 1956.

24. H. A. Jaynes and P. A. Godwin, Sterilization of White-pine Weevil with Gamma Radiation, *J. Econ. Entomol.*, **50**: 393 (1957).

25. D. J. Jefferies and P. B. Cornwell, Lethal and Sterilizing Effects of Single and Fractionated Doses of Gamma Radiation on *Calandra granaria* L., *Nature*, **182**: 402 (1958).

26. L. E. Brownell, J. V. Nehemias, and J. J. Bulmer, *The Design of a Gamma Irradiation Facility for the Control of Insect Infestation in Flour, Meal, or Grain*, U. S. Atomic Energy Commission, AECU–3050, 21 pp., 1955.

27. V. H. Baker, O. Taboada, and D. E. Wiant, Insect Control by Electron Irradiation, *Electronics*, **28** (5): 202 (1955).

28. D. W. Jenkins, Radioisotopes in Ecological and Biological Studies of Agricultural Insects, in *Radioisotopes and Radiation in Entomology*, p. 3, Intern. Atomic Energy Agency, Vienna, 1962.

29. T. Horne and L. E. Brownell, The Use of Radiation Sources for Insect Control, in *Radioisotopes and Radiation in Entomology*, p. 233, Intern. Atomic Energy Agency, Vienna, 1962.

30. L. Brownell and T. Horne, quoted in Irradiation Ship Would Eliminate Grain Loss Due to Insects in Tropics, Anon., *Nucleonics*, **19** (6): 88 (1961).

31. H. F. Krayhill, Are Irradiated Foods Harmful? *Nucleonics*, **18** (1): 112 (1960).

32. M. S. Read, Current Aspects of the Wholesomeness of Irradiated Food, *J. Agr. Food Chem.*, **8**: 342 (1960).

33. M. Milner, Application of Gamma Radiation to Grain Storage and Technology, *Mid-W. Conf. Ind. Use of Isotopes*, Manhattan, Kansas. USAEC #TID 7571, p. 150, Feb. 1959.

34. V. A. Arifov, I. D. Artmeladze, V. A. Barnov, T. N. Chkheidze, G. A. Gumansky, G. A. Klein, S. Z. Pashinsky, S. N. Shchenkov, L. M. Tkhelidze, and T. V. Tsetskhladze, The Use of Radiation to Kill Silkworm Cocoons, *Proc. 2nd. Intern. Conf. Peaceful Uses of Atomic Energy*, **27**: 444 (1958).

35. P. B. Cornwell, L. J. Crook, and J. O. Bull, Lethal and Sterilizing Effects of Gamma Radiation on Insects Infesting Cereal Commodities, *Nature*, **179**: 670 (1957).

CHAPTER 5

Biochemistry

The special feature of most work with insect tissues is the small quantity available. This is not always true when whole organisms can be utilized, for many insects can be reared in bulk, but to obtain reasonable quantities of individual tissues is often arduous or impossible. Nevertheless, the following pages will demonstrate that insect biochemistry has received much attention; indeed, an excellent text on the topic was recently published.[1]

One reason for this relatively extensive work has of course been the economic importance of insects; but insect biochemistry has flourished because of two factors that permit extensive work with very small amounts of material. One factor is that the study of enzymes can be made with large quantities of added substrate and tiny amounts of endogenous enzyme—a consequence of the catalytic property that constitutes enzyme action. However, this only provides an approach for *in vitro* work. *In vivo* work and many refinements of *in vitro* work are made possible largely because of the availability of radioactive compounds which can be added in minute amounts comparable to those of endogenous substrates and yet, because of the sensitivity of isotopic methods, can be detected with ease.

1. Carbohydrate Metabolism

One of the most important contributions that radioisotopes have made to biochemistry is the ability to assess the relative contributions of alternative metabolic pathways. For instance, the existence of two pathways for glucose utilization is well known both in mammals and insects—that is to say, enzymes have been shown to be present which could permit the operation of two pathways. These are: (1) the Embden-Meyerhof glycolytic pathway (glucose . . . fructose-1,6-diphosphate . . . pyruvate . . . acetyl-CoA), followed by oxidation of the acetyl-CoA through the citric acid cycle, to CO_2 and water; (2) the phosphogluconate cycle: glucose . . . glucose-6-phosphate . . . 6-phosphogluconate . . . ribulose-5-phosphate . . . fructose-6-phosphate . . . glucose-6-phosphate. This cycle oxidizes 6 moles of hexose to 6 moles of CO_2 plus 5 moles of hexose.

In evaluating the relative roles of these alternate pathways, one can add, say, glucose-1-C^{14}. All the CO_2 formed by the phosphogluconate route comes from the C^{14}-1.

$$
\begin{array}{l}
\text{H—C}^{14}\text{OH} \\
\;\;|\\
\text{(CHOH)}_3 \quad \text{O}\\
\;\;|\\
\text{CH} \\
\;\;|\\
\text{CH}_2\text{OH}
\end{array}
\quad
\xrightarrow[\substack{\text{lactonase, 6-phosphoglu-}\\ \text{conic dehydrogenase}}]{\substack{\text{Hexokinase, glucose-6-}\\ \text{phosphate dehydrogenase,}}}
\quad
\begin{array}{l}
\text{CH}_2\text{OH}\\
\;\;|\\
\text{C}=\text{O}\\
\;\;|\\
\text{(CHOH)}_2\\
\;\;|\\
\text{CH}_2\text{O}\,\textcircled{P}
\end{array}
\;+\; \text{C}^{14}\text{O}_2
$$

Glucose   Ribulose-5-phosphate

In this route, C^{14}-6 would not release $C^{14}O_2$ in the first turn of the cycle. But in glycolysis, the glucose gives rise to 2 moles of triose, so that both the C-6 and the C-1 are equally available for oxidation to CO_2, for the C-6 and C-1 are indistinguishable at and after the glyceraldehyde-3-phosphate step.

$$
\begin{array}{l}
\text{H—C}^{14}\text{OH} \\
\;\;|\\
\text{(CHOH)}_3 \quad \text{O}\\
\;\;|\\
\text{CH} \\
\;\;|\\
\text{CH}_2\text{OH}
\end{array}
\quad
\xrightarrow[\substack{\text{kinase, aldolase, phospho-}\\ \text{triose isomerase}}]{\substack{\text{Hexokinase, phosphohexose}\\ \text{isomerase, phosphofructo-}}}
\quad
\begin{array}{l}
\text{C}^{14}\text{H}_2\text{O}\,\textcircled{P}\\
\;\;|\\
\text{CHOH}\\
\;\;|\\
\text{CHO}\\[4pt]
\text{CHO}\\
\;\;|\\
\text{CHOH}\\
\;\;|\\
\text{CH}_2\text{O}\,\textcircled{P}
\end{array}
$$

Glucose   2 Moles of glyceraldehyde-3-phosphate

At first sight then, if the phosphogluconate pathway predominated, the ratio $(C^{14}O_2$ from glucose-1-$C^{14})$: $(C^{14}O_2$ from glucose-6-$C^{14})$ would be infinity, and if glycolysis plus citric cycle predominated, the ratio would be 1. The situation is far more complex in fact; for instance, each turn of the phosphogluconate cycle redistributes some of the C^{14}. To some extent the problems can be overcome by comparing several labeled positions.

Silva et al.[2] have utilized these techniques to evaluate the role of the two major pathways in the American cockroach Periplaneta americana. Their results are shown in Fig. 5.1. It is evident that the earliest carbon to appear as CO_2 is derived from the carbon atom 3 of glucose, and that carbon atom 6 contributes least in the first 4 hours of metabolism. Calculations based upon the $C^{14}O_2$ recovery over 6 hours from each type of labeled glucose showed that less than 10% of the injected glucose which was metabolized was oxidized by the phosphogluconate pathway; the remainder followed the glycolysis-citric-acid-cycle pathway.

By contrast, K. N. Mehrotra (unpublished) finds that with in vitro preparations of the two-spotted spider mite, Tetranychus telarius, 40–45% of glucose is utilized via the phosphogluconate pathway.

Russian work[3] has shown significant changes in carbohydrate pathways in the coelomic fluid of pupae from the silkworm, *Bombyx mori*. There were three phases of activity. Type I occurred during hystolysis; type II, during early histogenesis and differentiation; and then type I returned toward the end of development. In type I, sucrose-C^{14}* was readily utilized; in type II, it was not. During type II, pyruvate from sucrose-C^{14} was used mainly for the synthesis of dicarboxylic acids, primarily malate, fumarate, and succinate. During type I, the pyruvate was apparently oxidized in the usual way, and the C^{14} label was found in citrate. However, although citrate-C^{14} was not found during type II, unlabeled citrate was formed in large amounts, presumably from lipids.

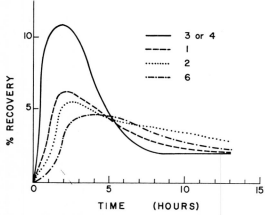

FIG. 5.1. Recovery of expired $C^{14}O_2$ from variously labeled glucoses after injection into the American cockroach. Recoveries are those within the preceding interval, i.e., are not cumulative. Numbers indicate the position of the C^{14}. (Redrawn from Silva *et al.*[2])

In this way, there is a parallel with mammalian development, in which at birth pyruvate is utilized by the liver primarily for dicarboxylic acid formation. Soon after, it returns to the prenatal pattern, the customary pattern of pyruvate oxidation. A comparable phenomenon is seen in starvation of mammals, when lipid utilization becomes prominent.[4] By deflecting pyruvate into dicarboxylate synthesis, the animal builds up its citric-acid-cycle intermediates to handle acetyl-CoA (derived, for example, from fat) more effectively.

The metabolism of glucose in the cockroach was examined by Treherne.[5] Assays of the hemolymph after injection of glucose-C^{14} showed a rapid and virtually complete conversion to the nonreducing disaccharide trehalose. Assays of the nerve cord showed more complex relations. After 3 hours the

* The position of the label was not given. Probably, labeling was random.

percentage composition of the radioactivity in the cord was: glutamate 25%, glutamine 20%, glycogen 20%, trehalose 13%, glucose 9%, aspartate 7%, and alanine 6%. Thus, almost two thirds had become involved in amino acid metabolism. Not more than 1% was actually degraded to $C^{14}O_2$, if the *in vitro* work may be used as an index of the above *in vivo* effects.

Labeled intermediates have also been used to evaluate the role of particular tissues. Clements[6] has examined reactions in whole fat body of the locust *Schistocerca gregaria*. Nonisotopic techniques had previously suggested that the enzymes of the tricarboxylic acid cycle were not all present. But since acetate-C^{14} gave rise to labeled glutamate and aspartate, it seemed probable that pathways to α-ketoglutarate (a precursor of glutamate) and oxaloacetate (a precursor of aspartate) were available, and such pathways constitute a part of the tricarboxylic acid cycle.

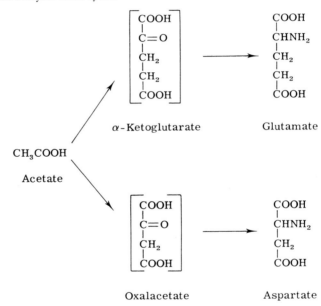

Furthermore, particular enzymes of the cycle, previously not detected, were demonstrated by Clements: the condensing enzyme, by showing indirectly that fluoroacetate could be converted to fluorocitrate; and succinic dehydrogenase, by showing $C^{14}O_2$ production from succinate-C^{14}. The succinic dehydrogenase activity was reduced 95% by homogenizing, perhaps owing to an endogenous inhibitor. This finding helped in part to account for previous failures to detect the enzyme.

Fat body utilized glycine-C^{14} and leucine-C^{14} for respiration much more effectively than did flight muscle (7 times more for glycine, 24 times for leucine). It utilized glucose-C^{14} almost exclusively for trehalose synthesis and little for glycogen synthesis. This was a marked difference from vertebrate liver, a tissue with which insect fat body is often compared. Labeled acetate, glycine, and leucine all gave rise to labeled fat, amino acids, and protein. This does not necessarily imply net synthesis of fat or protein in this preparation, for exchange without net synthesis would give the same result.

Later work by Candy and Kilby[7] showed that the locust fat body was an important site for conversion of glucose to trehalose, whereas hemolymph, muscle, and gut were largely inactive. The soluble fraction of the fat body contained the activity, much of which was lost after dialysis but could be replaced by adding UDP-glucose and ATP. This suggested that the pathway of trehalose synthesis was comparable to that proposed in the case of yeast:

glucose-6-phosphate + UDP-glucose $\longrightarrow$ trehalose phosphate $\longrightarrow$ trehalose

Fixation of CO_2 in *Drosophila* has been studied[8] in an attempt to demonstrate the mechanism whereby a certain virus-infected strain is killed by CO_2 under conditions in which the uninfected strain survives. The study revealed no differences between resistant and sensitive strains. It did show, however, quite extensive incorporation of $C^{14}O_2$ into organic acids. The counts per minute after 20 minutes gave a measure of the relative amounts of incorporation: malate 2000, citrate 1600, succinate 430, oxaloacetate plus pyruvate 95. Small amounts were also found in oxaloacetate and traces in glutamate, aspartate, and alanine.

Such fixation is probably caused by the operation of one or both of the following reactions:

(1) $CH_3C(O)COOH + CO_2 + NADPH + H^+$
         Pyruvate

$$\xrightarrow[\text{enzyme}]{\text{Malic}} HOOCCH_2CHOHCOOH + NADP$$
                          Malate

(2)

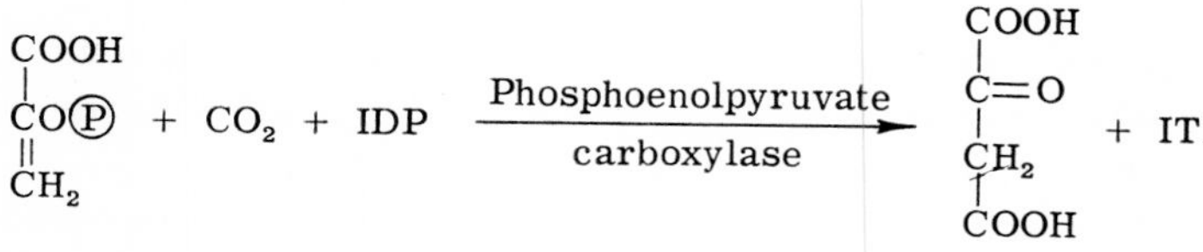

$$\begin{array}{l} COOH \\ | \\ CO\textcircled{P} \\ \| \\ CH_2 \end{array} + CO_2 + IDP \xrightarrow[\text{carboxylase}]{\text{Phosphoenolpyruvate}} \begin{array}{l} COOH \\ | \\ C=O \\ | \\ CH_2 \\ | \\ COOH \end{array} + ITP$$

Phosphoenol-   Oxalacetate
pyruvate

Most animals lack their own cellulose-degrading enzyme (cellulase), and if cellulose is an important dietary constituent, they rely upon symbiotic gut microorganisms to digest cellulose. Only in 1956 was this matter determined for an insect.[9] Uniformly labeled cellulose-C^{14} was fed to adult silverfish, and extensive respiratory production of $C^{14}O_2$ was found. Digestion must therefore have occurred. Sterile silverfish were reared and tested and produced comparable levels of $C^{14}O_2$ from the labeled cellulose. Clearly, the cellulose was being utilized, and cellulase would almost certainly be required to accomplish this. A search for such an enzyme was made, and it was located in the midgut.

2. Lipid Metabolism

Fat metabolism in insects is of particular interest because fat seems to play a more crucial and direct role in energy metabolism in insects than in mammals. For instance, respiratory quotients indicate that fat is utilized not only in rest but during high activity, and even in the presence of large quantities of glucose.

Unfortunately, fat metabolism has not been extensively studied in insects. Zebe and McShan[10] have shown that fat body from the southern army-worm *Prodenia eridania* can incorporate acetate-C^{14} into palmitic acid, and to a lesser extent into stearic, oleic, myristic, and lauric acids. The whole organ was more active than homogenates, which required several cofactors for optimal activity: coenzyme A, ATP, glutathione or cysteine, malonate, and, to a small extent, NAD or NADP, although the requirement for these was not imperative. Labeled glucose could also be utilized by these homogenates, but with only one-fifth of the efficiency for acetate.

When American cockroaches were injected with acetate-C^{14},[11] 17 fatty acids were labeled. Total incorporation into the saponifiable fraction (mainly fats, fatty acids, and phospholipids) was very dependent on sex; it was 18% of the dose in males and 4% in females. But the proportions of the fatty acids were extremely similar for both sexes; oleate was most important, representing in males 44% of the labeled fatty acids; palmitate and palmitoleate accounted for 31%; stearate for 10%; linoleate, 10%; and linolenate, 4%. All others were very minor.

These two studies suggest that fat metabolism in insects follows pathways substantially similar to those in mammals, but uptake of acetate is more rapid, which reflects perhaps a more dynamic metabolism.

Insects differ from mammals in requiring a dietary source of sterols. They therefore lack some or all of the enzymes needed for sterol synthesis. The biosynthetic pathway in mammals is shown in Fig. 5.2. Clark and Bloch[12,13] have explored this enzymic deficiency of insects, using the hide beetle, *Dermestes maculatus*. The larvae were reared on a diet containing C^{14}-1-labeled acetate or randomly C^{14}-labeled fructose (a source of "endogenous" acetate), but no radioactivity appeared in any sterol or in squalene. The only unsaponifiable lipids* which became labeled were a saturated, unbranched hydrocarbon, molecular weight 346, with 24 or 25 carbons, and an alcohol, molecular weight 395, perhaps ceryl alcohol. In an earlier report,[14] the latter

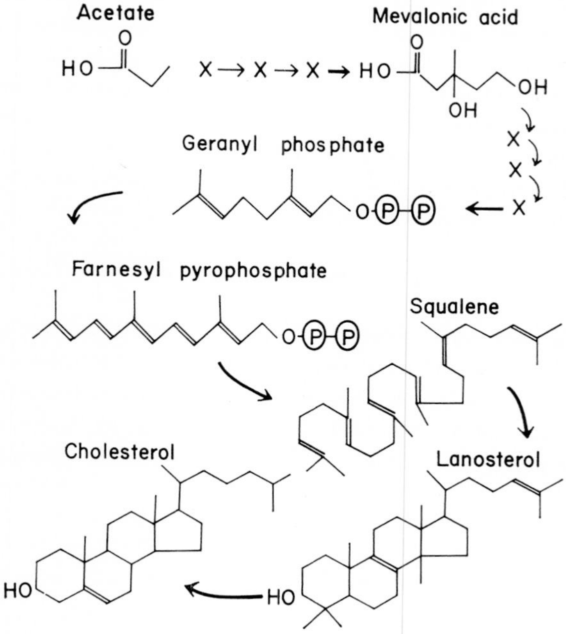

FIG. 5.2. Biosynthesis of cholesterol—a partial diagram. For simplicity, many known intermediates have been omitted, and their presence is shown by an X. (Based upon Wagner and Folkers.[76])

had been mistakenly reported as squalene. Since dietary cholesterol could not be replaced by mevalonic acid, squalene, or lanosterol, it seems (Fig. 5.2) that the whole apparatus of synthesis must be lacking in *Dermestes*.

Not all insects have precisely the same dietary requirements as *Dermestes*. It and other carnivorous insects need either cholesterol itself or closely related compounds (e.g., 7- or 24-dehydrocholesterol). But noncarnivorous insects can be raised on any sterol which contains a hydroxyl in the same position as

---

* That is, ether-extractable lipids other than esters (fats, phosphatides, etc.). Common "unsaponifiables" are steroids and alkanes.

cholesterol (Fig. 5.2) and has the same hydrocarbon side chain. It is true that Casida *et al.*[15] found that labeled acetate injected into the American cockroach was incorporated into "digitonides" as effectively as it was when injected into mice. "Digitonides" are those unsaponifiable lipids which can be precipitated by digitonin, and they are primarily steroidal. However, the quantity incorporated was very small (less than 0.1% of the injected dose), and characterization was not possible, so it cannot yet be said that acetate in the cockroach can be utilized for production of any known steroid.

Independent work[11] on the American cockroach also showed a very small incorporation of acetate-C^{14} into unsaponifiables—1% of the dose, of which about 7% behaved chromatographically like sterols, in good agreement with the earlier work. Males incorporated rather more than females. Duplicate digitonin precipitation suggested an even lower value for per cent of dose as sterols—10^{-2}% for females and 4×10^{-5}% for males. These minute quantities have little metabolic significance. No squalene-C^{14} was produced. The bulk (59%) of the unsaponifiables were hydrocarbons, but they differed from those in *Dermestes* in being a complex mixture including branched and unsaturated types.

The German cockroach, *Blattella germanica*, is another insect which can make a limited number of biochemical manipulations of steroids, as judged (for instance) by its ability to live on a diet containing ergosterol as the sole sterol. This sterol has two more unsaturations than cholesterol, one in the B ring and one in the side chain, and also an extra carbon (number 28).

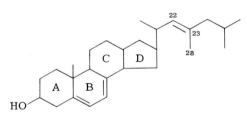

Ergosterol

The metabolism of labeled ergosterol was examined in the German cockroach.[16] When uniformly labeled ergosterol was fed, another radioactive sterol was obtained; but when C-28-labeled ergosterol was fed, no other labeled sterol was produced, so the new sterol must have had its C-28 removed. Further work showed that the product was 22-dehydrocholesterol, so that removal of C-28 and partial hydrogenation in the B ring had occurred.

In the housefly, injected acetate-C^{14} had a fate similar to that in *Dermestes*; a large portion was incorporated into the unsaponifiable fraction, which was primarily hydrocarbon in nature and had no sterol in it. The methods would have detected an incorporation of $2 \times 10^{-4}\%$ of the dose into a sterol. About 5% of the dose was recovered (after 18 hours) as fatty acids.[17]

22-Dehydrocholesterol

Since the housefly requires a dietary source of cholesterol, it was interesting to find[18] that it preserves a strict and efficient cholesterol economy. Only 2% of injected cholesterol-C^{14} was excreted, which is about one-tenth of the rate found in the rat. But the female passed on 78% of her dose to the eggs she laid. Most of the injected cholesterol (77–96%) was unchanged either in the adult or eggs. The major product was 7-dehydrocholesterol, and there were also sterol esters present.

Injection of mevalonate-C^{14} into houseflies[19] produced virtually no radioactive sterols. Therefore, the inability of the fly to synthesize sterols is not due to a deficiency in the acetate-mevalonate pathway. It seems likely that, as in *Dermestes*, the whole sterol-synthetic pathway is absent.

Agarwal *et al.*[20] have examined the nature of the sterols normally found in the housefly. The major sterol present in whole flies, both adult and pupal, was very like cholesterol; but on mixing a little cholesterol-C^{14} with this major compound and chromatographing the mixture on a silicic acid-celite column, the C^{14} peak always appeared one tube after the major sterol peak. This strongly suggested that the major sterol was not cholesterol. The structure of this major compound, which Agarwal *et al.* call "muscasterol," is not known, but evidence from elemental analyses, nuclear magnetic resonance, and infrared spectra suggested that the ring system was the same as cholesterol, but the side chain was different. Possible side chains postulated were (I), (II), and (III), the ring nucleus being attached at D.

(I)   (II)   (III)

When cholesteryl-4-C^{14} acetate was fed to the flies, no C^{14} was incorporated into muscasterol. It is therefore possible that muscasterol originates in the larval-rearing medium, so that one can modify the sterol content by dietary changes, just as the fat type of vertebrates may be influenced by the type of dietary fat.

3.   Amino Acid Metabolism

As in the lipids, much of the metabolic work on amino acids obtained its stimulus from nutritional findings. Extensive work by House with the German cockroach suggested that under aseptic conditions the sulfur acids, cystine and methionine, were needed for full development, although growth could occur without them.[21] But Hilchey found, on the contrary, that this insect could survive, mature, and apparently synthesize these acids, even under aseptic conditions.[22]

Later, Hilchey et al.[23] fed aseptic German cockroaches a diet lacking methionine and cystine and containing $S^{35}O_4{}^{2-}$. They found that S^{35} was incorporated into cystine and methionine, and incorporation was about 3 times higher in nonaseptic than in aseptic insects, suggesting that microorganisms normally played a role in synthesis. Incorporation was hundreds of times higher in nymphs than in adults, as one would expect. In the housefly, by contrast, $S^{35}O_4{}^{2-}$ was not incorporated into any amino acids.

Hilchey's isotope studies therefore supported his feeding experiments in showing that methionine and cystine can be synthesized in the German cockroach and are not needed in the diet. One would anticipate that feeding studies on houseflies should reveal a requirement for one or the other of these sulfur acids, but the housefly has not been so studied. In all the other nine insects so far studied,[1] methionine has proved essential, but cystine was essential only in one case, the *Aedes* mosquito. The majority of insects therefore follow the pattern found in mammals.

In Hilchey's studies the aseptic cockroaches lacked intestinal microflora. But German cockroaches also have intracellular microorganisms, located in organs called mycetomes, present in the fat body. Henry and Block[24] eliminated the intracellular organisms by aureomycin feeding and found that, under these conditions, when they injected $Na_2S^{35}O_4$ the only identifiable metabolite was sulfite. In normal and aseptic German cockroaches, a greater number of intermediates were found than in Hilchey's work: besides cystine and methionine, they found glutathione, methionine sulfoxide, and two major unknowns, as well as lesser amounts of taurine, sulfite, and minor unknowns.

It is apparent that it is the presence of intracellular symbionts in the German cockroach that bestows upon it its unusual independence of dietary cystine and methionine.

Thirteen other insects (not aseptic) were examined[25] for their ability to synthesize methionine from injected $Na_2S^{35}O_4$. As Table 5.1 shows, all five cockroaches could synthesize it, and so could the Japanese beetle. No other insect could. These results suggested that the Japanese beetle might have intracellular symbionts, although none has been reported.

TABLE 5.1[a]

ABILITY TO SYNTHESIZE METHIONINE FROM $SO_4{}^{2-}$

Capable of synthesis	Incapable of synthesis
Oriental cockroach, *Blatta orientalis*	Banded woolybear, *Isia isabella*
Florida cockroach, *Eurycotis floridana*	Southern army-worm, *Prodenia eridania*
Australian cockroach, *Periplaneta australasiae*	Mexican bean beetle, *Epilachna varivestis*
Madeira roach, *Leucophaea maderae*	Ground beetle, *Carabus*
Beetle roach, *Diploptera punctata*	Yellow mealworm, *Tenebrio molitor*
Japanese beetle, *Popillia japonica*	

[a] From Haines, Henry, and Block.[25]

The metabolism of thioacids in the housefly was investigated further[26] by feeding cystine-S^{35}. It seemed at first that taurine and sulfate were the main metabolites. With more adequate techniques, a far more complex situation was revealed.[27] Eight major metabolites and about a dozen lesser ones were seen when two-dimensional chromatograms were made.

The principal metabolites when cysteine-S^{35} was fed included glutathione, hypotaurine, taurine, cysteine, and a trace of cysteic acid. After injection, a different pattern was seen, and cysteinesulfinic acid, sulfate, and cysteamine were among the products. Possible routes for these metabolites are shown in Scheme I.

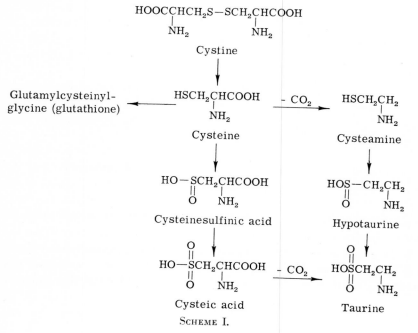

SCHEME I.

Feeding of taurine-S^{35} gave only isethionic acid and an unknown product:

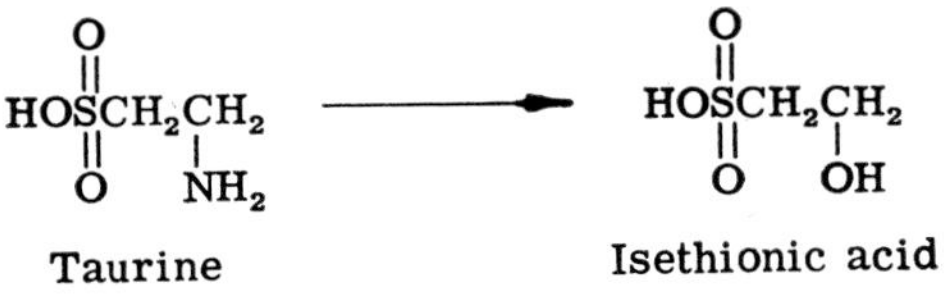

$$\underset{\text{Taurine}}{\overset{\displaystyle O}{\underset{\displaystyle O}{HO\overset{\displaystyle \|}{\underset{\displaystyle \|}{S}}CH_2\underset{\displaystyle NH_2}{CH_2}}}} \longrightarrow \underset{\text{Isethionic acid}}{\overset{\displaystyle O}{\underset{\displaystyle O}{HO\overset{\displaystyle \|}{\underset{\displaystyle \|}{S}}CH_2\underset{\displaystyle OH}{CH_2}}}}$$

Feeding of methionine-S^{35} gave principally methionine sulfoxide, cystine, cysteine, glutathione, cysteic acid, and taurine, suggesting that, as well as S oxidation, there was a pathway to cysteine (Scheme II). The cysteine so

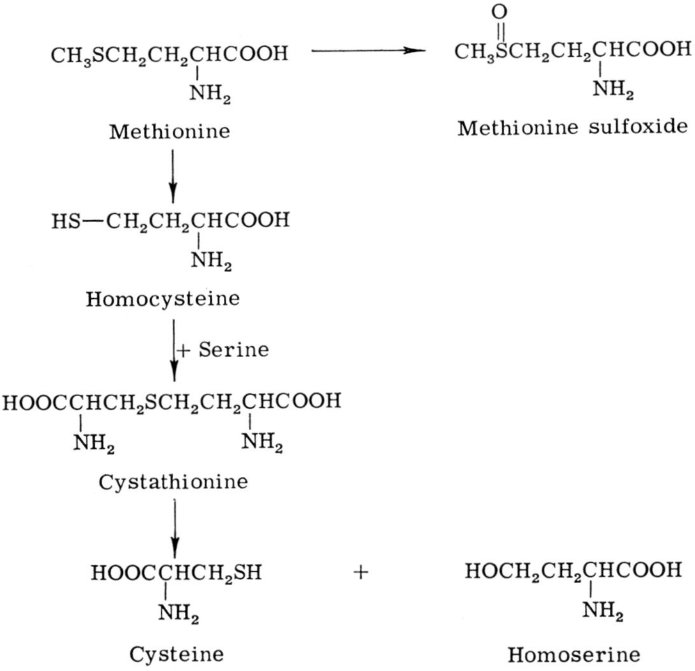

$$\underset{\text{Methionine}}{CH_3SCH_2CH_2\underset{\displaystyle NH_2}{CH}COOH} \longrightarrow \underset{\text{Methionine sulfoxide}}{CH_3\overset{\displaystyle \overset{O}{\|}}{S}CH_2CH_2\underset{\displaystyle NH_2}{CH}COOH}$$

$$\downarrow$$

$$\underset{\text{Homocysteine}}{HS-CH_2CH_2\underset{\displaystyle NH_2}{CH}COOH}$$

$$\downarrow + \text{Serine}$$

$$\underset{\text{Cystathionine}}{HOOC\underset{\displaystyle NH_2}{CH}CH_2SCH_2CH_2\underset{\displaystyle NH_2}{CH}COOH}$$

$$\downarrow$$

$$\underset{\text{Cysteine}}{HOOC\underset{\displaystyle NH_2}{CH}CH_2SH} \quad + \quad \underset{\text{Homoserine}}{HOCH_2CH_2\underset{\displaystyle NH_2}{CH}COOH}$$

SCHEME II.

produced could then give rise to the cystine, glutathione, cysteic acid, and taurine by routes shown in Scheme I.

These experiments on the housefly show that the basic pathways of sulfur acid metabolism are like those in mammals, except that in mammals small amounts of methionine can be synthesized from cystine. Cystine cannot be converted to methionine in the housefly, but methionine can be converted to cysteine and therefore (presumably) also to cystine. A number of questions, however, remain unanswered. Why were there different pathways following feeding and injection? If methionine was converted to cysteine according to Scheme II, why were none of the intermediates discovered? Which of the steps between cysteine and methionine are irreversible?

The possible role of —SH compounds in DDT resistance has been examined, since such compounds are at a higher level in resistant than in susceptible houseflies,[28] and glutathione is required for DDT-dehydrochlorinase activity *in vitro*.[29] The authors claimed that susceptible flies synthesized glutathione from cystine-S^{35} more rapidly. Their meager data hardly bear out the claim.

As described above, the normal (nonaseptic) German cockroach differs from the mammal in being able to utilize SO_4^{2-} for cysteine synthesis and in being able to convert cysteine to methionine. The metabolism of a variety of S^{35}-labeled acids was therefore examined in detail,[30] with the use of both normal and symbiont-free cockroaches.

Normal cockroaches fed labeled cystine or cysteine produced glutathione, methionine, taurine, and sulfate (cf. Scheme I). Labeled cysteic acid was decarboxylated to taurine:

$$
\begin{array}{ccc}
\text{COOH} & & \text{CH}_2\text{NH}_2 \\
| & & | \\
\text{CHNH}_2 & & \text{CH}_2 \\
| & \longrightarrow & | \\
\text{CH}_2 & & \text{O=S=O} \\
| & & | \\
\text{O=S=O} & & \text{OH} \\
| & & \\
\text{OH} & &
\end{array}
$$

Cysteic acid   **Taurine**

Taurine was metabolized (in normal insects only) to cysteine and glutathione and perhaps methionine, but all to a small extent. Cysteinesulfinic acid was converted almost completely to taurine and sulfate. Methionine was converted primarily to its sulfoxide, and also to cysteine, glutathione, and sulfate (cf. Scheme II). Methionine sulfoxide was metabolized, as was methionine, but methionine sulfone was not metabolized at all.

From these results it seemed that cysteine synthesis did not proceed via other sulfur acids to any great extent. Experiments with serine-C^{14} suggested that it provided the carbon moiety for cysteine synthesis. The synthesis could proceed by pathways (for which evidence is provided in other organisms) which involve prior conversion of sulfate to sulfide or thiosulfate (Scheme III).

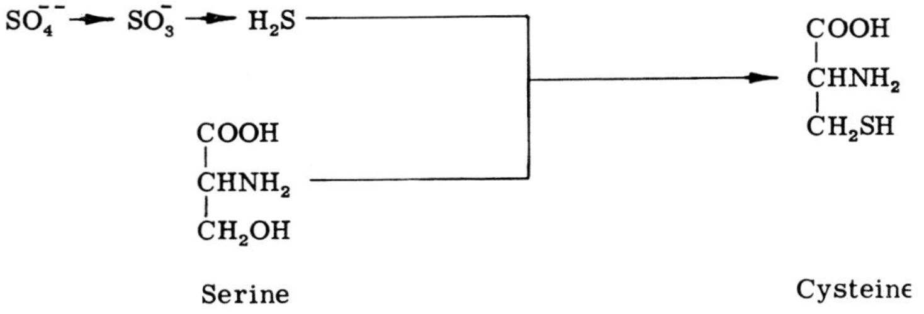

$$SO_4^{--} \rightarrow SO_3^{-} \rightarrow H_2S$$

COOH
|
CHNH$_2$
|
CH$_2$OH

Serine

COOH
|
CHNH$_2$
|
CH$_2$SH

Cysteine

or alternatively

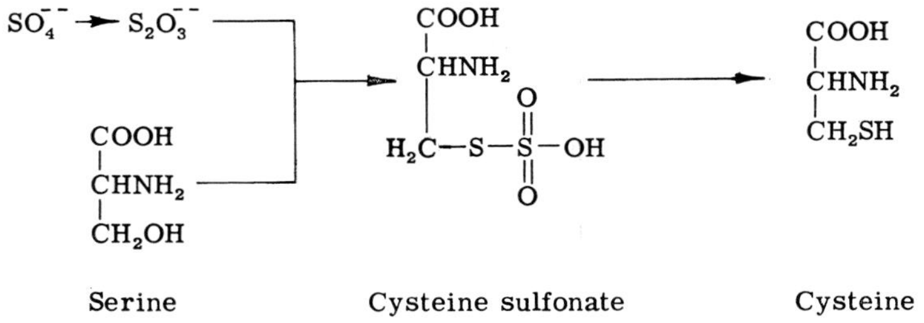

$$SO_4^{--} \rightarrow S_2O_3^{--}$$

COOH
|
CHNH$_2$
|
CH$_2$OH

Serine

COOH
|
CHNH$_2$
|
H$_2$C—S—S—OH (with O double bonds)

Cysteine sulfonate

COOH
|
CHNH$_2$
|
CH$_2$SH

Cysteine

SCHEME III.

Other information relevant to amino acid metabolism, but bearing directly on the problem of silk protein synthesis, will be given in the following section.

An isotopic method has been suggested[31] for the determination of the essentiality of particular amino acids in the diet. The classic procedure is, of course, to evaluate diets, made deficient in each amino acid in turn, in their ability to support growth. The isotopic method involves giving labeled glucose and later determining the specific activity of the various amino acids obtained by protein hydrolysis and chromatography. Where high activity is found, the implication is that the amino acid can be synthesized from glucose and is therefore not essential. In the case of the black blowfly, *Phormia regina*, injected as larvae and examined after 68 hours, the results showed high activities (over 14 counts per minute per micromole of carbon) only in serine, glycine, glutamate, and aspartate. These four had been found by classic procedures to be nonessential. Of the thirteen others evaluated (these had low activities—all less than 1 count/minute, except proline, 7.9 counts/minute, and alanine, 3.5 counts/minute), nine were found "classically" to be essential.

Clearly, the isotopic method is interesting, but it cannot yet replace the classical procedure. In some cases the discrepancies can be explained if sufficient biochemical knowledge is available. For instance, in the above isotopic study, phenylalanine and tyrosine both seemed essential, i.e., neither was synthesized from glucose; yet feeding studies showed tyrosine as nonessential. There is some evidence that tyrosine is actually formed from phenylalanine, so that omitting tyrosine only from the diet would have no ill effect. Consequently, the feeding study would show tyrosine as nonessential, and the isotope study would show it as essential.

4. Protein Synthesis

Radioactive amino acids have been widely used by biochemists to study protein turnover and synthesis. It is important to notice that incorporation of a labeled amino acid into protein does not necessarily mean that an overall synthesis of protein has occurred, for it can result from turnover as well as from net synthesis.

One of the earliest papers on the use of radioisotopes in protein synthesis bore the provocative title "Biological Synthesis of Radioactive Silk." In this paper, published in 1949, Zamecnik et al.[32] pointed out that the stability of the silk protein, fibroin, its ease of isolation, and its stable and known composition made it a highly suitable subject for studies on protein synthesis. They showed that C^{14}-labeled glycine and alanine, when injected into the cecropia silkworm, Hyalophora cecropia, were incorporated into fibroin. Isolated silk glands were also shown to form a radioactive protein from these amino acids. Subsequent workers have amply confirmed these findings. The posterior part of the silk gland is the most active; indeed, it is 200 times more active than rat liver in incorporation of glycine.[33] Ribonucleic acid (RNA) is undoubtedly involved, for low concentrations of ribonuclease (which hydrolyzes RNA) inhibit glycine incorporation.[33]

The amino acid content of mulberry leaves, the sole dietary source of Bombyx, differs substantially from that of silk fibroin which has, for instance, a high content (33%) of glycine. It follows that many of the dietary amino acids must be metabolized to others. Fukuda et al.[34] calculated that 70% comes unchanged from the diet ("direct"), and 30% requires preconversion ("indirect"). To examine this point further, they fed C^{14}-labeled mulberry leaves to larvae on various days. When pupation occurred, the silk was unwound, and the location of radioactivity in it was examined. The results of this ingenious experiment are shown in Fig. 5.3. Until the 4th day, ingested amino acids were not used, and silk synthesis had not begun. From then until the 8th day, ingested amino acids were built directly into the corresponding part of the fiber—e.g., on the 7th day, the portion from 400 to 650 m; on the 8th day, the portion from 650 to 1000 m. Then the last 300 m were formed from endogenous amino acids, as shown by the fact that material taken in on the first day and then not utilized but (presumably) incorporated in the body pool was only used for silk formation at the end of the thread.

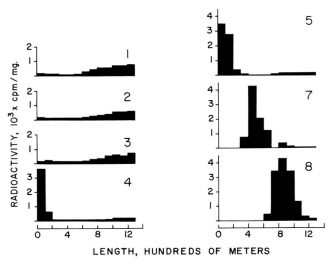

Fig. 5.3. Effect of feeding silkworms glycine-C[14] at various days of fifth instar upon labeling of different portions of the silk filament. (Plotted from data of Fukuda et al.[34])

Numerous experiments have been carried out to explore the paths available for interconversion of amino acids. The usual technique is to inject or feed a C[14]-labeled compound and isolate fibroin from the silk which is subsequently spun. This is then hydrolyzed, and its amino acids are separated chromatographically, at which time the radioactivity of any amino acid can be determined. The following have been administered.

(1) *Glycine*. Glycine-C[14] gives rise primarily to glycine in the fibroin.[35] It is also converted to serine and to glyoxylic acid.[36]

$$\underset{\text{Serine}}{\begin{array}{c}\text{COOH} \\ | \\ \text{CHNH}_2 \\ | \\ \text{CH}_2\text{OH}\end{array}} \longleftarrow \underset{\text{Glycine}}{\begin{array}{c}\text{COOH} \\ | \\ \text{CH}_2\text{NH}_2\end{array}} \longrightarrow \underset{\text{Glyoxylic acid}}{\begin{array}{c}\text{COOH} \\ | \\ \text{CH}_2\text{O}\end{array}}$$

The glyoxylic acid (which is found not in fibroin but in the coelomic fluid) is an interesting compound because of its high concentration in coelomic fluid, for it is absent in mammalian blood.[37] It does not appear to result from glucose metabolism, for silkworms fed with glucose-C^{14} produced extensive amounts of other keto acids (α-ketoglutarate and oxaloacetate) with only a trace of glyoxylate.[38] Belgian workers[39] found that carboxyl-labeled glycine gave rise to alanine as well as serine (both carboxyl labeled), but not to tyrosine. (Labeled carbon atoms will be indicated by asterisks.)

$$
\begin{array}{c}
\text{C*OOH} \\
| \\
\text{CH}_2\text{NH}_2
\end{array}
\quad\longrightarrow\quad
\begin{array}{c}
\text{C*OOH} \\
| \\
\text{CHNH}_2 \\
| \\
\text{CH}_3
\end{array}
$$

Glycine   Alanine

They also showed[40] that labeled glycine and serine in silk were formed after injection of labeled formate; both carbons of the glycine were labeled.

$$
\text{HC*OOH} \quad\longrightarrow\quad
\begin{array}{c}
\text{C*OOH} \\
| \\
\text{C*H}_2\text{NH}_2
\end{array}
$$

Formate   Glycine

(2) *Serine.* Uniformly labeled serine gives rise primarily to uniformly labeled glycine in silk,[41,42] with one-fifth as much alanine and no tyrosine.[41]

$$
\begin{array}{c}
\text{COOH} \\
| \\
\text{CHNH}_2 \\
| \\
\text{CH}_3
\end{array}
\;\longleftarrow\;
\begin{array}{c}
\text{COOH} \\
| \\
\text{CHNH}_2 \\
| \\
\text{CH}_2\text{OH}
\end{array}
\;\longrightarrow\;
\begin{array}{c}
\text{COOH} \\
| \\
\text{CH}_2\text{NH}_2
\end{array}
$$

Alanine   Serine   Glycine

(3) *Pyruvate.* Pyruvate is an important precursor for alanine, which is not ingested in sufficient quantity for silk synthesis.[43] The reaction is a simple transamination.

$$
\text{CH}_3\text{C*(O)COOH} \quad\longrightarrow\quad
\begin{array}{c}
\text{CH}_3\text{C*HCOOH} \\
| \\
\text{NH}_2
\end{array}
$$

Pyruvate   Alanine

The transamination was also catalyzed by a variety of tissue homogenates (silk glands, gut, fat body, etc.). Any of the 15 amino acids tested could act as amino donors, but glutamate and aspartate were best.

(4) *Phenylalanine*. Phenylalanine forms tyrosine in silk, and no glycine or alanine.[44,45,46] For instance, with a carboxyl label:

$$H_2NCH_2C*OOH \qquad\qquad H_2NCH_2C*OOH$$

Phenylalanine   Tyrosine

and thence to serine, labeled in an undetermined position.

The mechanism of protein synthesis, and particularly the role of RNA in governing synthesis, has also been studied in the silk gland. The gland is an organ of exceptionally high RNA content.

Work with mammalian liver preparations had shown that microsomes in the presence of "pH5 enzymes" and suitable cofactors could incorporate amino acids. The pH5 preparation contains all material which at $100,000 \times g$ is soluble under neutral conditions but precipitates at pH 5.1. Shimura and co-workers[35,47] found a different system in silkworms. A "large-particle" preparation of *Bombyx* silk gland could incorporate glycine-C^{14} in the absence of added materials such as pH5 enzymes. These large particles corresponded centrifugally to mitochondria; i.e., they were precipitated at $14,000 \times g$ in $0.4\,M$ sucrose. Treatment of the particles with deoxycholate destroyed the ability to incorporate, but subsequent addition of a supernatant preparation restored it. This supernatant preparation consisted of material which at $14,000 \times g$ was soluble under neutral conditions but precipitated at pH 4.9. Let us call this "4.9 enzyme."

The untreated large-particle preparation incorporated glycine better than alanine, and alanine better than leucine[48]: the ratio of the activities was $10 : 5 : 2$, approximately the ratios of these amino acids in fibroin. By contrast, rat liver contains more leucine than glycine, and its particles plus pH 5 enzyme incorporated leucine-C^{14} more than glycine. When deoxycholate-treated large particles of *Bombyx mori* silk gland were mixed with 4.9 enzyme from rat liver, glycine incorporation was predominant, whereas, when the sources were reversed, leucine incorporation was predominant. Therefore, the pattern of incorporation was dictated by that fraction of the large particles which were insoluble in deoxycholate.

In an attempt to elucidate the nature of these large particles,[49] glycine-C^{14} was injected into *Bombyx* larvae; 15 minutes later the larvae were homogenized, and radioactivity in various centrifugal fractions was determined. The large-particle fraction with most radioactivity was separable by special techniques from the fraction (presumable mitochondria) containing maximal succinic dehydrogenase. It was suggested that the effective particle was microsomal, probably having the nature of large vesicles. Much radioactivity was also found in a heavy fraction which consisted of a fibroin coagulum containing miscellaneous inclusions.

The 4.9 enzyme was later shown[50] to be separable into two components, both of which were required for activity. It was speculated that one component might activate the amino acids, while the other catalyzed the binding of the activated amino acids to the large particles.

Is protein synthesized by a more-or-less simultaneous condensation of a number of amino acids or peptides, or does the synthesis involve stepwise addition of amino acids? A way to distinguish these two alternatives is to add labeled amino acids during the synthesis. If they are incorporated uniformly into a variety of positions, one suspects simultaneous synthesis. If they are incorporated in a nonuniform way, the stepwise procedure is probable.

Shimura et al.[51] injected C^{14}-labeled glycine and alanine into Bombyx and then isolated the silk fibroin and degraded it progressively by a procedure which permitted them to distinguish between N-terminal* and non-N-terminal amino acids. They found that the N-terminal acid had two to five times more activity than the latter, and in one fraction of the protein the N-terminals were seven times more active. These results argue for a stepwise synthetic mechanism.

Incorporation of labeled amino acid into protein has been used to answer the question, "Is adult protein in the developing pupa of Lepidoptera synthesized from amino acids derived from histolysis of the larval tissues, or from proteins and polypeptides resulting from the lysis?" The experiment[52] was with pupae of the hawk moth, Sphinx ligustri, and, unfortunately, only five of them—two in diapause and three postdiapause. Labeled glycine was injected, and later the incorporation into protein glycine was determined. The conclusion tentatively favored the concept of utilization of free amino acids for adult tissue formation, for glycine incorporation was higher in the postdiapause pupae.

Glycine incorporation into blood proteins has been shown by Telfer and Williams[53] to be a convenient index of those various metabolic activities of the pupating Cecropia which are depressed when the pupa enters the phase of diapause and are re-excited by termination of diapause or by injury. The

---

* An N-terminal amino acid is one situated at the end of a protein chain and attached by its COOH group, so that its NH_2 group is free.

incorporation thus parallels oxygen utilization. Furthermore, carbon monoxide has no effect on oxygen utilization or glycine-C^{14} incorporation during diapause but inhibits them 90% during adult development.

5. The Labeled-Pool Technique

An important contribution which entomology has made to the radioisotope field is the development of the labeled-pool technique. The pioneers and principal exponents are F. P. W. Winteringham and his group in Slough, England.[54]

The principle is simple. One selects a basic metabolic pool, most commonly acetate or phosphate, with which numerous intermediates in the organism are in dynamic equilibrium. One then adds into the pool—usually working with the intact animal—the appropriate labeled compound, such as acetate-C^{14} or $H_3P^{32}O_4$. The label is progressively taken up into the various intermediates which, directly or indirectly, draw upon the pool. One can at any time take the animal or parts of it, extract and then separate the metabolites chromatographically, and study the extent of labeling of each intermediate. By this means one can obtain ". . . the spectrum of labeled metabolites which obtained in the living tissue at the instant of death."[55]

Two kinds of application of such knowledge have been made. First, one can find what intermediates are in contact with the pool; this can be particularly useful in comparing metabolism in different organisms or in various tissues. Alternatively, one can study the effect of poisons or other treatments upon the metabolism of an organism or tissue. All the work to be described concerns insects. However, the technique is extremely valuable in its essential simplicity (once chromatographic techniques are developed), and, particularly, in that it allows evaluation of a whole set of potential reactions of interest in a single experiment. It seems probable that the applications of this technique will become greatly increased in the near future.

Before embarking on a description of the work of Winteringham's group, we should point out that independent workers in the U.S.A. used the technique almost simultaneously with the first English work. In 1955 Fang and Allen[56] carried out an experiment with the Douglas-fir beetle, *Dendroctonus pseudotsugae*. The insects were fed on sucrose which contained $H_3P^{32}O_4$, and the various labeled intermediates were identified chromatographically, with the results shown in Table 5.2.

The first full account of the use of the labeled-pool technique by the Slough group was in 1955[57] with the housefly, using P^{32}. At that time less fractionation was obtained than in later studies; thus, arginine phosphate, glucose-6-phosphate, AMP, and an unknown all chromatographed together. Better separation was reported in 1958,[58] when six well-known compounds were identified, and four unidentified compounds and phosphate were also found. Table 5.3 shows some results for the thorax; values for the head were not radically different. It will be noticed that both the ATP and AMP fractions

TABLE 5.2

Per Cent of P[32] Incorporated into Intermediates of the Douglas-Fir Beetle, *Dendroctonus pseudotsugae*[a]

Inorganic phosphorus	25
ATP	3
α-Glycerophosphate	6
Fructose-1,6-diphosphate	9
3-Phosphoglycerate	15
Fructose-6-phosphate	7
Glucose-6-phosphate	5
Glucose-1-phosphate	10
Phospholipid	0.2
Unidentified	3

[a] Data rounded off from Fang and Allen.[56] Total is 82% (using original data) presumably due to chromatographic losses.

TABLE 5.3

Compounds of the Housefly Thorax in Equilibrium with the PO_4^{3-} Pool, and the Effect of Methyl Bromide and Iodoacetate[a,b]

Compound	Two minutes in methyl bromide		Two hours after 5 μg per fly of iodoacetate	
	Control	Treated	Control	Treated
AMP + ?[c]	4	8	0	7
ADP	3	3	0	0
ATP + ?[c]	27	11	37	17
Arginine phosphate	9	3	14	6
α-Glycerophosphate	16	16	15	6
Glucose-6-phosphate	10	8	12	17
Phosphate	25	50		

[a] Data rounded off from Winteringham *et al.*,[58] as corrected by Winteringham.[75]
[b] Figures show per cent of recovered P[32] in the thorax present as the indicated compounds. Insects were unanesthetized. In abdomen, compounds were not well resolved, and so results are not shown here. Resolution of phosphate from unknowns incomplete in columns 3 and 4.
[c] Question mark indicates contamination by an unknown impurity.

were contaminated with unidentified compounds. The effects of methyl bromide and iodoacetate are also shown in the table: both lowered the ATP levels and correspondingly raised the AMP, which suggests that treatment provoked the reaction $ATP \rightarrow AMP + 2PO_4^{3-}$, a change usually considered to be deleterious.[59] If recovery of the insect occurred—e.g., by only brief exposure to methyl bromide—the ATP and AMP levels returned to normal.

Prolonged exposure to methyl bromide resulted in an effect on α-glycerophosphate: its level was depressed as in iodoacetate poisoning.

The effect of other unpleasant treatments was subsequently reported.[60] The level of labeled α-glycerophosphate in the thorax was now reported as 20.9% of the radioactivity when the insects were "resting," i.e., under light cyclopropane anesthesia. It was reduced to 12.7% during nonflying activity and somewhat more by induced flight. Drowning raised the level to 29%. Starvation had little effect until prostration was achieved, and the level then fell to about 11%; at death by starvation, it was 5.9%. These findings are compatible with current views on α-glycerophosphate in insect flight muscle: it is the primary device for "shuttling" electrons across the mitochondrial membrane[61]; it is the major and product of anaerobic glycolysis (hence its rise in drowning); and it is the most readily utilized substrate for mitochondrial oxidation (hence its fall during activity). Presumably, the starvation effect was a reflection of a general depletion of energy-yielding intermediates, although, oddly enough, glucose-6-phosphate was little affected by starvation.

Other observations were that thoracic phosphate levels rose during flight from 20.4% (unanesthetized) to 28%, probably owing to utilization of arginine phosphate. The levels of ATP were not, in general, excellent indexes of energy utilization, although much reduced by drowning—from 34.7% in resting down to 3.9% after a 2-hour immersion. Starvation to prostration profoundly lowered head ATP (from 35.9% down to 14.8%), with little effect on thoracic levels; the effect was reversed when glucose was given.

In 1961 a study of American cockroach nerve[62] by the labeled-pool technique revealed 17 phosphorus compounds, after allowance of a 7-day period for P^{32} to equilibrate with P^{31}. The results are shown in Table 5.4, along with the original authors' somewhat hazardous estimate of the actual concentration of each compound in the tissue. They measured total phosphorus chemically and assumed that the total phosphorus was distributed in the same ratios as the P^{32}. Probably this is approximately accurate for compounds with a rapid turnover, such as the compounds of Table 5.4. An independent assay procedure gave an ATP value of 1350 μg/g in the nerve, compared with 850 radiometrically; agreement is thus only approximate. With larger molecules, some may turn over very little or not at all; e.g., the phospholipids of rabbit-brain white matter are "metabolically inert," although those of the gray matter exhibit turnover.[63] It is apparent from Table 5.4 that two-thirds of the injected phosphate was recovered in identifiable form.

The acetate pool has been labeled in order to examine amino acids in the housefly. In a comprehensive study, Price[64] used six paper-chromatographic systems in appropriate combinations for identification. The amino acid concentrations were first assayed directly, instead of making assumptions as in the results of Table 5.4. That is, instead of measuring total amino acid nitrogen and assuming that, within this total, the unlabeled amino acids were distributed in the same ratios as the labeled ones, Price chemically assayed each amino acid and obtained for each a conversion factor to enable the determination of that amino acid's concentration from the count rate of its

TABLE 5.4

COMPOUNDS OF AMERICAN COCKROACH NERVE IN EQUILIBRIUM WITH THE $PO_4{}^{3-}$ POOL[a]

Compound	Percentage of P^{32} as compound	Estimated tissue concentration, μg/g (wet)
Adenosine-5-phosphate (AMP)	0.3	30
Adenosine-5-diphosphate (ADP)	3.0	180
Adenosine-5-triphosphate (ATP)	18.5	850
Cytidine-5-phosphate (CMP)	0.2	20
Cytidine-5-diphosphate (CDP) + ?[b]	2.2	< 120
Cytidine-5-triphosphate (CTP)	2.4	100
Guanosine-5-diphosphate (GDP)	1.1	70
Guanosine-5-triphosphate (GTP)	1.8	90
Uridine-5-diphosphate (UDP)	1.5	80
Uridine-diphosphoglucose	1.2	90
Uridine-5-triphosphate (UTP)	3.4	150
Nicotinamide-adenine dinucleotide (NAD)	2.3	210
Nicotinamide-adenine dinucleotide phosphate (NADP) + ?[b]	0.5	< 30
H_3PO_4	25.4	660
Glucose-6-phosphate	1.1	80
Arginine phosphate	7.8	540
α-Glycerophosphate + ?[b]	3.7	< 170
Unidentified	33.6	
	110.0	

[a] From Heslop and Ray.[62]

[b] Question mark indicates contamination of the fractions by an unknown impurity.

spot on the chromatogram. One reason that this was necessary was that it was desired to study uptakes within minutes after injection, so that equilibrium condition could certainly not be assumed.

Price found that four amino acids became rapidly labeled: their specific activities in the whole insect 30 minutes after injection of 4 μc of acetate (5.3 μc/micromole) were 0.28 μc/micromole for proline, 0.77 for alanine, 1.15 for glutamine, and 1.74 for glutamic acid. Autoradiography showed that labeling of asparate and γ-aminobutyrate had also occurred, presumably to a much smaller degree. The time course of the labeling was followed for 3 hours, by which time the ratios of activities were quite different, with glutamine most active and alanine least. Analysis of protein hydrolyzates at 3 hours showed that these contained C^{14}-labeled alanine, proline, glutamate, and aspartate, but not glutamine.

An important metabolite which can be produced from the acetate pool is CO_2. After a dose was injected as above, CO_2 production rose to a peak at 1 hour and declined to zero at $5\frac{1}{2}$ hours. The data do not show what percentage appeared as CO_2.

In a comparison of DDT-resistant and DDT-susceptible strains of house-flies,[65] inorganic P^{32} was fed in a larval medium, and some simple fractiona-tion of the adults was carried out, which indicated P^{32} in protein and fat. No profound differences were found between strains. One might refer to such experiments as being related to the full labeled-pool technique.

6. Miscellaneous Topics

Iodine metabolism in insects was first studied by Wheeler[66,67] in *Drosophila gibberosa* by using inorganic I^{131}. She found that the only tissues which were very effective in accumulating iodine (like the vertebrate thyroid gland) were "skeletal parts" such as foregut lining, larval "skin," and tracheae. It was possible to distinguish between nonmetabolic uptake, which occurred with excised cuticle and only when it was tanned, and metabolic, which oc-curred in tanned and untanned cuticle. The whole treated larva was shown to contain labeled iodine as monoiodotyrosine and diiodotyrosine.

Inorganic I^{131} utilization in 13 insect species was later described by Limpel and Casida.[68,69] Some of the results are given in Table 5.5. Evidently, the main pathways involve incorporation into di- and monoiodotyrosine. Also

Tyrosine   Monoiodotyrosine   Diiodotyrosine   Thyroxine

evident is the extreme species variation: for instance, monoiodotyrosine varied between 8% for the dragonfly to 99% for the cicada.

The individual tissues of the American cockroach were examined in detail after *in vivo* treatment with inorganic I^{131}. The cuticle was most effective in utilizing it, being four times better than the average of all tissues and the only one to achieve higher total iodine than blood. In this respect, the cuticle

TABLE 5.5

UTILIZATION OF INORGANIC I^{131} BY INSECTS[a]

Insect	Per cent as following compounds				
	Inorganic	Monoiodo-histidine	Monoiodo-tyrosine	Diiodo-tyrosine	Thyr-oxine[b]
Dragonfly, *Aeschna* sp.	2	trace	8	72	18
American cockroach, *Periplaneta americana*	52	trace	27	3	18
Cicada, *Tibicen* sp.	trace	trace	99	trace	0
Squash bug, *Anasa tristis*	trace	3	18	60	20
Beetle, *Trogoderma versicolor*	18	6	73	4	0
Locust borer, *Megacyllene robiniae*	trace	1	12	63	24
Gay Harlequin, *Euchaetias egle* (larva)	1	3	39	34	23
Mud-dauber, *Sceliphron cementarium*	trace	trace	8	88	4
Yellow fever mosquito, *Aedes aegypti* (larva)	20	5	58	6	13
Housefly, *Musca domestica*	13	1	28	52	10

[a] From Limpel and Casida.[68]

[b] Triiodothyronine may also occur in this fraction.

resembled the thyroid of mammals. However, virtually the sole iodinated product in cuticle was monoiodotyrosine, so the analogy with the thyroid is not close. Furthermore, thiouracil was without effect on iodine uptake by cuticle,[69] whereas it inhibits thyroxine synthesis in the thyroid. It is likely that the high levels of tyrosine and its derivatives associated with tanning of the cuticle provide a substrate for iodination. Nerve cord, fat body, and muscle all contained appreciable thyroxine, which constituted 20, 27, and 20%, respectively, of their iodine content. Iodine was excreted as monoiodohistidine.

The metabolism of I^{131}-labeled monoiodohistidine and thyroxine by the American cockroach *in vivo* was also reported.[69] The only metabolites identified were from the former, which gave mono- and diiodohistidine, monoiodo-tyrosine, and iodide.

Frontali[70] has recently shown the presence of glutamic acid decarboxylase in honey bee brain. Her technique involved addition of C^{14}-labeled substrate to homogenates and chromatographic separation of the labeled product, γ-aminobutyric acid.

$$
\begin{array}{ccc}
\underset{|}{NH_2} & & \underset{|}{NH_2} \\
\underset{|}{CHCOOH} & & \underset{|}{CH_2} \\
\underset{|}{CH_2} & \longrightarrow & \underset{|}{CH_2} \\
\underset{|}{CH_2} & & \underset{|}{CH_2} \\
COOH & & COOH
\end{array}
$$

Glutamate γ-Aminobutyrate

The observation may turn out to be of major importance in the hunt for insect neurohumors; γ-aminobutyrate has received much study as a possible neurohumor in the mammal, in which glutamic acid decarboxylase is localized in nervous tissue.

The fate of single-carbon fragments has been of great general interest in bio-chemistry over the past 10 years. It has become evident that certain single-carbon-atom compounds, such as formate, are typical "currency" in the body. The fragments are probably transferred to acceptor molecules by transient combination with tetrahydrofolic acid. In the mammal, molecules formed by such acceptance include purines and the amino acids methionine, histidine, and serine.

In studies on the American cockroach[71,72] in which C^{14}-labeled formate was injected, 20% of the C^{14} appeared as CO_2, and about 5% appeared as uric acid, in the C-2 and C-8 positions only; 7% appeared in serine. However, the cockroach differed from mammals in that 1.5% appeared in proline and 0.2% in glutamate (positions not determined), and virtually no incorporation into methionine or histidine was found (Fig. 5.4).

The metabolic abilities of the American cockroach fat body *in vitro* were then examined. Whole tissue and homogenates both incorporated formate-C^{14} into serine in the 3 position, and this incorporation was stimulated fivefold by glycine. This finding favored the occurrence of the over-all reaction, as found in mammals:

$$
\text{H--C*COOH} + \text{NH}_2\text{CH}_2\text{COOH} \longrightarrow \underset{\underset{NH_2}{|}}{\text{HOC*H}_2\text{CHCOOH}} + \text{O}
$$

Formate   Glycine   Serine

Although whole fat body could accomplish the incorporation into uric acid described above, homogenates could not. Presumably some necessary cofactor or intermediate was diluted away by homogenizing.

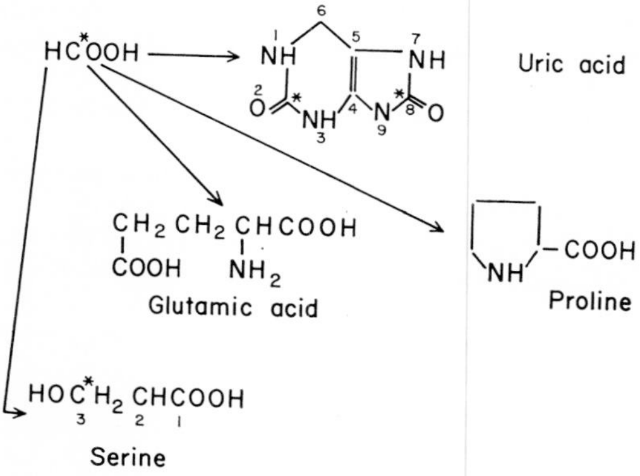

FIG. 5.4. Compounds which incorporate formate in the American cockroach; labeled carbon atoms are indicated by asterisks.

Yamafuji has presented evidence[73] of an oximase in *Bombyx*, which in the presence of NAD and FAD could reduce oximes to amines

$$R—CH=NOH \longrightarrow R—CH_2NH_2$$

and also of a transoximase which could transfer the hydroxyimino group to a carbonyl acceptor

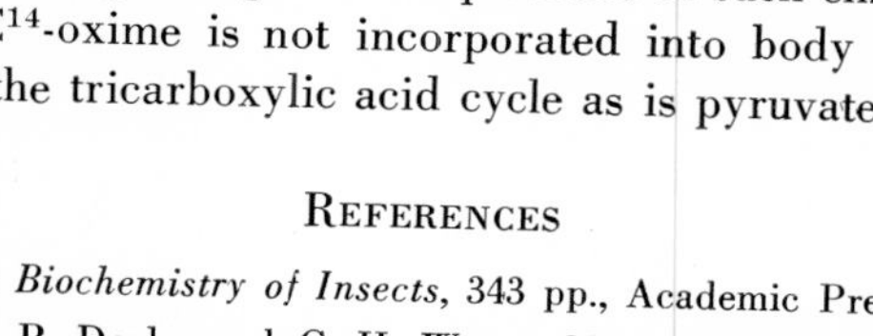

Bheemeswar[74] has argued against the presence of such enzymes in *Bombyx*, since pyruvate-2-C^{14}-oxime is not incorporated into body protein, nor is it oxidized through the tricarboxylic acid cycle as is pyruvate itself.

REFERENCES

1. D. Gilmour, *The Biochemistry of Insects*, 343 pp., Academic Press, New York, 1961.
2. G. M. Silva, W. P. Doyle, and C. H. Wang, Glucose Catabolism in the American Cockroach, *Nature*, **182**: 102 (1958).

3. E. I. Vyskrebentseva, Pathways of Carbohydrate Metabolism in the Coelomic Fluid of the Mulberry Silkworm during Metamorphosis, *Biochemistry (Leningrad)*, **22**: 613 (1957).

4. A. White, P. Handler, E. L. Smith, and DeW. Stetten, *Principles of Biochemistry*, 2nd ed., p. 480, McGraw-Hill, New York, 1959.

5. J. E. Treherne, The Nutrition of the Central Nervous System in the Cockroach, *Periplaneta americana* L. The Exchange and Metabolism of Sugars, *J. Exptl. Biol.*, **37**: 513 (1960).

6. A. N. Clements, Studies on the Metabolism of Locust Fat Body, *J. Exptl. Biol.*, **36**: 665 (1959).

7. D. J. Candy and B. A. Kilby, Site and Mode of Trehalose Biosynthesis in the Locust, *Nature*, **183**: 1594 (1959).

8. M. Somlo and H. Fukuhara, Etude de la Sensibilité au Gaz Carbonique et de la Fixation du CO_2 chez *Drosophila melanogaster*, *Biochim. Biophys. Acta*, **36**: 221 (1959).

9. R. Lasker and A. C. Giese, Cellulose Digestion by the Silverfish *Ctenolepioma lineata*, *J. Exptl. Biol.*, **33**: 542 (1956).

10. E. C. Zebe and W. H. McShan, Incorporation of (^{14}C) Acetate into Long Chain Fatty Acids by the Fat Body of *Prodenia eridania* (Lep.) *Biochim. Biophys. Acta*, **31**: 513 (1959).

11. S. P. Louloudes, J. N. Kaplanis, W. E. Robbins, and R. E. Monroe, Lipogenesis from C^{14}-acetate in the American Cockroach, *Ann. Entomol. Soc. Am.*, **54**: 99 (1961).

12. A. J. Clark and K. Bloch, The Absence of Sterol Synthesis in Insects, *J. Biol. Chem.*, **234**: 2578 (1959).

13. A. J. Clark and K. Bloch, Function of Sterols in *Dermestes vulpinus*, *J. Biol. Chem.*, **234**: 2583 (1959).

14. K. Bloch, R. G. Langdon, A. J. Clark, and G. Fraenkel, Squalene C^{14} from acetate C^{14}-fed *Dermestes*, *Biochim. Biophys. Acta*, **21**: 176 (1956).

15. J. E. Casida, S. D. Beck, and M. J. Cole, Sterol Metabolism in the American Cockroach, *J. Biol. Chem.*, **224**: 365 (1957).

16. A. J. Clark and K. Bloch, Conversion of Ergosterol to 22-dehydrocholesterol in *B. germanica*, *J. Biol. Chem.*, **234**: 2589 (1959).

17. W. E. Robbins, J. N. Kaplanis, S. J. Louloudes, and R. E. Monroe, Utilization of 1-C^{14}-acetate in Lipid Synthesis by Adult House Flies, *Ann. Entomol. Soc. Am.*, **53**: 128 (1960).

18. J. N. Kaplanis, W. E. Robbins, and L. A. Tabor, The Utilization and Metabolism of 4-C^{14}-cholesterol by the Adult House Fly, *Ann. Entomol. Soc. Am.*, **53**: 260 (1960).

19. J. N. Kaplanis, R. C. Dutky, and W. E. Robbins, Lipid Biosynthesis from C^{14}-mevalonate in Adult House Flies, *Ann. Entomol. Soc. Am.*, **54**: 114 (1961).

20. H. C. Agarwal, J. E. Casida, and S. D. Beck, An Unusual Sterol from House Flies, *J. Insect Physiol.*, **7**: 32 (1961).

21. H. L. House, Nutritional Studies with *Blatella germanica* (L.) Reared Under Aseptic Conditions. III. Five Essential Aminoacids, *Can. Entomol.*, **81**: 133 (1949).

22. J. D. Hilchey, Studies on the Qualitative Requirements of *Blatella germanica* (L.) for Aminoacids under Aseptic Conditions, *Contrib. Boyce Thompson Inst.*, **17**: 203 (1952).

23. J. D. Hilchey, R. J. Block, L. P. Miller, and R. M. Weed, The Sulfur Metabolism of Insects. VII. The Utilization of Sulfate for the Formation of Cystine and

Methionine by the German Cockroach, *Blatella germanica* (L.), *Contrib. Boyce Thompson Inst.*, **18**: 109 (1955).

24. S. M. Henry and R. J. Block, The Sulfur Metabolism of Insects. IV. The Conversion of Inorganic Sulfur Compounds in Cockroaches. The Role of Intracellular Symbionts, *Contrib. Boyce Thompson Inst.*, **20**: 317 (1960).

25. T. H. Haines, S. M. Henry, and R. J. Block, The Sulfur Metabolism of Insects. V. The Ability of Insects to Use Sulfate in the Synthesis of Methionine, *Contrib. Boyce Thompson Inst.*, **20**: 363 (1960).

26. J. D. Hilchey, V. F. Cotty, and S. M. Henry, The Sulfur Metabolism of Insects. II. The Metabolism of Cystine-S^{35} by the House Fly, *Musca domestica* (L.), *Contrib. Boyce Thompson. Inst.*, **19**: 189 (1957).

27. V. F. Cotty, S. M. Henry, and J. D. Hilchey, The Sulfur Metabolism of Insects. III. The Metabolism of Cystine, Methionine, Taurine and Sulfate by the House Fly, *Musca domestica* (L.), *Contrib. Boyce Thompson Inst.*, **19**: 379 (1958).

28. R. C. Sanborn, *Interactions Between Respiratory Enzymes and Insecticides*, The Armed Forces Research and Development Report on Insect and Rodent Control, No. 23, 101, 1953.

29. J. Sternburg, C. W. Kearns, and H. Moorefield, DDT Dehydrochlorinase, an Enzyme Found in DDT-resistant Flies, *J. Agr. Food Chem.*, **2**: 1125 (1954).

30. S. M. Henry and R. J. Block, The Sulfur Metabolism of Insects. VI. Metabolism of Sulfur Aminoacids and Related Compounds in the German Cockroach, *Blatella germanica* (L.), *Contrib. Boyce Thompson Inst.*, **21**: 129 (1961).

31. R. Kasting and A. J. McGinnis, The Use of Glucose Labelled with C^{14} to Detect the Aminoacids Essential for an Insect, *Nature*, **182**: 1380 (1958).

32. P. C. Zamecnik, R. B. Loftfield, M. L. Stephenson, and C. M. Williams, Biological Synthesis of Radioactive Silk, *Science*, **109**: 624 (1949).

33. S. Tukeyama, H. Ito, and Y. Miura, Fibroin Synthesis and Ribonucleic Acid Metabolism in the Silk Gland, *Biochim. Biophys. Acta*, **30**: 233 (1958).

34. T. Fukuda, M. Sudo, M. Matuda, T. Hayashi, T. Kurose, Y. Horiuchi, and M. Florkin, Formation of the Silk Proteins During the Growth of the Silkworm Larva (*Bombyx mori*), *Fourth Intern. Congr. Biochem.*, Vienna, Sept. 1958, *Proc.*, **12**: 90 (1959).

35. K. Shimura, H. Fukai, S. Suto, and R. Hoshi, Studies on the Biosynthesis of Silk Fibroin. I. Incorporation of Glycine-1-C^{14} into Fibroin *in vivo*, *J. Biochem.* (*Japan*), **45**: 481 (1958).

36. T. Fukuda, Biochemical Studies on the Formation of the Silk Protein. VII. The Conversion of Glycine to Serine in the Silkworm Larva, *J. Biochem.* (*Japan*), **47**: 720 (1960).

37. T. Fukuda and T. Hayashi, Biochemical Studies on the Formation of the Silk Protein. V. Conversion of Glyoxylic Acid to Glycine in the Silkworm Larva, *J. Biochem.* (*Japan*), **45**: 469 (1958).

38. T. Fukuda and T. Hayashi, Biochemical Studies on the Formation of the Silk Protein. VIII. The Synthesis of α-Ketoglutaratic Acid, Oxalacetic Acid, and Glyoxylic Acid from Glucose in Silkworm, *J. Biochem.* (*Japan*), **48**: 9 (1960).

39. S. Bricteux-Grégoire, W. G. Verly, and M. Florkin, Utilization of the Carboxyl Group of Glycine for the Synthesis of the Aminoacids of Silk by *Bombyx mori*, *Nature*, **182**: 1515 (1958).

40. S. Bricteux-Grégoire and W. G. Verly, Utilization of Formate for the Biosynthesis of Glycine Carbon-1 and -2 in *Bombyx mori*, *Nature*, **182**: 1515 (1958).

41. T. Fukuda, Biochemical Studies on the Formation of the Silk Protein. VI. Conversion of Serine to Glycine in the Silkworm Larva, *J. Biochem. (Japan)*, **47**: 581 (1960).
42. M. Muramatsu, H. Nagayama, and K. Shimura, Studies on the Biosynthesis of Glycine in the Silkworm. I. Formation of Glycine from Serine, *J. Biochem. (Japan)*, **49**: 55 (1961).
43. T. Fukuda, Biochemical Studies on the Formation of the Silkprotein. IV. The Conversion of Pyruvic Acid to Alanine in the Silkworm Larva, *J. Biochem. (Japan)*, **44**: 505 (1957).
44. S. Bricteux-Grégoire, W. G. Verly, and M. Florkin, Utilization of the Carboxyl Carbon of L-phenylalanine for the Synthesis of the Aminoacids of Silk by *Bombyx mori*, *Nature*, **177**: 1237 (1956).
45. T. Fukuda, Conversion of Phenylalanine into Tyrosine in the Silkworm Larva (*Bombyx mori*), *Nature*, **177**: 429 (1956).
46. T. Fukuda, Biochemical Studies on the Formation of the Silk Protein. III. The Conversion of C^{14}-labeled Phenylalanine to Tyrosine in the Silkworm Larva (*Bombyx mori*), *J. Biochem. (Japan)*, **43**: 137 (1956).
47. I. Suzuka and K. Shimura, Biosynthesis of Silk Fibroin. I. Incorporation of Glycine-C^{14} into Particles of Posterior Silk Gland *in vitro*, *J. Biochem. (Japan)*, **47**: 551 (1960).
48. I. Suzuka and K. Shimura, Biosynthesis of Silk Fibroin. II. Incorporation of Specific C^{14}-labeled Aminoacids into Protein of Posterior Silk Gland *in vitro*, *J. Biochem. (Japan)*, **47**: 555 (1960).
49. S. Suto and K. Shimura, Studies on the Biosynthesis of Silk Fibroin. III. In vivo Incorporation of Glycine-C^{14} into Proteins of Posterior Silk Gland Fractions, *J. Biochem. (Japan)*, **49**: 69 (1961).
50. I. Suzuka, S. Tanaka, and K. Shimura, Aminoacid Incorporation Enzyme in Posterior Silk Gland, *J. Biochem. (Japan)*, **48**: 774 (1960).
51. K. Shimura, H. Kobayashi, R. Hoshi, and J. Sato, Studies on the Biosynthesis of Silk Fibroin. II. Non-uniform Labeling of Silk Fibroin Synthesized *in vivo*, *J. Biochem. (Japan)*, **46**: 849 (1959).
52. S. Bricteux-Grégoire, W. G. Verly, and M. Florkin, Protein Synthesis in *Sphinx liqustri* Pupae, *Nature*, **179**: 678 (1956).
53. W. H. Telfer and C. M. Williams, The Effects of Diapause, Development and Injury on the Incorporation of Radioactive Glycine into the Blood Proteins of the *Cecropia* Silkworm, *J. Insect Physiol.*, **5**: 6 (1960).
54. F. P. W. Winteringham, The Labeled Pool Technique with Particular Reference to Pesticide Research, *Advan. Pest Control Res.*, **3**: 76 (1960).
55. F. P. W. Winteringham and A. Harrison, Study of Anticholinesterase Action in Insects by a Labeled Pool Technique, *Nature*, **178**: 81 (1956).
56. S. C. Fang and D. Allen, Distribution and Incorporation of Radioactive Phosphorus in the Douglas-fir Beetle, *J. Econ. Entomol.*, **48**: 79 (1955).
57. F. P. W. Winteringham, P. M. Bridges, and G. C. Hellyer, Mode of Insecticidal Action Studied with Labelled Systems. Phosphorylated Compounds in the Muscle of the Adult Housefly, *Musca domestica*, *Biochem. J.*, **59**: 13 (1955).
58. F. P. W. Winteringham, G. C. Hellyer, and M. A. McKay, Effects of Methyl Bromide on Phosphorus Metabolism in the Adult House Fly, *Musca domestica*, *Biochem. J.*, **69**: 640 (1958).
59. E. Baldwin, *Dynamic Aspects of Biochemistry*, 1st ed., p. 341, Cambridge University Press, Cambridge, England, 1957.

60. F. P. W. Winteringham, Phosphorylated Compounds in the Head and Thoracic Tissues of the Adult House Fly, *Musca domestica* L., During Flight, Rest, Anoxia and Starvation, *Biochem. J.*, **75**: 38 (1960).

61. G. E. Boxer and T. M. Devlin, Pathways of Intracellular Hydrogen Transport, *Science*, **134**: 1495 (1961).

62. J. P. Heslop and J. W. Ray, Nucleotides and other Phosphorus Compounds of Cockroach Nerve, *Nature*, **190**: 1192 (1961).

63. A. N. Davison and J. Dobbing, Phospholipid Metabolism in Nervous Tissue. III. The Anatomical Distribution of Metabolically Inert Phospholipid in the Central Nervous System, *Biochem. J.*, **75**: 571 (1960).

64. G. M. Price, Some Aspects of Aminoacid Metabolism in the Adult Housefly, *Musca domestica*, *Biochem. J.*, **80**: 420 (1961).

65. F. H. Babers and C. C. Roan, Distribution of Radioactive Phosphorus in Susceptible and Resistant Houseflies, *J. Econ. Entomol.*, **47**: 973 (1954).

66. B. M. Wheeler, Halogen Metabolism of *Drosophila gibberosa*. I. Iodine Metabolism Studied by Means of I[131], *J. Exptl. Zool.*, **115**: 83 (1950).

67. B. M. Wheeler, The Iodine Metabolism of *Drosophila gibberosa* Studied by Means of Radioiodide (I[131]), *Proc. Nat. Acad. Sci.*, **33**: 298 (1947).

68. L. E. Limpel and J. E. Casida, Iodine Metabolism in Insects. I. *In vivo* Metabolism of Radioiodide, *J. Exptl. Zool.*, **135**: 19 (1957).

69. L. E. Limpel and J. E. Casida, Iodine Metabolism in Insects. II. *In vivo* Distribution and Metabolism of Iodoamino acids and Related Studies with *Periplaneta*, *J. Exptl. Zool.*, **136**: 595 (1957).

70. N. Frontali, Activity of Glutamic Acid Decarboxylase in Insect Nerve Tissue, *Nature*, **191**: 178 (1961).

71. W. D. McEnroe and A. J. Forgash, The *in vivo* Incorporation of C[14]-formate in the Ureide Groups of Uric Acid by *Periplaneta americana* (L.), *Ann. Entomol. Soc. Am.*, **50**: 429 (1957).

72. W. D. McEnroe and A. J. Forgash, Formate Metabolism in the American Cockroach, *Periplaneta americana* (L.), *Ann. Entomol. Soc. Am.*, **51**: 126 (1958).

73. K. Yamafuji, Metabolism of Silkworm in Relation to Biochemical Virus Induction, *Fourth Intern. Congr. Biochem., Vienna, Sept. 1958, Proc.*, **12**: 100 (1959).

74. B. Bheemeswar, Some Aspects of Aminoacid Metabolism in Insects, *Fourth Intern. Congr. Biochem., Vienna, Sept. 1958, Proc.*, **12**: 78 (1959).

75. F. P. W. Winteringham, Presence and Significance of Alpha-glycerophosphate in Insect Tissue, *Biochem. J.*, **71**: 21P (1959).

76. A. F. Wagner and K. Folkers, The Organic and Biological Chemistry of Mevalonic Acid, *Endeavour*, **20**: 177 (1961).

CHAPTER 6

Physiology

The area of insect physiology is one in which the use of radioisotopes should be of tremendous assistance. In fact, their possibilities have been exploited only to a small extent. It is a gloomy experience to read the account of gut absorption in "Insect Physiology," published in 1953.[1] The traditional and often ineffectual procedures involving dyes, qualitative microscopic examination, and osmometric techniques have led to a good deal of dispute. Fortunately, several radioisotopic studies have been made since then. They are described below, and it will be apparent that far more definitive information is obtained when such procedures are used.

Other areas where a modest amount of work has been done include the movements of inorganic ions within the body and the functions of the Malpighian tubules, but very obvious fields for isotope use have been studied by only one or two investigators. Examples are the permeability properties of the integument and the nerve sheath, the blood volume and "spaces" (such as glucose space) in the insect body, and water movements.

1. Digestion and Absorption

Treherne has published a comprehensive series of papers on this topic. In a study of the uptake of glucose-C^{14} by the American cockroach *Periplaneta americana*,[2] a mixture of glucose with a dye (Amaranth, or Azo-Rubrin S) was fed to starved cockroaches. The dye was shown to be unabsorbed and to be recoverable to an extent of 99% from the intestine. It was therefore possible to determine quantitatively the progress of the dye-glucose mixture down the gut as a function of time. By measuring the radioactivity of the contents of particular gut parts and finding the dye:glucose ratio, the per cent absorption from that part was established. It was found that the caecae of the midgut absorbed most of the glucose, and the contribution of other gut parts was negligible. A diagram of the gut is shown in Fig. 6.1.

It was also shown that the amount of mixture which had left the crop at any given time was linearly related to the extent of glucose uptake from the caecae at that time; the relationship was not dependent on the glucose concentration fed. However, the rate of crop emptying was linearly related to the concentration of the glucose which was fed. Consequently, the rate at which glucose was removed was not controlled by the rate of movement across the caecal membrane but by the rate of crop discharge. A consequence of this was that, if salts were fed along with the glucose so that extra water was drawn osmotically into the crop and its rate of discharge of glucose thereby reduced, the rate of glucose absorption by the caecae was severely reduced: addition of 1.17% sodium chloride decreased the glucose absorption by 60%.

This control by the crop made it impossible to determine whether other gut parts could absorb glucose if given an opportunity, for, normally, the crop only passed out enough for the caecae to remove rapidly. Consequently, studies were shifted[3] to the locust *Schistocerca gregaria*, into whose gut glucose could be introduced, anally or orally, in order to bypass the crop. It was shown in this way that the caecae, and to a far less extent the ventriculus, were capable

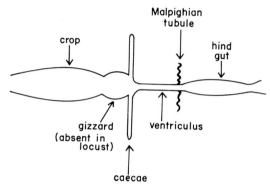

FIG. 6.1.   Diagram of the alimentary tract of the American cockroach.

of absorption. However, at high glucose concentrations,[4] the caecae and ventriculus were equally active. Chromatography of the hemolymph radioactivity[3] showed that after low concentrations $(0.02\,M)$ of glucose were fed, complete conversion to trehalose* occurred immediately after absorption. Only when high levels of glucose $(0.2\,M)$ were fed was appreciable glucose-C^{14} found in the hemolymph. It was shown that conversion followed uptake rather than preceding it, which demonstrated that all of the radioactivity in the gut was as glucose.

The rate of glucose uptake from excised guts suspended in a large volume (1 liter) of saline containing cyanide and iodoacetate was identical with that found *in vivo*. It was therefore suggested that the mechanism of absorption *in vivo* was by simple diffusion, and that, to maintain the steep concentration gradient (comparable to the *in vitro* experiment), the glucose was rapidly

---

* An unusual disaccharide, nonreducing because it is formed from two glucose molecules condensed at their reducing groups.

removed by conversion to trehalose. This mechanism is unlike that found in mammals, in which active transport occurs, and the rapid conversion in blood does not.

The sugar studies on *Schistocerca* were also made with fructose and mannose.[4] Both were converted to trehalose, and the efficiency of their conversion accounted for variations in their rate of absorption. With glucose and fructose it was shown that conversion to trehalose was comparable whether the monosaccharide was fed or injected, so that gut-wall conversion was probably not a factor.

The above mechanism operates when relatively high concentrations of glucose (e.g., $0.01\,M$) are in the gut. At very low levels, the gut concentration is comparable with the hemolymph level, and it was found (by injecting glucose-C^{14} into the hemolymph) that exchange rather than net absorption occurred. This finding supports the theory of passive diffusion.

The combination of an unabsorbable dye and an absorbable nutrient was also used to study amino acid absorption, following introduction into the gut via the rectum.[5] Carbon-14-labeled glycine and serine were used, at concentrations similar to those in hemolymph, that is, about $0.034\,M$. As with sugars, maximum uptake occurred in the caecae, less in the ventriculus, and very little anywhere else. In the caecae, about 60% absorption of both occurred in 1 hour. The uptake rate fell off exponentially.

The above paragraph appears to give a succinct statement of the fate of ingested serine. But in fact it does not, for reasons which are worth analyzing because they illustrate a recurrent problem in isotope use—the problem of distinguishing between exchange and net movement of molecules. The situation was analyzed in detail by Treherne in this amino acid study. Figure 6.2 (a) shows that the concentration of labeled glycine in the caecae fell steadily, as described above, but the concentration of total glycine (labeled plus unlabeled) actually increased. In other words, the loss of labeled glycine from the caecae, expressed as a concentration, was more than balanced by an influx of unlabeled glycine from the blood. Yet, a net loss of glycine from the caecae did in fact occur, for water was also slowly lost from the caecae, so that, although the concentration of total glycine rose, the quantity fell, as shown in Fig. 6.2 (b). The figure shows that the quantity of total glycine fell at about one-third of the rate of the quantity of labeled glycine.

Problems of this sort arise when the labeled compound which is added can equilibrate with an unlabeled endogenous compound. If the gut is suspended in a large beaker of buffer (as in the sugar experiments described above), then the loss of radioactivity is a precise measure of the loss of total compound. But whenever significant back-diffusion can occur, loss of radioactivity only gives information about permeability to the compound, not about net loss of compound.

From these experiments it was concluded that amino acid absorption from the gut occurred by passive diffusion. Since no rapid facilitating mechanism comparable to the glucose-trehalose conversion occurs with amino acids, the net absorption is fairly slow. From 0.03-M solutions in the caecae, 54% of glucose, but only 8% of serine, would be absorbed.

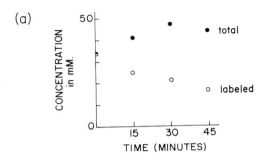

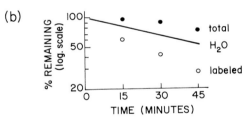

FIG. 6.2. Uptake of glycine-C[14] from gut of the intact locust: (a) concentration of glycine within the gut; (b) quantity of glycine within the gut, and water content. (From Treherne.[5])

The topic of fat absorption has long been of interest and dispute among students of vertebrates. Only a single quantitative study has appeared for the insect, a paper by Treherne[6] on tripalmitin-C[14] fed to the American cockroach. After feeding, the crop contents were recovered, and the radioactivity was still 77% as unaltered fat. Using the combined dye-and-substrate method described above for sugars, Treherne found once more that uptake was maximal from the caecae and negligible in the crop. This appeared to be in opposition to previous histological studies (e.g., see Eisner[7]) which suggested that the crop was an important organ for fat uptake on the basis of droplets appearing in its epithelium after a meal. The resolution of the paradox is presumably that the foregut absorbs fat and stores it and, from the point of view of the whole body, is an organ of storage and not of transmission.

As with sugars, the rate of crop emptying appeared to control the rate of caecal uptake. This argues for the hypothesis that fats can be absorbed without prior hydrolysis; however, rapid hydrolysis in the midgut cannot be excluded.

In 1939 a pioneer study on the role of the Malpighian tubules was made by Patton and Craig[8] by using the chloride of an unidentified radioactive sodium

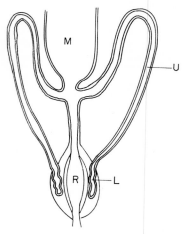

Fig. 6.3. Diagram of the Malpighian tubules of *Tenebrio molitor*, with two of the many tubules shown: M is the midgut; R, rectum; U, upper portion of Malpighian tubule; and L, lower portion. (Based on Patton and Craig.[8])

isotope. The tubules of the yellow mealworm *Tenebrio molitor* have the conformation shown diagrammatically in Fig. 6.3. Clearly, there are two portions, the upper portion (U) in the figure which hangs free in the body cavity and the lower portion (L) which is bound to the rectal wall. In the experiment, part U was placed in a vessel with radioactive sodium: another vessel contained part L and the excised, ligated rectum. Radioactivity appeared in the L vessel. When labeled sodium was placed with L and not with U, no activity appeared in the U vessel. The tubules therefore represent a one-way diffusion system.

The Malpighian tubules of the insect are analagous to the kidney of the mammal. But do they operate (1) as the glomerulus of the kidney, i.e., permitting all dialyzable solutes to enter and therefore requiring selective removal of useful solutes later, as in the mammalian renal tubule; or (2) by selectively secreting unwanted solutes into the tubules?

In view of the lack of evident structural differentiation in the insect Malpighian tubules, one might expect possibility (2). But Ramsay[9] has shown that various "metabolically useful" substances, such as amino acids and sugars, pass into the tubule in the case of the stick insect *Carausius morosus*. The experiments were carried out by placing a tubule in a medium containing a known concentration (P) of a labeled compound, collecting the urine secreted by the tubule, and measuring its concentration (U) of label.

With six amino acids, alanine, arginine, glycine, lysine, proline, and valine, the U/P ratio varied little with P, even though P was varied 1000-fold. There

TABLE 6.1

PENETRATION OF AMINO ACIDS INTO EXCISED MALPIGHIAN TUBULES OF THE STICK INSECT, *Carausius morosus*[a]

	$P(mM)$ [b]	U/P [c]
DL-Alanine	4.4	0.23
L-Arginine	0.34	0.39
L-Arginine	53	0.35
L-Arginine	105	0.40
L-Arginine	158	0.62
Glycine	4.5	0.14
L-Lysine	0.15	0.13
L-Proline	0.16	0.22
DL-Valine	6.3	0.24

[a] From Ramsay.[9]

[b] P is the concentration applied outside the tubule.

[c] U is the concentration found in the urine.

was, therefore, no threshold for absorption, nor was there any upper limit. Among all six acids (see Table 6.1), U/P varied only from 0.13 (lysine at 0.15 mM) to 0.62 (arginine at 158 mM). All these facts indicate passive diffusion.

Glucose, fructose, sucrose, and urea were also studied; at low concentrations the values for U/P were 0.32, 0.45, 0.47, and 1.03, respectively. For fructose and glucose the values of U/P were somewhat dependent on P, a fact which Ramsay attributed to metabolism of these sugars (compare Treherne's observations above). Thus, for glucose, U/P was 0.32 when P was 0.17 mM, but 0.85 when P was 158 mM.

The Malpighian tubule permits diffusion of urea and sucrose in either direction, for Ramsay showed that, if the distal end of the tubule was placed in a drop containing labeled urea or sucrose and the middle portion was placed in an unlabeled drop, radioactivity appeared in the second drop. Considering this fact and that the value of U/P was never above 1, it is apparent that the tubules themselves are passive and nonselective; it must be the rectal glands, which reabsorb useful solutes, that control solute levels in the insect. The two-way effect differs from that reported by Patton and Craig for sodium in *Tenebrio*. It is impossible to say whether this difference is due to variations in mechanism, species, or technique, or to the fact that one study dealt with ions.

The Malpighian tubules of the insect therefore resemble the glomerular part of the vertebrate kidney, and the selective function of the vertebrate's renal tubules is carried out by the insect's rectal glands.

2. Uptake and Distribution of Inorganic Materials

Most radioisotopes fed for tagging purposes are in an inorganic form. This fact, as well as fundamental interest, has prompted several studies on the uptake of inorganic materials and their subsequent retention.

Barium[140] was readily absorbed from food by larvae of *Drosophila repleta*.[10] In this case absorption was from the anterior part of the midgut, and, to a lesser extent, from the bases of the caecae; a sharp boundary "about 5 cell-widths up the caecae from their bases" was described, above which no absorption occurred, as evidenced by radioautographs. The absorbed barium appeared promptly in the Malpighian tubules and stayed there. The author viewed this as a phenomenon of dissolved foods in general and not a behavior peculiar to barium. For male hornets of the genus *Vespula* fed with Ba[140], a qualitative study[11] indicated that the barium was mostly voided without absorption. However, a distinct uptake into the epithelial cells of the midgut was found. A little uptake by Malpighian tubules was found, and some was transferred to the genital system.

The manganese metabolism of hornets and wasps was examined by Bowen,[12] using Mn[56]. Unfortunately, this isotope has a half-life of only 2.6 hours. Manganese-56 dichloride fed to the hornet *Vespa crabro* was later found radioautographically only in the crop and midgut. Times of up to 12 hours after feeding were selected. Similarly, for *Vespa maculata*, in which Geiger counting was employed, the midgut had 289 counts/minute; the hindgut, 9 counts/minute. Most of the activity was restricted to the distal third of the epithelial cells of the midgut; this appears to contrast rather strongly with the barium study above. A third pattern is reported for Cu[64] fed to various *Drosophila* species[13]: a high proportion appeared in the middle portion of the midgut.

The distribution of ingested inorganic P[32] was reported in 1942 for several species: greater wax moth, *Galleria melonella*; *Tenebrio*; German cockroach,

Blatella germanica; and firebrat, *Thermobia domestica*.[14] Both frozen and paraffin sections were prepared and radioautographed. Little P^{32} was found in fat body, strangely enough, or in salivary glands, or hind- or foregut. Most was in the epithelium of the midintestine (cf. results with barium, etc., above) and in the reproductive organs.

In other insects, somewhat contrary results have been reported. When *Drosophila* was reared[15] on a medium containing inorganic P^{32} deposition was particularly marked in fat body and nervous tissues, doubtless owing to high phospholipid levels. Esophagus, mid- and hindgut, gonads, and Malpighian tubules all contained much P^{32}. High P^{32} in salivary glands was reported for yellow fever mosquitoes, *Aedes aegypti*, reared as larvae in P^{32} in water,[16] or fed as adults on P^{32} in water and glucose.[17] In the larvae, the principal uptake sites were Malpighian tubules, mid- and hindgut, and fat body.

It is apparent that many patterns have been reported, and in some cases, such as the labeling of the salivary glands, important differences have been described. These discrepant results may reflect genuine species variation, but it would be unwise to rely on this without confirmatory work.

The larva of the mosquito *Aedes* absorbs salts from its fresh-water medium into the hemolymph against a steep concentration gradient. The mechanism of this ion uptake was examined by Treherne[18] with the use of Na^{24}. He confirmed an earlier nonisotopic proof of Wigglesworth that the anal papillae were responsible for most of the uptake, for destroying them reduced uptake by 80%. If the mouthparts were blocked as well, uptake was reduced another 15%, which showed that uptake from the gut was also significant. The kinetics of sodium uptake fitted remarkably well with the theoretical values for diffusion from one simple compartment into another. The uptake rate was unaffected by doubling the external sodium level, and if the larvae were loaded with Na^{24} and placed in distilled water, they held tenaciously to the sodium. Some form of metabolically energized pump with a fixed capacity must be involved. A 25-fold increase in the external potassium level had no effect on the rate of Na^{24} uptake, so it is clear that the pump is highly specific and also potassium insensitive (cf. results, p. 125, for the sodium pump of nerve).

Independent work[19] largely confirmed Treherne's, and showed also that the extent of the sodium flux was highly dependent on feeding, being reduced sevenfold by starvation; the halflife of the exchange was about 10 hours in fed larvae. Nevertheless, sodium balance was retained in the starved larvae, which suggests that both entry and exit of sodium are metabolically controlled rather than having a single "pump" working against a steady passive efflux. A similar conclusion follows from Treherne's demonstration of sodium retention even in distilled water.

A few studies exist on the distribution of elements of no conceivable metabolic importance.

The utilization of yttrium-91 by *Drosophila*[20,21] and the housefly[21] has been studied in Norway. When injected as the citrate into *Drosophila*, yttrium was completely retained in the body through the experimental period of 3 weeks. It appeared to stay in the injection zone, but, apart from this, discrepant results were reported.

By contrast, when Y^{91} citrate was fed, it was rapidly and almost completely excreted. Most of the small residual fraction was retained in a remarkably localized band in the midgut—the posterior portion in *Drosophila* and the middle portion in the housefly. Clearly, there is considerable species variation, but, unfortunately, these data do not fit with the Cu^{64} results above. In the housefly, Y^{91} was also found to a small extent in the heart and pericardium, so a little translocation must have occurred. Unfortunately, such rare-earth studies appear to be peculiarly susceptible to small variations in preparation of the labeled material, and one cannot say to what extent these results reflect the properties of certain physical preparations rather than the chemical constitution of yttrium.

Lanthanum[140] was not absorbed at all by larvae of *Drosophila repleta*, nor was it excreted when formed endogenously by breakdown of Ba^{140}.[10]

3. Elemental Turnover

In the chapter on biochemistry, the fate of ingested, specifically labeled compounds is discussed. The current view of the dynamic state of body constituents gives the picture of a continuous breakdown and reformation of most of the components of the body. Any given element has an average turnover rate which expresses the average turnover rate of the principal compounds as well as the age, sex, and metabolic status of the organism.

In order to measure the turnover rate of an element, one measures the biological half-life, usually by allowing the animal to feed on the radioisotopically labeled element until this has equilibrated with the element in the body and by then removing the animal to an unlabeled diet and observing the time for the body's radioactivity to decay to half its equilibrium value. The biological half-life measures the rate at which a material is removed from the body but is also dependent on the size of the pool of that material in the body. For instance, sodium might be rapidly excreted, but, because the body's sodium pool is large, it would take some time for half of it to be excreted. Many other such problems exist. For instance, in adult houseflies reared as larvae in a P^{32} medium, the half-life for P^{32} loss was several days, whereas in adults fed on labeled milk, the half-life was 0.8 days.[22] Presumably, in the latter case true equilibrium with the phosphorus pool had not occurred.

The values for a given strain of a given species can vary a great deal with minor variations in technique. Thus, King[23] reported that P^{32} was lost from female *Drosophila* in two phases, fast and slow, with half-lives of 0.94 and 2.25 days; for males the figures were larger, 1.59 and 3.08 days. A year later King and Wilson[24] reported values for the same insects of 0.26 and 3.39 days (females), and 0.43 and 5.32 days (males). The differences were that in the first experiments the insects were fed P^{32} in a cornmeal-molasses-yeast-agar medium and were often etherized. In the later experiments they were fed on P^{32}-labeled yeast and were not etherized. These changes altered some values almost fourfold, as one can see. It is apparent that in comparing different species, only enormous variations in half-life should be considered to reflect fundamentally different physiological or biochemical processes.

In such "P^{32}-equilibrated" *Drosophila*, most of the P^{32} was in the thorax (e.g., 33% in males), hemolymph (17%), and head (16%). Data for the turnover in these and other tissues were reported; the female gonads turned over 96% of their phosphorus in a day, compared to 18% for male gonads. Presumably, this is a reflection of the vigorous phosphorus metabolism involved in egg formation. Further studies[24] showed that the balance is preserved by a gigantic uptake and output: the female insect weighed 1.5 mg and took in and put out daily 1.12 mg of yeast, which contained 6.4 µg of phosphorus. The efficiency of utilization of ingested P^{32} was 80%, compared with 70% in mammals. In the process, 58% of the body phosphorus was turned over in one day, being replaced by phosphorus from the medium.

In the locust (*Locusta migratoria*), the half-life of ingested inorganic P^{32} was approximately 10 days.[25] For the German cockroach fed on milk with P^{32}, the half-life was 9 days for males and over 14 days for females.[22] For female two-spotted mites, *Tetranychus telarius*, fed on P^{32}-tagged bean plants, the half-life was 1.5 days.[26] For screw-worm fly adults reared as larvae on a P^{32} medium, the half-life was 7 days.[27]

For other elements, data are scarce. After feeding Sr^{89} to adults, the half-lives reported were 18 hours for houseflies of both sexes, 3.5 days for male German cockroaches, and 0.95 days for females.[28]

4. The Permeability of the Central Nervous System

The matter of ion permeability of the insect central nervous system is of utmost importance. Most phytophagous insects have a high blood potassium level which would kill vertebrates by blocking the nervous system. This anomaly appeared to be resolved when Hoyle[29] showed in 1953 that in the

Locusta there was, around the nervous system, a sheath impermeable to potassium. When potassium was injected under this sheath, blockade occurred. This finding led to other experiments which generated the picture of a rather nonspecific ion barrier around the insect central nervous system.[30,31] However, a series of recent papers by Treherne seems to cast doubt on the validity of this picture.

From experiments in which he injected Na[24] and K[42] into American cockroaches and measured the amounts which appeared in the nerve cord at various times, Treherne[32] calculated a half-time for the exchange process of 24 minutes for potassium, and from his graph one can estimate a value of about 14 minutes for sodium. It is important to note that in these and subse-

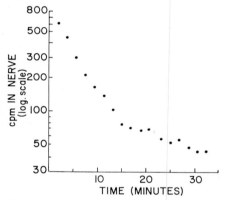

Fig. 6.4.   Efflux of Na[24] from the isolated nerve cord of the American cockroach; the nerve cord itself was monitored. (From Treherne.[33])

quent experiments Treherne arranged that the total sodium level (radioactive plus nonradioactive) in blood was in the normal range; the concentration selected was 0.157 M.

Next, the efflux rate from the nerve cord was measured.[33] The cord was loaded with Na[24] by injecting a large dose of up to 50 μc of Na[24]Cl into the intact insect and removing the cord 30 minutes later. This was transferred to a vessel which allowed continuous washing of the cord and monitoring of its radioactivity. It was found that the Na[24] declined rapidly and exponentially at first, and then at about 30 minutes there was an abrupt change to a slower rate (Fig. 6.4). The first rapid phase could be severely inhibited by the respiratory inhibitors KCN and 2,4-dinitrophenol and by washing with potassium-free solution. Washing with sodium-free solution had no effect.

It is clear that the fast effect is something more than simple diffusion: it involves some kind of metabolic pump, and it seems to require intake of potassium coupled with output of sodium. No satisfactory explanation exists for the biphasic nature of the efflux, unless it is that the cord deteriorates about 30 minutes after removal, and afterward only passive diffusion occurs.

What is the tissue that controls the efflux rate? The outer layers of the nerve cord include a sheath or perilemma which has two components: an outer fibrous layer (the neural lamella), and an inner cellular layer (the perineurium). "Desheathing" by removal of the perilemma had been shown by Twarog and Roeder[30] to increase greatly the susceptibility of the cockroach ganglion to ionic inhibitors (including high concentrations of potassium) which normally have little effect upon insect nerves. Consequently, it seemed probable that some part of the perilemma controlled ion flux. But Treherne[34] used an isolated ganglion to show that desheathing had absolutely no effect on the rate of Na^{24} loss, and that therefore the perilemma must be freely permeable to sodium. Oddly enough, this ganglion preparation, although behaving like the whole cord in its rate of loss of Na^{24} and its sensitivity to 2,4-dinitrophenol or low potassium, differed from it in showing only the first rapid phase of Na^{24} efflux and not the second slow phase.

In the experiments so far described, Treherne made his first measurement at 1 minute after washing began. In a new study,[35] the technique was modified so that about 10 readings could be made during the first minute. The major technique change was that measurements were made on the washings rather than on the cord itself. With whole nerve cords there was a rapid drop in the efflux rate during the first 200 seconds before the "rapid early exponential" phase described above was achieved (Fig. 6.5). Further graphical analysis showed that during the first 200 seconds there was a brief phase (I) lasting about 30 seconds of rapidly changing efflux, and that for the next 150 seconds there was simultaneously a rapid exponential loss (II), with a half-time of 28 seconds, and a less rapid exponential loss (III), with a half-time of 277 seconds. By the end of this 150-second period, (II) had run its course. It was (III) which was measured as the "rapid early" phase in previous experiments.

Although 2,4-dinitrophenol (0.5 mM) had no effect on (II), it about halved the rate of (III). The effect on (I) was not readily determined. With isolated ganglia, which showed substantially the same kinetics of efflux as whole cords, desheathing was found not to affect (II) or (III), and it was not possible to determine if (I) was affected.

Presumably, these different phases represent losses of sodium from different sources within the nerve cord. Some sodium may be on the surface of the cord, but, since the sodium in (II) was calculated to occupy 30% of the nerve cord water, that sodium could not originate solely from surface water. Treherne considers that the (II) sodium is in the intercellular water, which he measured as "inulin space" and found to be 10% of the nerve cord water.

The inulin space was found by equilibrating with inulin-C^{14} and measuring the radioactivity in the cord. It is generally assumed that this foreign polysaccharide cannot diffuse into cells and consequently occupies only intercellular water (but see Section 5, p. 128). Treherne's arguments are that (1) the calculated diffusion constant for sodium efflux (II) was one-thirtieth of that for free diffusion of sodium, and such a retardation is consonant with "the increase in the effective path length for ions diffusing between a complex collection of cellular structures," and (2) there was good agreement between the ratio of efflux rates for sodium and inulin and the ratio of free diffusion rates for sodium and inulin. Against these arguments stands the fact that the inulin space was 10% of the nerve cord water, but the (II) sodium was in 30% of the water.

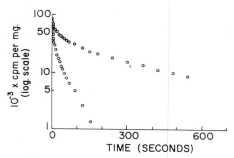

FIG. 6.5. Efflux of Na^{24} from the isolated nerve cord of the American cockroach; the nerve cord washings were monitored. The top curve represents direct measurements, and after 150 seconds it displays phase (III). By extrapolating the linear portion back to the origin and substracting its contribution to the prelinear phase, the bottom points are obtained, showing a rapidly changing period (I) followed by a rapid linear phase (II) at from 30 to 150 seconds. (From Treherne.[35])

Acceptance of Treherne's argument explains why the rate of (II) was unaffected by metabolic inhibitors; it is a purely passive process. A corollary is that (III) represented loss from the intracellular space. The early experiments showed in effect that (III) is reduced in a potassium-free medium; one assumes that (II) would be unaffected, but this experiment was not done.

We are left with a paradox: Treherne finds that penetration through the perilemma is rapid, for the intercellular sodium must penetrate it, and with a half-time of 28 seconds. Yet Twarog and Roeder[30] found that removal of the perilemma reduced the time for blockade caused by high external potassium (0.14 M) from 26 minutes to 75 seconds. Perhaps inward diffusion of potassium is not governed in the same way as outward diffusion of sodium. Further studies along Treherne's lines could answer this. More likely, it is ionic materials which penetrate the cell that are important, and these are subject to the more stringent conditions of phase (III), whose sodium efflux had a half-time of 277 seconds.

It is also most important to consider the particular preparation used. O'Brien, studying the penetration of organophosphates,[36] showed that in excised American cockroach nerve cords an ionic compound penetrated almost as well as a nonionic, but with intact cords (i.e., those left in place in an opened cockroach), ionic penetration was greatly inhibited. All of Treherne's experiments except his first one[32] involved excised cords.

Efflux of glucose-C^{14} from the American cockroach nerve cord was studied[37] by the same procedure as that described for sodium. In this case only two phases were observed: a rapid exponential one (half-time 19 seconds) and a slow exponential one (half-time 580 seconds). Although the hypothesis was not advanced at the time, one may presume that Treherne would interpret this too as loss of extracellular and cellular solute, respectively. It was interesting to note that, if the cord was only soaked in glucose-C^{14} for 1 second, subsequently efflux showed only the rapid phase. Presumably, under these conditions little glucose had entered the cells.

Influx of sugar into the nerve cord after injection of glucose-C^{14} into the whole insect was also fairly rapid, but its time course was complex because of the extremely rapid condensation of the glucose to trehalose, which penetrated 2.5 times more slowly. Consequently, the total influx rate went through a short burst of activity due to glucose and then settled down to a slow rate due primarily to trehalose penetration. The rate difference (2.5-fold) for these sugars is much greater than the difference of free diffusion in water, which is only 1.2-fold. Some sort of activated transport of glucose is implied.

5. Miscellaneous Studies

In the evaluation of results from physiological experiments on solute concentrations within tissues, it is often important to distinguish between cellular and intracellular water. The only procedure used for insects has been Levenbook's,[38] which employed C^{14}-labeled inulin. Its original application was to larvae of the southern army-worm, *Prodenia eridania*. The inulin was injected, and samples of blood were removed at various times for assay of radioactivity. Later, the tissues were individually assayed for total water and radioactivity. By using the assumption that inulin is distributed only in the extracellular water, the latter was estimated as 28% of the total water for fat body and for gut. However, it must be pointed out that the "extracellular space" in mammalian brain, often evaluated by use of inulin, is currently believed to be an artifact,[39] and such a procedure is therefore suspect.

An important measurement in vertebrates is that of the circulation time of the blood. The insect has an open mixing system rather than a true circulation, and in this case one can only measure the time for uniform mixing of the blood. Inorganic P^{32} has been used for this measurement.[40] The results were rather dependent upon the details or the procedure—primarily on the injection site and the sampling site. For instance, when the harlequin bug, *Murgantia histrionica*, was injected in the head, the time for mixing in the antenna was about 2 minutes, but in the wing was about 20 minutes. One can only select the longest time measured with all injection and sampling sites and give this as the estimate of complete mixing throughout the body. These values were 25 minutes for *Murgantia histrionica*, 35 minutes for the squash bug, *Anasa trist:s*, and 10 minutes for *Tenebrio*; all were adults. These figures compare with 2–4 minutes for man and 5 minutes for the dog.

REFERENCES

1. D. F. Waterhouse and M. F. Day, Function of the Gut in Absorption, Excretion and Intermediary Metabolism, in *Insect Physiology*, K. D. Roeder (Ed.), p. 331, John Wiley and Sons, New York, 1953.
2. J. E. Treherne, Glucose Absorption in the Cockroach, *J. Exptl. Biol.*, **34**: 478 (1957).
3. J. E. Treherne, The Absorption of Glucose from the Alimentary Canal of the Locust *Schistocerca gregaria* (Forsk.), *J. Exptl. Biol.*, **35**: 297 (1958).
4. J. E. Treherne, The Absorption and Metabolism of some Sugars in the Locust, *Schistocerca gregaria* (Forsk.), *J. Exptl. Biol.*, **35**: 611 (1958).
5. J. E. Treherne, Amino Acid Absorption in the Locust *Schistocerca gregaria* (Forsk.), *J. Exptl. Biol.*, **36**: 533 (1959).
6. J. E. Treherne, The Digestion and Absorption of Tripalmitin in the Cockroach, *Periplaneta americana* L, *J. Exptl. Biol.*, **35**: 862 (1958).
7. T. Eisner, The Digestion and Absorption of Fats in the Foregut of the Cockroach, *Periplaneta americana* (L), *J. Exptl. Zool.*, **130**: 159 (1955).
8. R. L. Patton and R. Craig, The Rates of Excretion of Certain Substances by the Larvae of the Mealworm, *Tenebrio molitor* L., *J. Exptl. Zool.*, **81**: 437 (1939).
9. J. A. Ramsay, Excretion by the Malpighian Tubules of the Stick Insect, *Dixippus morosus* (othoptera, phasmidae): Amino Acids, Sugars and Urea, *J. Exptl. Biol.*, **35**: 871 (1958).
10. V. T. Bowen, The Uptake and Distribution of Barium140 and Lanthanum410 in Larvae of *Drosophila repleta*, *J. Exptl. Zool.*, **118**: 509 (1951).
11. V. T. Bowen, Barium Metabolism in Hornets Studied by Means of Radioisotopes, *Trans. N. Y. Acad. Sci., Ser. II*, **11**: 68 (1949).
12. V. T. Bowen, Manganese Metabolism of Social Vespidae, *J. Exptl. Zool.*, **115**: 175 (1950).
13. D. F. Poulson and V. T. Bowen, The Copper Metabolism of *Drosophila*, *Science*, **114**: 486 (1951).
14. E. Lindsay and R. Craig, The Distribution of Radiophosphorus in the Waxmoth, Mealworm, Cockroach and Firebrat, *Ann. Entomol. Soc. Am.*, **35**: 50 (1942).
15. R. L. Irwin, J. W. T. Spinks, and T. J. Arnason, Deposition of P^{32} in Developing *Drosophila*, *Can. J. Res.*, **28D**: 137 (1950).
16. C. C. Hassett and D. W. Jenkins, The Uptake and Effect of Radiophosphorus in Mosquitoes, *Physiol. Zool.*, **24**: 257 (1951).
17. P. F. Hahn, V. A. Haas, and A. Wilcox, Arrest of Development of *Plasmodium*

gallinaceum in Mosquitoes (*Aedes aegypti*) by Radiation, *Science*, **111**: 657 (1950).

18. J. E. Treherne, Exchange of Labeled Na in the Larvae of *Aedes aegypti* (L), *J. Exptl. Biol.*, **31**: 386 (1954).

19. R. H. Stobbart, Studies on the Exchange and Regulation of Sodium in the Larva of *Aedes aegypti* (L.), *J. Exptl. Biol.*, **36**: 641 (1959).

20. P. Oftedal, Studies with Radioactive Yttrium in Flies. I. Retention and Distribution in *Drosophila* after Injection, *Intern. J. Radiation Biol.*, **3**: 211 (1961).

21. P. Oftedal, Studies with Radioactive Yttrium in Flies. II. Retention and Distribution in *Drosophila* and *Musca* after Ingestion, *Intern. J. Radiation Biol.*, **3**: 222 (1961).

22. F. H. Babers and C. C. Roan, Distribution of Radioactive Phosphorus in Susceptible and Resistant Houseflies, *J. Econ. Entomol.*, **47**: 973 (1954).

23. R. C. King, Studies with Radiophosphorus in *Drosophila*. II. The Turnover and Distribution in Adult *Drosophila*, *J. Exptl. Zool.*, **125**: 331 (1954).

24. R. C. King and L. P. Wilson, Studies with Radiophosphorus in *Drosophila*. V. The Phosphorus Balance of Adult Females, *J. Exptl. Zool.*, **130**, 71 (1955).

25. H. B. D. Kettlewell, Labelling Locusts with Radioactive Isotopes, *Nature*, **175**: 821 (1955).

26. J. G. Rodriguez, Radiophosphorus in Metabolism Studies in the Two-spotted Spider Mite, *J. Econ. Entomol.*, **47**: 514 (1954).

27. R. D. Radeleff, R. C. Bushland, and D. E. Hopkins, Phosphorus-32 Labeling of the Screw-worm Fly, *J. Econ. Entomol.*, **49**: 714 (1956).

28. N. Mitlin and F. H. Babers, The Action of Radiostrontium in the House Fly and German Cockroach, *J. Econ. Entomol.*, **49**: 714 (1956).

29. G. Hoyle, Potassium Ions and Insect Nerve Muscle, *J. Exptl. Biol.*, **30**: 121 (1953).

30. B. M. Twarog and K. D. Roeder, Properties of the Connective Tissue Sheath of the Cockroach Abdominal Nerve Cord, *Biol. Bull.*, **111**: 278 (1956).

31. R. D. O'Brien, An Ion-impermeable Barrier in the Roach, *Proc. Tenth Intern. Congr. Entomol., 1956*, **2**: 378 (1958).

32. J. E. Treherne, Sodium and Potassium Fluxes in the Abdominal Nerve Cord of the Cockroach, *Periplaneta americana* L, *J. Exptl. Biol.*, **38**: 315 (1961).

33. J. E. Treherne, The Movements of Sodium Ions in the Isolated Abdominal Nerve Cord of the Cockroach, *Periplaneta americana*, *J. Exptl. Biol.*, **38**: 629 (1961).

34. J. E. Treherne, The Efflux of Sodium Ions from the Last Abdominal Ganglion of the Cockroach, *Periplaneta americana* L, *J. Exptl. Biol.*, **38**: 729 (1961).

35. J. E. Treherne, The Kinetics of Sodium Transfer in the Central Nervous System of the Cockroach, *Periplaneta americana* L, *J. Exptl. Biol.*, **38**: 737 (1961).

36. R. D. O'Brien, Effect of Ionization upon Penetration of Organophosphates to the Nerve Cord of the Cockroach, *J. Econ. Entomol.*, **52**: 812 (1959).

37. J. E. Treherne, The Nutrition of the Central Nervous System in the Cockroach, *Periplaneta americana* L. The Exchange and Metabolism of Sugars, *J. Exptl. Biol.*, **37**: 513 (1960).

38. L. Levenbook, Intracellular Water of Larval Tissues of the Southern Armyworm as Determined by the Use of C^{14}-carboxylinulin, *J. Cellular Comp. Physiol.*, **52**: 329 (1958).

39. H. M. Pappius, I. Klatzo, and K. A. C. Elliott, Further Studies on Swelling of Brain Slices, *Can. J. Biochem. Physiol.* **40**: 885 (1962).

40. R. Craig and N. H. Olsen, Rate of Circulation of the Body Fluid in Adult *Tenebrio molitor* (Linnaeus), *Anasa tristis* (de Geer), and *Murgantia histrionica* (Hahn), *Science*, **113**: 648 (1951).

CHAPTER 7

Insects and Light

1. Introduction

Since life began on this planet about 500 million years ago, living things have been dependent on or have made use of sunlight in some way. Parasitic forms may seem to be an exception, but even their life cycles are influenced through the effects of light on the host. Light is broadly defined as visible radiant energy, that is, the narrow band of the electromagnetic spectrum of wavelengths from about 3500 to 7500 A. Undoubtedly, one of the fundamental factors in the evolution of life as we know it today has been the constant bathing of our planet with solar energy of the right intensity and wavelength to produce excited molecules which can then undergo reactions otherwise unfeasible in their ground state. The most obvious and important photochemical reaction in nature is photosynthesis, a process made possible through the unique properties of a porphyrin pigment, chlorophyll. The development of the ozone layers of the upper atmosphere is probably a consequence of photosynthesis. Through the protection they afford from the harmful effects of ultraviolet rays, they assure the unique balance of environmental conditions necessary for the development of animal organisms.

Light arriving at a living organism can be reflected, transmitted, scattered, or absorbed. It is only the absorbed energy which can have a chemical effect, and so for light energy to be effective biologically it must first be absorbed by particular light-sensitive pigments. For example, chlorophyll is the active pigment involved in initiating photosynthesis; carotenoids are involved in the phototropic responses of the sporangiophores of the mold, *Phycomyces*, the coleoptile of the oat seedling, *Avena sativa*, the phototactic responses of *Euglena*, and vision in molluscs, arthropods, and vertebrates.

An important way in which pigments initiating a photoreaction are identified is through the study of action spectra and a comparison with the adsorption spectra of extracted pigments. Action spectra are determined by plotting the effectiveness of different wavelengths of light in causing a particular reaction to take place. For example, the striking resemblance in the visible region between the action spectrum for the phototropic reaction of the *Avena* coleoptile to that of a carotenoid extracted from the coleoptile tips is good evidence indicating a primary role of these pigments in phototropism. The measurement of action spectra is one of the best ways to begin investigations of the photoreceptive process, and it is unfortunate that so few are available for the phototactic responses and photoperiodically controlled processes of insects.

Consider now another aspect of our natural environment inextricably associated with the biological effects of solar energy. Living organisms throughout evolution have been exposed to a number of geophysical periodicities: the 24-hour cycle of day and night; the annual cycle of $365\frac{1}{4}$ solar days passing through spring, summer, autumn, and winter; the lunar daily cycle of 24 hours, 50 minutes; and the lunar monthly cycle of $29\frac{1}{2}$ days. Many of the activities of plants and animals are directly linked to these repetitive changes of the physical environment. The biological literature is replete with examples of diurnal, lunar tidal, lunar monthly, annual, and seasonal rhythms of innumerable physiological processes, but it is obvious that the two most important are the diurnal and seasonal cycles.

What are some of the consequences of these geophysical oscillations to animals and plants? Those that inhabit middle and high latitudes are subject to seasonal climatic conditions often unfavorable for growth, reproduction, and survival. Consequently, it is imperative that the organism predict or anticipate seasons far enough in advance to initiate appropriate adaptive physiological responses. The changing duration of the daily photoperiod or, more probably, the duration of the dark period acts as a biological calendar, the study of which presents one of the most challenging and fascinating problems in biology.

In this chapter it is proposed to outline the structure, physiology, and biochemistry of the eyes of arthropods, including recent work on the fine structure of the rhabdomere, the site of the visual photochemical reaction. This is followed by illustrations of the way in which insects orient to light, from the simplest phototaxes to the most complex time-compensated sun orientation of bees. Next, the effect of seasonal changes in photoperiod on growth and differentiation, particularly with regard to diapause, is examined. In conclusion, the contributions of field and laboratory studies to an understanding of the nature, properties, and origin of diurnal rhythms is discussed.

2. Photoreceptors in Arthropods

2.1. Compound Eyes

Localized, light-sensitive organs of arthropods are of two types: the compound or faceted eyes, and the simple eyes, such as the stemmata of many larvae and the ocelli of adult insects and arachnids. The nervous system, or possibly neurosecretory cells within it, appear in special circumstances (e.g., aphids, crayfish tail ganglion) to be directly sensitive to light. The compound eye, however, is the most important visual structure in arthropods. It differs structurally, functionally, and optically from the vertebrate eye.[1] It is built up from many basic units or ommatidia, each with its own facet. Each separate optical unit has a fixed focus and principally concentrates light that is normal to the unit. The amount of detail seen is limited by the number and size of the ommatidia. Great variety in the number of ommatidia is found among different species of insects and even among different insect castes. Certain worker ants may have less than a dozen units, whereas the housefly has 4000, and some dragon-flies may have other 20,000 to each eye. Ommatidia may vary in size in different parts of the eye as, for example, in the males of biting midges, horse flies, certain beetles, and mayflies. These different divisions of the eye are adaptations which serve the needs for greater sensitivity of perception of variations in light intensity and movement or better visual acuity, and their distribution within the eye is closely connected to the particular behavior patterns of the insect.

Although the compound eye is capable in a rudimentary way of forming an image, which is really a mosaic picture of the partial images from separate ommatidia, its important feature lies in its ability to detect movement and changes in the brightness of objects. Two visual functions are concerned in the perception of moving objects: visual acuity and persistence time. The latter is the time for which a sensation persists after the stimulus has ceased and is measured by determining the flicker fusion frequency, that is, the lowest stimulation rate which gives a homogeneous response. The shorter the persistence time or the higher the fusion frequency, the more quickly a moving object can be perceived. Each ommatidium of the insect eye recovers very rapidly following each light stimulus. The fusion frequency of the blowfly, *Calliphora erythrocephala*, for example, under conditions of light adaptation is 250 flashes per second, the highest value so far recorded for any eye.[2] The fusion frequency of the human eye under the same conditions is about 50 flashes per second.

2.2. THE OMMATIDIUM

Each ommatidium of the compound eye rests on a fenestrated basement membrane, below which lies the optic ganglion and through which penetrate nerve fibers and branches of the tracheal system. In the center of the ommatidium is a refractile rod, the rhabdom, derived from the modified central portions of several retinula cells which are arranged around it (Fig. 7.1). In insects there are usually four to eight retinula cells. Each retinula cell in those insects studied so far is the primary neurone whose axons form an optic nerve of as many fibers as there are retinula cells which run out through the basement membrane to join other nerves and form the main optic nerve

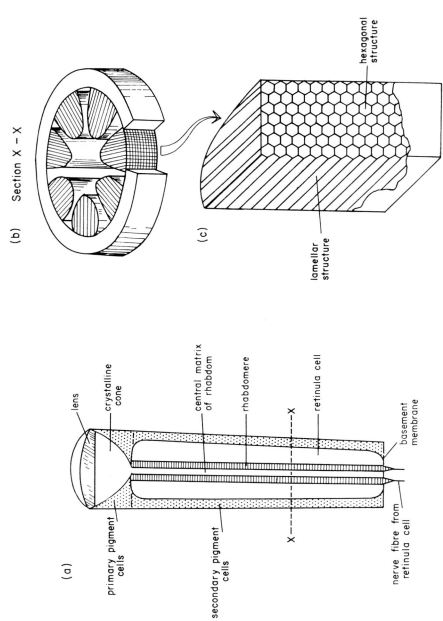

FIG. 7.1. Diagrammatic sections through an ommatidium: (a) A longitudinal section of a complete ommatidium. (b) Three-dimensional cross section through the ommatidium which shows the lamellar pattern in the radially arranged rhabdomeres. The rhabdomere area has been enlarged at the expense of the retinula cells and the pigment sheath. (c) Three-dimensional section of a rhabdomere showing the lamellar and hexagonal structures. (After Wolken, Capenos, and Turano.[3,7])

trunk. The central rhabdom is made up of a number of rhabdomeres, associated one with each retinula cell, and a central matrix. Two main types of rhabdomere arrangement are found in insects[3]: a closed type in which the rhabdomeres of the inner margin of the retinula cells are in close proximity with one another, which occurs in grasshoppers, locusts, dragon-flies, moths, and butterflies; and an open type in which the rhabdomeres project into a large axial cavity of the rhabdom, found among the Diptera and Hymenoptera. The different ommatidia are surrounded by a sleeve of pigment cells serving to isolate them structurally and optically. At the distal end of each ommatidium is a transparent conical structure, the crystalline cone, formed from several cone cells. This is the principal focusing device in most insects. It is surrounded by a sheath of primary pigment cells. Overlying each crystalline cone and in direct contact with the external world is the transparent cornea made up of numerous facets, one for each ommatidium. Incident light penetrates the corneal facets and the crystalline cone, is reflected and refracted to some extent, and passes through the length of the rhabdom. The extraordinary regularity of the pattern in which the cells of each ommatidium are arranged is one of the most striking features of the anatomy of the insect eye.

2.3. Fine Structure of the Rhabdomeres

Examination of the structure of the rhabdom under the electron microscope[4-10] has shown that the rhabdomeres consist of closely packed hexagonal arrays of tubules arranged with their long axes all parallel to one another and at right angles to the long axis of the rhabdomere (Fig. 7.1). The rhabdomeres are actually formed from infoldings of the external plasma membrane of the retinula cells.[11] Evidence that the rhabdomeres are derived from cell membranes is further shown by the continuity of the membranes of each tubule with the retinula cell membrane.

There seems little doubt that the rhabdomeres are the sites of photoreception in the ommatidium and are, in fact, specialized parts of the primary sensory neurones, the retinula cells. The striking feature of these cells is the large number of mitochondria they contain, and this may indicate an important metabolic linkage to the rhabdomeres. The rods and cones in vertebrates are homologous structures. There is undoubtedly a fundamental structural similarity among photoreceptors, whether they be in the eyes of molluscs, arthropods, or vertebrates, or in the chloroplasts of plants.

2.4. Visual Pigments

Wald and co-workers[12,13] showed that the outer segments of the rods in the vertebrate eye contain the visual pigment rhodopsin and that they are the site of the initial photochemical reaction of vision. There were many difficulties encountered in the early work on the extraction of insect visual pigments. Pigment was extracted from pigment cells rather than the visual structures. Attempts to extract the carotenoid, vitamin A_1, (Fig. 7.2) from the head of a fruit fly, a grasshopper, or a dragonfly at first were negative.

However, the aldehyde of vitamin A_1, retinene$_1$, has been isolated recently from heads of the honey bee, *Apis mellifera*.[14] It was found only in the acetone extracts and not in the petroleum ether extracts. The visual pigment differed from all others in being soluble in water without the aid of digitonin, the most commonly used extractive. After partial purification of the retinene-protein complex, it was shown to bleach on exposure to light and to contain a photosensitive pigment of absorption maximum at 440 mµ close

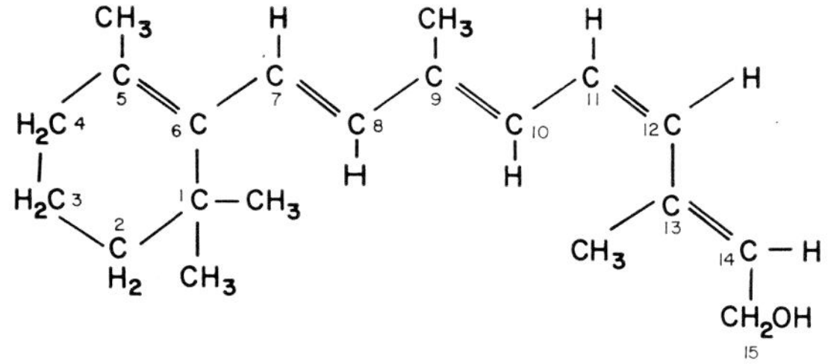

FIG. 7.2. The structural formula of vitamin A_1, 11-*cis* isomer.

to the human violet pigment (Fig. 7.3). Other light-stable pigments, however, were extracted in vast amounts in comparison to the retinene$_1$. Extractions of retinene$_1$ have also been made from cockroaches; it has been calculated that there are enough retinene$_1$-protein or rhodopsin molecules to form an oriented monomolecular layer at the aqueous lipoprotein surfaces of the rhabdomere tubules.[7,8] The chemical principles underlying photoreception of arthropods appear, therefore, in principle, to be no different from those in other phyla and are based on the characteristics of the 11-*cis* isomer of retinene$_1$. So far, no alcohol dehydrogenase which is necessary for the formation of the retinene$_1$ from vitamin A_1 has been found in insects.

It is likely that there are also other visual pigments in the eyes of insects, probably involved in color vision, which is well developed in flower-visiting insects.[15] A special pigment has been suggested as the basis of the analysis of polarized light by insects, particularly in bees.[16] However, the rhabdom structure itself may act as an analyzer, and this ability may be just a structural consequence of the particular type of vision developed in arthropods.[17]

The spectral sensitivities of insects further suggest requirements for light-sensitive pigments other than carotenoids. The honey bee and fruit fly, *Drosophila melanogaster*, are sensitive to the ultraviolet part of the spectrum to a much greater extent than man. In general, insects show maximum sensitivity in the blue region of the spectrum extending into the ultraviolet and in the blue-green but are insensitive to red or the far-red region. The eye-gnat, *Hippelates collusor*, for instance, shows maximum sensitivity to light at

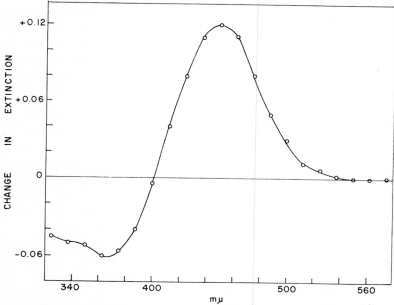

Fig. 7.3. The difference spectrum of a photosensitive pigment from the honey bee. An aqueous extract from the heads of dark-adapted bees was irradiated with yellow light, and the absorption spectrum was recorded. This was subtracted from the absorption spectrum of the extract before irradiation to give the difference spectrum. The maximum is about 450 mμ. The true absorption spectrum of the photopigment has a maximum somewhat shorter, close to 440 mμ. (From Goldsmith.[14])

440–450 mμ and minimum at 600 mμ. The wavelengths causing maximum response shift to shorter wavelengths as the energy level decreases.[18] Thus, the spectral sensitivity of insects is different from plants, which show maximum sensitivity for photoperiodic behavior in the red wavelengths (620–660 mμ). In fact, the red and far-red regions of the spectrum inhibit growth and molting of the nymphs of the German cockroach, *Blattella germanica*, and the large milkweed bug, *Oncopeltus fasciatus*.[19,20] Of considerable interest is the recent work of Ziegler,[21] who has extracted light-sensitive tetrahydrobiopterins as the N-ribosides from the skin and retina of frogs, the eyes of *Drosophila*, the cluster fly, *Pollenia rudis*, and some crustaceans. This compound is changed in ultraviolet light to the dihydro compound with the liberation of hydrogen. A tetrahydro-dihydrobiopterin equilibrium may be of importance in the ultraviolet sensitivity of insects.

2.5. FUNCTIONAL ADAPTATIONS

Two types of arrangement of pigment cells in the eyes of insects occur. In one type, the appositional eye, which occurs in most diurnal insects, the pigment cells completely ensheath the ommatidia and, consequently, retinula cells are stimulated only by light entering each ommatidium. In the other type, the superpositional eye, found in most nocturnal insects, the pigment cells only partially cover the ommatidia, so that retinula cells from neighboring ommatidia may be stimulated by light entering a single ommatidium. However, in all compound eyes there is a movement of pigment during light and dark adaptation so that the eyes often function as an appositional type when light adapted and as a superpositional type when dark adapted. Of interest in this connection are the 24-hour rhythms of pigment migration that are persistent in constant darkness. They have been observed in nocturnal insects such as noctuid moths as well as in many crutaceans. Such rhythms, although probably synchronized by the diurnal light-dark rhythm, are apparently determined by a complex physiological timing mechanism. The nature of similar rhythms is discussed in greater detail later in this chapter.

The physiological investigations of Autrum[2,22] on the electroretinograms of insects have revealed two physiological types of eye, a slow and a fast type. The slow type of eye shows a negative monophasic potential which is dependent upon the state of dark adaptation. The fast type of eye has a diphasic electroretinogram, the amplitude being independent of the state of dark adaptation. It has been pointed out that the slow type of eye is characteristic of nocturnal insects in which the rhabdom of the ommatidium is large and contains wedge-shaped rhabdomeres in close proximity to one another. The fast type of eye is characteristic of diurnal insects, Hymenoptera and Diptera, which have small rhabdoms and rhabdomeres that project into the axial rhabdom cavity.[3] The eyes of dragon-flies (e.g., *Anax junius*), however, are an exception in that the rhabdom is not composed of individual rhabdomeres separated by a central matrix but subdivided into three pieces, each third representing the fusion of three rhabdomeres.[6] They therefore have an eye structure closer to that of cockroaches, even though they are diurnal insects. There does seem to be a relationship among the arrangement of the rhabdomeres, the form of the electroretinogram, and the habits of the insect.

Differences in rhabdom structure and pigment movements are not the only adaptations of compound eyes for the detection of low light intensities.

Lüdtke has shown that the whole rhabdom of the eye of the backswimmer, *Notonecta glauca*, moves.[23] During dark adaptation the rhabdom moves peripherally and protrudes between the cells of the crystalline cone, thus achieving a position best suited to intercept low light intensities reaching the eye. This rhabdom movement is suggestive evidence that the visual pigment is located in it. Nocturnal insects, particularly the noctuid moths, have another remarkable adaptation to night flying. It is well known that the eyes of noctuid moths shine with glistening colors in the dark. This appearance is produced by many fine tracheae grouped around the retinula cells, especially at the basal end of the rhabdom, which reflect light back through the ommatidium and cause the pigments to glisten. A similar adaptation is found in the vertebrate eye in which the tapetum lucidum acts as a reflective layer in the choroid, which increases the sensitivity of the eye.

2.6. THE SIMPLE EYE

The simplest arthropod eyes are the stemmata found in many insect larvae. Stemmata are most highly developed in the larvae of certain beetles. They contain several structures similar to ommatidia, particularly well developed in the cincindelids and all located beneath a single lens. They probably do not form images but do perceive movements. The dorsal ocelli occurring on the heads of insects, often between the compound eyes or distributed over the cephalothorax of arachnids, are similar in structure to the stemmata. The ocelli of damsel-flies and dragon-flies possess a pigmented layer like a tapetum which moves across the ocelli when these insects are brought from darkness to bright light. Sphingid and noctuid moths lack ocelli. Little is known of the function of the ocelli. One suggestion is that they increase the sensitivity of the brain to light stimuli received through the compound eyes. Thus, if the compound eyes of *Drosophila* are blackened, the flies behave as if blind, but, if only the ocelli are blackened, the light responses through the compound eyes are much slower.[24] It has been shown that the ocellar nerve fibers are spontaneously active in the dark, and that illumination inhibits this activity.[25,26] There are two functions of light sense organs: a phototactic or orientating function and a photokinetic or stimulatory function.[24] Ocelli may increase the efficiency of phototactic responses in those insects in which they are present together with compound eyes.

3. Responses of Insects to Light

One of the most widespread reactions, not only in insects but in most living organisms, is movement toward or away from light. Many of the light reactions of insects were studied by Loeb.[27] His theory was that the tone of the muscles on either side of the insect is determined by the intensity of the stimulus received by bilateral sense organs, and that the insect orients so that the stimulation on either side is equal, the muscular tone is then equal, and the insect moves in a straight line. Although this scheme explains some of the simple responses of insects, it is of little value in consideration of the complex and highly specialized behavior of many Diptera and Hymenoptera. A striking example is seen in the asilid fly, *Proctacanthus*, which becomes immobile and whose legs collapse when the eyes are blackened. When the eyes are uncovered, the fly raises its body off the ground. Covering one eye leads to an exaggerated tonus on the uncovered side.[24]

Much of the early work on orientations and directed movements of animals was inadequately controlled, and the terminology was confused and inconsistent. Fraenkel and Gunn's book "The Orientation of Animals," published in 1940[28] and extensively revised in 1962, removed much of this confusion and is indispensable to any student of animal behavior, particularly that of insects. The word taxis means simply an oriented locomotory reaction which leads directly toward or away from an undifferentiated source of stimulation. Therefore, phototaxis is simply movement to or away from light. Phototropisms are the directed growth-curvature movements seen in many plants in response to light, and among animals the term can strictly be applied only to sessile forms such as some hydroids and polychaete worms. There is an important distinction between these two reactions. Tropisms involve growth mechanisms, whereas taxes involve the organs of movement. In arthropods, phototaxis is usually brought about by a light stimulus to the eyes or ocelli which initiates coordinated reflex activity within the nervous system affecting the muscles of the legs or wings.

Responses to light which result only in a change in the velocity of movement, dependent on the light intensity but with no directional orientation, are termed photokineses. When the response is just a variation of linear velocity, it is orthokinesis. When the response is a variation in the rate of change of direction of turning, it is klinokinesis. In kineses performed with the simplest types of intensity-sensitive receptors, the animal reaches its optimal position purely by random movements. The land crustaceans of the superfamily Oniscoidea, the woodlice and garden slaters, illustrate this simple form of behavior. Woodlice are unable to control water loss through the cuticle and so are found in dark, damp places such as under logs, stones, or bark. If they are placed in open dry places under the influence of light, they run aimlessly in all directions. As they approach a zone of damp air their speed decreases (orthokinesis), and they turn more frequently (klinokinesis).[29] This undirected behavior results in the animal's becoming trapped in moist dark places. Taxes are a considerably more efficient behavioral response than kineses because the animal moves directly toward or away from the source of stimulation. Some examples of the different types of orientation of insects to light will illustrate the variety and elaborations of phototactic responses, from the simplest kind in the larvae of Diptera to the complex sun orientations of ants and bees.

3.1. PHOTOKLINOTAXIS

The maggots of such common flies as the housefly, *Musca domestica*, the greenbottle, *Lucilia sericata*, or the blowfly, *Calliphora erythrocephala*, are photonegative. Maggots will crawl directly along a light beam away from its source. If presented with a second light beam at right angles to the first beam which is then put out, the maggots undergo a series of regular deviations determined by the position of the animal at the time the stimulation changes until they are again moving directly away from the second light.[30] If two beams of light are directed on each side of a maggot, it will go between them. This type of behavior, Fraenkel and Gunn have pointed out, involves a comparison of the light intensities from various directions at successive points in time.[28] The photoreceptors of these larvae are incapable of discriminating the direction of a light source instantly without going through a series of trial movements. The maxillary lobes are probably the site of the maggot photoreceptors. In some higher dipterous larvae it may be that specialized photoreceptors appear to be absent and the response is assumed to be due to a sensitivity of certain cells within the anterior nervous system to light transmitted through the unpigmented cuticle.

3.2. PHOTOTROPOTAXIS

In this type of reaction it is necessary for the insect to have paired light receptors so that a simultaneous comparison of the two intensities of incident light can be made. The animal moves directly toward or away from the light stimulus or turns so that the bilaterally situated sense organs are equally stimulated. Blackening one eye leads to turning toward the seeing side if the insect is photopositive and toward the blind side if photonegative. Unilateral blinding experiments result in continuous turning or the cricus movements characteristic of tropotaxes. The larvae of the Mediterranean flour moth, *Anagasta kühniella*, are photonegative, and their behavior toward light is a good example of tropotaxis.[28] On each side of the head are groups of six ocelli. In the dark the larvae are disoriented but orient in a straight path in light, exhibit turning movements on unilateral blinding in uniform light, and in two-light experiments follow a path between the beams. The hover fly, *Eristalis tenax*, after dark adaptation is strongly photopositive and reacts tropotactically, but with one important difference: after unilateral blinding it can go straight toward a light beam instead of deviating toward the seeing side. This is due to a division of each eye into two functionally different regions so that a state of balance can be achieved in one eye only. The antero-median ommatidia, when stimulated, lead to contralateral turning movements, whereas the frontolateral, lateral, and posterior ommatidia lead to ipsilateral turning movements.[28]

3.3. PHOTOTELOTAXIS

The essential feature of this behavior is that bilateral balance is not necessary for orientation to occur. The insect can orient exclusively to one of two sources of illumination, continuously or temporarily disregarding the other. A capacity for central inhibition has developed in the central nervous system whereby the response to one of the two lights is inhibited. The honey bee shows both tropotactic and telotactic behavior toward light.[28] Each eye contains areas which initiate ipsilateral and contralateral turning movements as well as a region of fixation. Its behavior is distinguished from *Eristalis* in its ability to inhibit the effect of a second light. The phenomenon of central inhibition is a basic requirement before complex behavior patterns can develop. Bees, when placed in a dark room with two lights, move toward one of the lights. If the lights shine on the bees with equal intensity, they go equally often toward one or the other of the lights. If one is stronger in intensity, the bees go toward this one but follow a zigzag track first toward one and then toward the other so that at any moment orientation is exclusively toward one of the light sources. Unilaterally blinded bees orient efficiently in a light beam through the operation of the functional divisions in each eye, as does *Eristalis*.

3.4. THE LIGHT-COMPASS REACTION

There are many insects which are capable of moving at a constant angle to a source of light and not in line with rays of light as in telotaxis. The term "light-compass movement" originated from the work of Buddenbrock, who used it to describe the orientation to light of the caterpillar of the tortoise-shell butterfly, *Vanessa urticae*.[31] In this case although light was necessary for a directed orientation, the insect did not necessarily travel in line with the light. The light served only as a fixed point, and the animal maintained the angular relationship between its direction of movement and a line which joined the light source to the eye. This angle of orientation could be changed spontaneously, allowing movement to occur in a new direction. The over-all effect of the light-compass reaction is that the insect is kept moving in a constant direction, regardless of whether the place it is directed to is favorable or not. Many insects show a high degree of accuracy in maintaining the orientation angle. The anatomical basis of such reactions is found in the structure of the compound eye. Each ommatidium points in a slightly different direction. Only a few ommatidia at a time are stimulated by a directed light source. The insect moves so as to maintain the image of the light source on the same ommatidia. The light-compass reaction is involved in the remarkable homing behavior of ants and bees. They can maintain a constant direction with respect to the sun by keeping the image of the sun on a particular ommatidium. The importance of the sun in the homing of ants was demonstrated many years ago by Santschi[32] by ingenious experiments using suitably placed mirrors to reflect sunlight and so induce ants to go in any direction in relation to the image of the sun in the mirror.

3.5. The Dorsal Light Reaction

Certain aquatic insects, notably the nymphs of mayflies, water-boatmen, *Notonecta*, and whirligig beetles or Gyrinidae, maintain their position by keeping the dorsal surface perpendicular to the light which passes through the surface of the water. They can also maintain their position in running water by keeping constant the image of objects on the bank. Removal of these objects will cause the insect to move with them. Fraenkel and Gunn classify the light-compass and dorsal-light reactions as transverse orientations. In both, the animals orient at a temporarily fixed angle to the source of stimulation rather than in line with it as in the phototaxes.[28]

3.6. Time-Compensated Sun Orientation

Forel, over 60 years ago, concluded from a few simple experiments that honey bees have a time memory or, as he called it, a "Zeitgedächtnis."[33] Subsequently, Beling[34] and Wahl[35] confirmed the observations of Forel and further showed that bees trained to feed at a certain time of day did not lose this punctuality when kept under conditions that excluded the effect of important environmental factors such as changes in illumination, temperature, humidity, air ionization, or cosmic radiation. An inherent time sense was postulated to occur in bees. Ants also possess a time sense and establish regular feeding rhythms.[36] This time memory is closely connected to the natural 24-hour cycle, and bees cannot be trained to other rhythms. For example, bees fed at 48-hour intervals also come for food after 24 hours and when fed at 19-hour intervals show no conditioning. Further, bees reared in an incubator and never exposed to a 24-hour rhythm cannot be trained to rhythms unrelated to a 24-hour periodicity. Drugs such as thyroxine and quinine, which alter cellular metabolism, have no influence on the time sense.[37,38,39] Severe cooling or carbon dioxide narcosis does affect the time sense but causes the bees to be approximately as many hours late for feeding as the duration of the cooling or anesthesia. The mechanism, probably within the nervous system, was thus insensitive during the period of hypothermia or anesthesia. Carefully controlled translocation experiments (i.e., bees were trained in a certain latitude and longitude and subsequently tested at another) showed that bees are able to function independently of diurnal, exogenous factors.[40,41] Bees kept under constant conditions in closed chambers and trained to feed at a particular local time in Paris fed in New York 24 hours after the trained feeding time although, of course, the time of the day was different. If the translocation experiments were carried out under the natural conditions of exposure to changes in sun altitude and day-night alternations, different results were obtained. The searching activity of the time-trained bees showed two maxima after 3 days in the new locality, one 24 hours from the training time, and another at the day time in the new location corresponding to the training day time. Therefore, in nature the time sense depends on both exogenous and endogenous factors. Only under constant light conditions can the time orientation occur solely by the mechanism of the endogenous clock with a 24-hour periodicity.

What is the biological significance of this time sense? It is simply that, if this ability is linked to the light-compass reaction, the animal has a means of navigation. It has been known for some time, largely owing to the excellent studies of von Frisch,[42,43,44] that bees use the sun to find compass directions and compensate for the movement of the sun during the day; that is, they show time-compensated sun orientation. This ability is also found in birds. It appears clear now that bees can orient by the sun azimuth.[41] This is the direction toward the sun on a horizontal plane measured in degrees clockwise from north. Although the angular velocity of the sun's movement is nearly constant at $15°$ per hour, the angular velocity of the sun azimuth, depending on the latitude, varies at different times of the day because of the variation in the steepness of the sun's path. In middle latitudes the sun azimuth changes very slowly in the morning and evening and relatively fast around midday. The experiments of Renner[45] clearly indicate that the bee also compensates for the change in sun angle, thus achieving a remarkably accurate orientation. The experimental proof for these results, which cannot be presented here, can be found in the papers of Renner and Lindauer.[41,46] An interesting aspect of sun-azimuth orientation is that during the midday hours the time orientation of animals might be expected to show less precision.* This has not been observed so far and has led some workers to question whether the sun azimuth is the only means of keeping compass direction.

---

* This has been observed recently by D. A. T. New et al., Nature, **189**, 155, 1961.

The presence of an innate chronometer which, together with celestial data, can be used for orientation has recently been demonstrated in a variety of arthropods. The littoral amphipod or beach flea, *Talitrus saltator*, possesses a time sense and allows for the change in the sun's position or plane of polarization during the day. Each population of these crustaceans orients at a different angle to the sun's direction to enable it to get across the beach to the moist sand and the sea by the quickest route.[47] The dung beetle, *Geotrupes silvaticus*, and the pond skater, *Velia currens*, have also been shown experimentally to possess chronometer orientation.[48] There is, however, a fundamental difference in the time-compensated sun orientations of these arthropods and those of honey bees. In *Talitrus* and *Velia* the compensation for the movement of the sun is clockwise during the daytime but reverses its direction after sunset and runs backward throughout the night. The honey bees, as well as certain fishes, lizards, and birds, possess a very accurate clock which tells them that each 24 hours the sun makes one complete revolution. These animals compensate for sun movement as if the sun moves in a clockwise direction during 24 hours.[49]

The studies of von Frisch[43,50,51] have shown that bees are sensitive to polarized light, and that light from a 10° sector of blue sky was enough to secure correct orientation to the sun. Not only does the degree of polarization in the sky increase as one passes across the sky away from the sun but the plane of polarization from different parts of the sky bears a consistent relationship to the sun's position. It is this pattern of polarization that the bee "remembers," and when this is coupled with a time sense it is able to orient to the sun, compensating for its movement even though it is not visible. It is only on completely cloudy days when the degree of polarization of light is small that bees are unable to orient to the sun. It should be mentioned that terrestrial clues such as a row of trees, the edge of a forest, a road, or a lake shore take preference over sun orientation when these landmarks lead in almost an unbroken line from the hive to the feeding area.

The discovery, description, and experimental proof of the astonishing orientation abilities of bees is surely one of the most fascinating stories in animal behavior of this century. This is not the place to go into the details of how the information obtained by these orientations is accurately communicated by the scout bees in the form of the dance "language" discovered by von Frisch.[44,52,53] The bee, dancing on the vertical comb, transposes vertically the angle of orientation toward the sun azimuth, thus giving the direction of a food source relative to the position of the sun and indicates, as well, the distance of it from the hives. It will do this at any time of the day and even at nighttime. Thorpe[54] points out that this behavior involves an elementary form of map making and reading.

A fundamental problem is which components of the time-compensated sun orientation are inherited and which are learned. Kalmus[55] tried to answer this by translocating bees from the northern to the southern hemisphere and found no adjustment in the next generation to the new situation. Accordingly, the direction of compensation of the sun's movement, either clockwise or counterclockwise, must have been inherited. However, Lindauer[46] repeated these experiments and carried out similar translocations from Ceylon to Munich and found adjustment to the direction of sun movement after several days. It is unfortunate that these translocation experiments were not carried out from extratropical areas. In intertropical regions reorientations must occur to the sun, since in the northern hemisphere at midsummer noon the sun would be north and in midwinter, south. Even so, there can be no question that the behavior of bees adapts as a result of experience; i.e., they learn. The bee is born with a 24-hour chronometer and an awareness that the sun is important, but it learns why and how it is important. The ant, *Formica rufa*, has been shown to compensate for the movement of the sun in the summer only after its movement has been experienced daily. It does not compensate for the movement of the sun in the spring.[56] It is most likely, therefore, that ants learn that the sun is moving.

4.   Photoperiod and Diapause

Periodic arrest of growth can occur at any stage of development in insects. All degrees of arrest are found, from a simple dormancy induced directly by unfavorable environmental conditions to true diapause in which a prolonged arrest supersedes development even though environmental conditions are favorable. In the diapause state the insect does not excrete or feed, the respiratory rate is exceedingly low, and resistance to cold is increased. It functions primarily to enable survival to the next breeding season. The induction of diapause among temperate-zone insects and arachnids and, in a few cases, its termination are often controlled by the duration of the light and dark periods of the daily cycle of solar illumination. Tropical species often develop without diapause, and photoperiod has no influence on development. The obvious adaptive significance of a response either to particular durations of light or dark periods or to a progressively changing photoperiod or dark period, whichever is the significant inducer, is that the absolute length of these periods or the direction of their change is a precise and invariable indicator of season. Thus, animals perceptive to such photoperiodic stimuli are able to adjust critical physiological processes before seasonal changes occur and so achieve synchronization of their life cycles with the seasons. The effect of day length can be modified by environmental factors such as temperature, quantity and quality of food, and population density. It is not possible here to consider these interactions, and only the effect of photoperiod will be discussed.

4.1. INDUCTION OF DIAPAUSE

Two directions of response to photoperiodic stimuli are possible. Either short days can be diapause inducing and long days diapause suppressing or the opposite circumstance can occur. By analogy with plants, the terms "long day" and "short day" are frequently used to describe the effect of photoperiod in inhibiting or inducing the onset of diapause. Diapause in most species of insects is a long-day response; i.e., long day lengths are diapause preventing, and short or medium day lengths are diapause inducing.[57] The best example of a short-day species is seen in the egg diapause of the silkworm, *Bombyx mori*. In fact, it was from the studies of Kogure more than 30 years ago on diapause in *Bombyx* that the significance of day length in controlling diapause was first recognized.[58] Some examples of long-day insects are the oriental fruit moth, *Grapholitha molesta*, the agrotid moth, *Diataraxia oleracea*, the imported cabbageworm, *Pieris rapae*, the Tussor silkmoth, *Anthereae pernyi*, the noctuid moth, *Acronycta rumicis*, the Colorado potato beetle, *Leptinotarsa decemlineata*, the Western grape leaf skeletonizer, *Harrisina brillians*, the dragonfly, *Anax imperator*, and the pitcherplant midge, *Metriocnemus knabi*.[57,59,60,61] Among arachnids, the European red mite *Metatetranychus ulmi* is a long-day species.[62,63] Frequently, those insects which depend on plants are the most sensitive to the duration of light and dark periods. Such species must have an accurate indication of the season to survive. The effect of photoperiod on the induction of diapause is illustrated in Fig. 7.4.

In those arthropod species which are distributed over a wide geographical area, significant variations in the critical photoperiod for diapause initiation are found at different latitudes. At low latitudes the critical photoperiods are shorter. Three interesting examples of geographical adaptations of the diapause mechanism are cited by Lees[64]: (1) The critical photoperiod for diapause initiation in a Cambridge, England, strain of two-spotted spider mite, *Tetranychus telarius*, is approximately two hours less than that of a Leningrad population 8° further north. (2) The moth *Acronycta* has a wide geographical range in Russia. The critical photoperiod for pupal diapause in Leningrad (60°N) strains is almost 20 hours whereas for strains from Vitebsk (55°N), Byelgorod (51°N), and Sukhumi (43°N) the photoperiods are 18, 17, and 14½ hours, respectively. The pupae are released from diapause earlier in the season in more southerly latitudes, and the higher temperatures more effectively prevent diapause. Together, these characteristics, as well as the longer period of long-day conditions, enable three generations to occur each year. The Leningrad insects invariably have one generation a year, i.e., are univoltine, and diapause is obligatory. However, a latent capacity to respond to photoperiod is still present. It can readily be seen how these variations in diapause adjustments could function in the isolation of geographical races. (3) The Japanese cabbage moth, *Barathra brassicae*, has two generations a year throughout its range and also shows two forms of arrest in growth, a

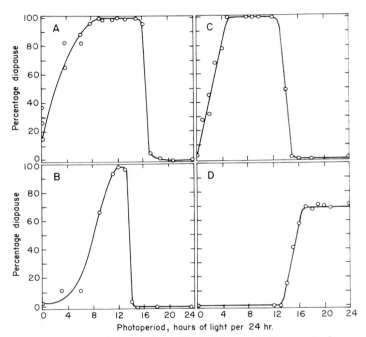

Fig. 7.4. The effect of photoperiod on the incidence of diapause in four species of Lepidoptera: (A) *Acronycta rumicis* at 27–28°C; (B) *Grapholitha molesta* at 24°C; (C) *Antheraea pernyi*; (D) *Bombyx mori* at 15°C. (From Lees.[57])

transient one in the summer induced by long photoperiods, and an enduring one in the winter induced by short photoperiods. It is only in populations of moths in southern Japan (Honshu) that estivation occurs, and this delays development sufficiently to allow the second generation to be exposed to short days which induce a long-lasting winter diapause. Northern Japanese strains (Hokkaido) do not estivate and show only the usual response of diapause induced by short days and prevented by long days.

Generally, arthropods, unlike many vertebrates, respond to the actual duration of the light and dark periods and not to gradual changes in either component.[57] *Anax imperator*, a slowly developing dragonfly, is probably an exception. The onset of diapause in the final instar of this insect is influenced by the progression of the photoperiod.[59] The importance of photoperiodic timing mechanisms varies widely among species. In mammals, photoperiodic control of seasonal cyclic functions such as gonadal development and migration varies from a direct dependence of the function on increasing or decreasing photoperiod to just a monitoring of the phase and frequency of an internal rhythm by the changing photoperiod. In arthropods, the determination of diapause by photoperiod is more absolute. A sensitive period which is most influenced by photoperiod occurs in development, and during this period the physiological processes controlling the diapause or nondiapause conditions are determined. Again, the duration of this sensitive period and the stage in development in which it occurs are highly variable among insects. It should be noted, however, that the environmental stimuli operate only at a period of development when neural, neurosecretory, and hormonal systems are present.[57]

So far, the control of diapause by the length of the photoperiod has been emphasized. The length of the dark period has been shown to be no less important. A long-night requirement for diapause induction is found in several Lepidoptera and also in *Metatetranychus*. In this species, although long dark periods induce diapause and long light periods inhibit, the former is the more potent.[63] Under permanent darkness or unnaturally short photoperiods, diapause in many species is frequently absent, or the response is variable. Another feature in arthropods is the cumulative effect of the light-dark cycle during the sensitive periods, which suggests an accumulation of a chemical substance to a certain threshold. One or two light-dark cycles of critical duration are usually ineffective. The ineffectiveness of short, interspersed light or dark periods during the dark or light phases, respectively, on diapause responses of arthropods is in contrast to the photoperiodic responses of plants. Again, this emphasizes the importance of light and dark periods of particular durations for the control of diapause.

Photoperiodic induction of diapause is independent of light intensity above certain thresholds. The minimal light intensity necessary for a reaction varies with the species but is always very low. *Metatetranychus* requires 1–2 ft-c; most Lepidoptera, about 1 ft-c; the embryos of *Bombyx*, 0.01 ft-c; and the midge *Metriocnemus*, 0.0025 ft-c. The latter is in the range of the light intensity of moonlight, but this is ineffective because 10–14 cycles of 8–12-hour photoperiods of this low intensity are required at $23°C$ to maintain diapause. As regards spectral sensitivity, ultraviolet, violet, blue, and green light up to around 500 mμ are generally the most effective. Longer wavelengths are much less effective. Unfortunately, accurate action spectra are not yet available, and the chemical nature of the photosensitive pigments is unknown. The photoperiodic response is not reversed by wavelengths in the red or far-red spectral regions as is found for plants. The site of the photoreceptors for diapause control is uncertain. Experiments with the silkworm *Anthereae* cited by Lees,[57] in which the larval ocelli were destroyed or covered, showed that diapause pupae were still formed in response to short day lengths. It is possible that neurosecretory cells in the central nervous system are the photoreceptors.

4.2. TERMINATION OF DIAPAUSE

Whereas photoperiod is frequently the most important factor in the induction of diapause, termination of diapause is often thermally controlled. There are a few insects in which photoperiod also controls the breaking of diapause. The larvae of the pine lasiocampid, *Dendrolimus pini*, continue growth at a time in response to long daily photoperiods.[65] Other examples are certain planthoppers[66] and the midge, *Metriocnemus knabi*.[61] Photoperiodic control of diapause termination has also been reported for the winter eggs of the mosquito, *Aedes triseriatus*.[67] The spruce budworm, *Choristoneura fumiferana*, is a species with an obligatory diapause, most individuals entering diapause in the second instar without feeding, regardless of the photoperiod to which they have been exposed since the egg stage.[68] However, exposure of diapausing second-instar larvae to continuous light at 21°C induces emergence of larvae that have received inadequate cold treatment of 6 weeks at 0°C. No such effect was observed following the normal periods of cold of about 20 weeks. The action of continuous light in breaking diapause appears to stimulate the endocrine activity of the brain and prothoracic glands.

4.3. THE NERVOUS SYSTEM AND HORMONES

Within the nervous systems of arthropods are groups of specialized cells which show cytological evidence of secretion and are called "neurosecretory cells." These cells link the function of the nervous system and the endocrine system. It appears very likely that in all forms of diapause one form or another of hormonal control exists, as suggested by Wigglesworth many years ago.[69] Pupal diapause in the cecropia silkworm *Hyalophora cecropia* was demonstrated by Williams to be due to failure of neurosecretory cells in the brain to supply a diffusible hormone activating the prothoracic glands.[70] Diapause can be terminated by injection of the prothoracic gland hormone.

When diapause is photoperiodically determined, the way in which photoperiodic fixation of the functional endocrine response system occurs at an early stage of development is still largely unknown. Diapause in bivoltine strains of *Bombyx* is controlled maternally.[58] The type of egg that is laid, i.e., diapause or nondiapause, is determined by the conditions of temperature and photoperiod which prevailed during the late embryonic development of the maternal generation. A secretion from the subesophageal ganglion controls the type of egg laid. When this hormone is present in the hemolymph, diapause eggs form in the ovaries; when it is absent, nondiapause eggs develop. The subesophageal ganglion is also controlled by higher centers in the brain and by the corpora allata, which inhibit hormonal secretion in insects previously determined as nondiapause egg producers. Cutting the circumesophageal connectives in the pupal stage leads to the production of diapause eggs, even though previous photoperiodic and temperature conditions may have determined nondiapause eggs. Transplantation of subesophageal ganglia also leads to the production of diapause eggs regardless of the previous determination.

The reproductive diapause of the adult *Leptinotarsa*, which is photoperiodically determined, has also been shown to be under endocrine control.[71] In this insect it appears that diapause is produced by a deficiency of hormonal secretion of the corpora allata (juvenile hormone or neotenin) rather than the prothoracic glands. Diapause behavior is produced by allatectomy in female beetles reared under the inhibitory effect of long-day conditions. These diapause reactions are normally produced by insects reared under a 10-hour photoperiodic regime from the egg. Implantation of active corpora allata does not affect the normal short-day, diapause-inducing effect but reverses the allatectomy diapause. In this insect, the corpora allata control not only egg formation and yolk deposition but also diapause behavior in the adult.

4.4. PHOTOPERIOD AND POLYMORPHISM

It is among the aphids that some of the most remarkable seasonal changes in form occur. The recent studies of Lees have beautifully demonstrated the photoperiodic control of polymorphism in the single-host aphid, *Megoura viciae*.[64,72,73] When these aphids are reared under uncrowded conditions at moderate temperatures (15°C) and exposed to long-day conditions (16 hours of light), they give birth to a succession of parthenogenetic offspring termed "virginoparae." However, if the virginoparous generations are exposed to short-day conditions (8–12 hours of light), they produce egg-laying offspring termed "oviparae," and also males. The transition from the short-day effect to the long-day effect takes place within a 30-minute increase in photoperiod from $14\frac{1}{2}$ to 15 hours. As in diapause, it is the exact duration of the light-dark cycle which is most significant. Under continuous darkness, production of oviparae is favored. The form of the offspring is governed by a photoperiodic response set up in the mother and begins while the mother is still an embryo. Thus, the light stimulus must act on the embryo within the ovarioles of the grandmother. It appears likely that the control of embryonic development operates through an endocrine mechanism linked with the photoreceptive system. In *Megoura*, 4–6 light-dark cycles are required for photoperiodic determination: this suggests that a threshold amount of some hormone is necessary to initiate the response in development of the embryos. The site of the photoperiodic receptors in aphids has been studied experimentally by Lees.[73] The eyes are not involved, because cauterizing or painting of them in no way interferes with the response. Illumination of the head and thorax over restricted areas showed that the midline area of the head was the most sensitive. Illumination of the abdomen had no effect, even though the embryos in the abdomen must have received some light transmitted through the transparent body wall. Consequently, the effect of light on the embryos must be operative through a maternal controlling system. The most reasonable suggestion at present is that the photoreceptors and pigments are in the dorsum of the brain, and the photoperiodic effects are initiated here, which causes subsequent changes in neurosecretory activity, which in turn controls the form determination of the embryos.

Other aphid species in which day length has been shown to control the determination of parthenogenetic and sexual forms (wingless, egg-laying females and winged males) are the bean aphid, *Aphis fabae*, the cabbage aphid, *Brevicoryne brassicae*, the green peach aphid, *Myzus persicae*, and the pea aphid, *Macrosiphum pisi*.[64] *Aphis fabae* alternates between two plant hosts. Short day lengths act on summer generations of parthenogenetic virginoparae to produce winged offspring or gynoparae which migrate from the summer to the winter plant host. The offspring of the gynoparae (oviparae) then lay diapause eggs on the winter host.[74]

A number of insects show striking seasonal changes in form. Often, the determination of form in these species is controlled by photoperiod.[57,64,73] The nymphalid butterfly, *Araschnia*, is a dimorphic species and shows differences in wing patterns of the spring (levana) and summer (prorsa) generations. Under natural conditions of temperature, nondiapause pupae of the first generation, which have been exposed in the larva to long photoperiods, give the summer form. Diapausing pupae always yield the spring form. A similar connection between diapause and form determination is found in psyllid homopterans. The pear sucker, *Psylla pyricola*, exhibits a dimorphism in which the form of the overwintering generation differs in size, color, and wing length from the summer generation. A reproductive diapause occurs in the winter generation. The alternate paths of development and the determination of form are controlled by the photoperiod experienced by the early nymphal instars. Another example is the jassid hemipteran, *Euscelis*, in which the spring (incisus) and summer (plebejus) generations differ in size, pigmentation, and penis shape.

5. Diurnal Rhythms

Rhythms which take place at 24-hour intervals or around dawn and sunset occur throughout the animal and plant kingdoms. Strictly, they should not be termed diurnal, but 24-hour rhythms, since they can occur during the day or the night, unless it is understood that diurnal is used in its archaic or astronomical sense. By far the greatest volume of evidence for such rhythms in insects comes from the observations of field naturalists on flight, activity, biting, feeding, oviposition, and emergence cycles. To be of value, such field observations must be accurate, planned, detailed, and prolonged, must take into account all aspects of the behavior of the insect species in their natural environment, and must be studied in relation to microclimatic variables. The experimental approach to the study of rhythmical activity in insects has recently received more attention. The particular rhythm can be observed under controlled conditions in the laboratory, and the effects of alterations of certain physiological functions by surgical excisions of specific structures, parabiotic procedures, or treatment with specific drugs and hormones can be examined.

It is generally agreed that the primary environmental factor which controls the positioning of the phases of 24-hour rhythms in insects with diurnal or nocturnal habits is the daily light-dark cycle and, more particularly, the rapid changes in light intensity which take place at sunrise and sunset. Because receptor organ responses are approximately proportional to the logarithm of the incident intensity, the disruptive effects of random daily fluctuations, such as changing cloud cover, are avoided. The insect, in effect, perceives sunrise and sunset almost as if a light were turned on in the morning and off at night and positions its particular behavioral activity according to the time at which these events occur. Other factors such as temperature, relative humidity, or internal digestive functions can, in certain circumstances, override the influence of light.

One of the most important discoveries that has arisen from the laboratory approach has been the demonstration that a number of the 24-hour rhythms persist for some days in the absence of natural environmental changes of light intensity, and that these rhythms are temperature independent.[75] The general conclusion of Uvarov[76] that the daily activities of insects are directly dependent on the daily changes of the weather and are influenced by combinations of several meteorological factors is only partially true. It is now usual to divide 24-hour rhythms into two types: exogenous rhythms which are directly dependent on environmental changes, and endogenous, persistent, or circadian (i.e., about a day) rhythms which continue under constant conditions and which reflect an intrinsic ability of the animal to measure absolute time. There has been considerable speculation and conflict of opinion over the nature of the "internal," "physiological," or "biological" clocks postulated to control the phases of endogenous rhythms.

Much of the quantitative information on 24-hour cycles of behavior in nature has been obtained by measuring flight, biting, or egg-laying activities of nocturnal or crepuscular (twilight active) species.[75,77,78] These recurrent activities are controlled through the interaction of both exogenous and endogenous factors. Which is the most important depends on the species, the activity being observed, the developmental stage, and the physiological state of the insect. Light is the major factor determining and positioning the activity patterns. Haddow,[78] in a review of the biting habits and diurnal activity of African mosquitoes, concluded that light was the most important microclimatic factor which released these insects into activity. In general, during the daytime light is inhibitory, and this may lead to the accumulation of hungry mosquitoes which are released into activity as the light intensity falls at sunset.[79] It is only when temperature, humidity, and wind velocity are outside a certain range that the 24-hour activity patterns established by the light-dark cycle are modified.

The importance of particular levels of low light intensity in inducing flight-activity peaks at dawn and dusk has been shown for certain mayflies (Ephemeroptera), caddisflies (Trichoptera), black flies (Simuliidae), fruit flies (Drosophilidae), and mosquitoes (Culicidae).[80-84] In the pulpwood forests of Quebec, Canada, the black fly, *Simulium venustum*, the commonest man-biting species, shows a morning and evening flight-activity rhythm.[82] Provided the temperature was not below 45°F, the wind velocity not above 2 mph, and the relative humidity not below 50%, the flight activity was correlated with a particular level of low light intensity. In the morning, activity was greatest at higher levels of light intensity (20 ft-c) than in the evening (5 ft-c). At night, a vertical movement of black flies occurred from the ground to the tops of the trees, again associated with the more suitable light intensities at the higher levels just before darkness. Mosquitoes also show a vertical migration in forested areas. The activity of mosquitoes at ground level in tropical forests is poorly synchronized, but in the exposed situations, such as in the forest canopy, a well-synchronized crepuscular behavior occurs.[85]

Caution is necessary in interpreting diurnal flight activity as general for the whole population. For example, the rhythmic flight patterns of tropical mosquitoes refer only to a limited section of the total population and include those individuals which are not swarming, feeding, resting, or egg laying. The flight pattern of the mosquito *Mansonia fuscopennata* resembles that of oviposition activity and occurs at particular times in the day-night cycle. However, whether flight or egg-laying activity occurs depends on the physiological condition of the females.[84] Flight activity takes place only in a limited period between emergence and the acquisition of a blood meal. Freshly fed females rest until egg laying.

The way in which the effect of light can be modified by other climatological factors is well illustrated in the food-seeking activity in the morning and before sunset of the fruit fly, *Drosophila subobscura*.[86] In the summer, the peaks of activity are correlated with low levels of light intensity, but, in the early spring and autumn, temperature is the determining factor.

Experimental investigations of 24-hour rhythms have shown that some of these persist under constant conditions and can be modified by alterations in the cycle of light and darkness. It is impossible to consider here the various kinds of persistent rhythms found among arthropods. The review of Harker[75] and the symposium on "biological clocks"[87] should be consulted for further details. There are several basic criteria required before a rhythm can be termed endogenous or circadian. First, its characteristic period of about 24 hours must persist for at least 2–3 days in a constant environment; second, it must be little affected by temperature; and, third, the timing of the peaks of activity or phases must be determined by an environmental time giver such as temperature or a change from light to darkness. Light is almost always the most powerful phase setter. There is much variation in the degree to which exogenous or endogenous components control a particular rhythm. Light and dark cues are of overriding importance for the manifestation of the oviposition cycle of the yellow-fever mosquito, *Aedes aegypti*.[96] Light-dark regimes other than 24 hour are readily adopted and completely mask any endogenous rhythm. Endogenous rhythms become unrecognizable in constant light. The locomotory rhythms of certain cockroaches, beetles, and flies exhibit all the characteristics of endogenous rhythms, the phase being set in nocturnal insects by the light-dark transition. Figure 7.5 illustrates such a locomotory rhythm in *Drosophila robusta*. A striking example of an endogenous rhythm is the pupal emergence or eclosion of *Drosophila*, which has been extensively studied by Pittendrigh.[97,98] In nature, eclosion takes place at dawn, and the time it occurs is measured from the previous dawn. The adaptive significance of this is connected to the water economy necessary in the newly emerged fly. The evaporating power of the atmosphere is lowest at dawn. An eclosion rhythm can be established in an arrhythmic population of flies by a single light stimulus of only 1/2000 second. Further, existing, overt rhythms in a fly population can be reset by a single stimulus. The new rhythm is not established instantaneously but passes through a period in which transient cycles greater or less than 24 hours were found, depending on the time of the cycle in which the stimulus was applied. The entrainment to a new light stimulus over a certain range was temperature independent. Anoxia or cooling to 0°C stopped the rhythm, but, following such treatment, the cultures continued out of phase with the normal control.

On the basis of an interesting paper by Pringle[99] which made use of entrainment phenomena of oscillators in the development of a theory of learning, Pittendrigh has formulated a coupled oscillator model to explain the eclosion rhythms of *Drosophila*. One temperature-independent oscillator is

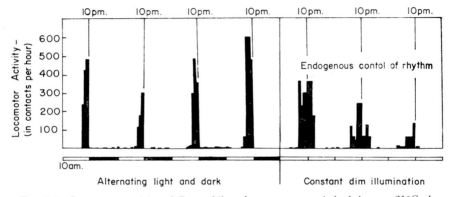

Fig. 7.5.   Locomotor activity of *Drosophila robusta* over a period of days at 21°C. Activity was measured as number of contacts made when a fly stepped on a pair of grid wires on the inside walls of a cage. Under conditions of alternating light and dark, the photoperiods are 12 hours, with "dawn" at 10 A.M., E.S.T. (From Roberts.[88] Reprinted from *Science* by permission.)

self-sustaining and is entrained by the environmental light regime. When it is free running or aperiodic, its phase can be shifted by a single light stimulus. It is coupled to and drives a second oscillator whose phase and time are immediately reflected in the overt emergence rhythm of the flies.

The hormonal control of diurnal activity rhythms has been investigated by Harker[89-92] in the American cockroach, *Periplaneta americana*. Cockroaches that have been allowed to become arrhythmic by prolonged exposure to continuous light become rhythmic when joined in parabiosis to a cockroach which shows a clear activity rhythm. The activity could be relayed by transplanting subesophageal ganglia from normally rhythmic cockroaches. The neurosecretory cells of the subesophageal ganglia were found to show 24-hour rhythms of secretion. Secretion appeared in the neurosecretory cells soon after darkness, apparently through the effect of light on the ocelli. The experimental evidence also suggests that a neurosecretory rhythm is present in the brain as well, which influences the timing of the neurosecretory phases of the subesophageal ganglion via the recurrent nerve and the corpus allatum-subesophageal ganglion nerves. An interesting finding is that extracts of cockroach corpus cardiacum which contain material that originates from the neurosecretory cells in the brain modify the spontaneous nerve activity of isolated cockroach nerves, as well as the locomotor behavior, following injection into intact roaches.[93] There is a similarity between linked brain-subesophageal neurosecretory cycles and the coupled oscillators of Pittendrigh.

An observation that may have considerable importance is that, if the secretory cycle of the subesophageal ganglion becomes completely arrhythmical by repeated implantation of ganglia 12 hours out of phase with the animal's own ganglia, tumors which are transplantable and which metastasize form in the gut.[94] Tumors in the guts of cockroaches have been reported by Scharrer to result after recurrent nerve section.[95] Plants can also be injured by abnormal light regimes owing to a failure of the synchronization of cellular functions. It is not unlikely that disruption of diurnal rhythms in man may be one of the factors that incites or stimulates the growth of certain tumors. It is sobering to think of the possible consequences of prolonged travel in space in an environment where no light or other environmental time givers are provided and cellular functions become desynchronized.

Are endogenous rhythms inherited or learned? Evidence is accumulating for the existence of a fundamental inherited rhythm in many insects. However, some of these rhythms may also be examples of a special learning process called "imprinting."[54] In this process, a very rapid unrewarded adjustment of a behavior pattern which is of crucial importance to the life of the organism can occur after a single stimulus.

REFERENCES

1. M. H. Pirenne, *Vision and the Eye*, p. 96, Pilot Press, London, 1948.
2. H. von Autrum, Die Belichtungspotentiale und das Sehen der Insekten, A, *Z. Vergleich. Physiol.*, **32**: 176 (1950).
3. J. J. Wolken and P. D. Gupta, Photoreceptor Structures. The Retinal Cells of the Cockroach Eye. IV. *Periplaneta americana* and *Blaberus giganteus*, *J. Biophys. Biochem. Cytol.*, **9**: 720 (1961).
4. W. H. Miller, Morphology of the Ommatidia of the Compound Eye of *Limulus*, *J. Biophys. Biochem. Cytol.*, **3**: 421 (1957).
5. H. Fernandez-Moran, Fine Structure of the Insect Retinula as Revealed by Electron Microscopy, *Nature*, **177**: 742 (1956).
6. T. H. Goldsmith and D. E. Philpott, The Microstructure of the Compound Eyes of Insects, *J. Biophys. Biochem. Cytol.*, **3**: 429 (1957).

7.   J. J. Wolken, J. Capenos, and A. Turano, Photoreceptor Structures. III. *Drosophila melanogaster*, *J. Biophys. Biochem. Cytol.*, **3**: 441 (1957).

8.   J. J. Wolken, A Comparative Study of Photoreceptors, *Trans. N. Y. Acad. Sci.*, **19**: 315 (1957).

9.   M. F. Moody and J. D. Robertson, Fine Structure of Some Retinal Photoreceptors, *J. Biophys. Biochem. Cytol.*, **7**: 87 (1960).

10. H. Fernandez-Moran, Fine Structure of the Light Receptors in the Compound Eyes of Insects, *Exptl. Cell Res., Suppl.*, **5**: 586 (1958).

11. C. H. Waddington and M. M. Perry, The Ultrastructure of the Developing Eye of *Drosophila*, *Proc. Roy. Soc., B.*, **153**: 155 (1960).

12. G. Wald, The Distribution and Evolution of Visual Systems, in *Comparative Biochemistry*, M. Florkin and H. S. Mason (Eds.), Vol. I, p. 311, Academic Press, 1960.

13. G. Wald, The Visual Functions of Vitamins A, in *Vitamins and Hormones*, **18**: 417 (1960).

14. T. H. Goldsmith, The Visual System of the Honeybee, *Proc. Natl. Acad. Sci.*, **44**: 123 (1958).

15. H. Eltringham, *The Senses of Insects*, Methuen's Biological Monographs, London, 1933.

16. K. Stockhammer, Zur Wahrnehmung der Schwingungsrichtung linear polarisierten Lichtes bei Insekten, *Z. Vergleich. Physiol.*, **38**: 30 (1956).

17. H. von Autrum and H. Strumpf, Das Bienenauge als Analysator für polarisiertes Licht, *Z. Naturforsch.*, **56**: 116 (1950).

18. R. W. Dorner and M. S. Mulla, Response of the Eye Gnat *Hippelates collusor* to Light of Different Wave Lengths, *Ann. Entomol. Soc. Am.*, **54**: 69 (1961).

19. H. J. Ball, The Effect of Visible Spectrum Irradiation on Growth and Development in Several Species of Insects, *J. Econ. Entomol.*, **51**: 573 (1958).

20. S. Marcovitch, Migration of Aphididae and the Appearance of Sexual Forms as Affected by the Relative Length of Daily Light Exposure, *J. Agr. Res.*, **27**: 573 (1924).

21. I. von Ziegler, Tetrahydrobiopterin-Derivat als lichtempfindliche Verbindung bei Amphibien und Insekten, *Z. Naturforsch.*, **156**: 460 (1960).

22. H. von Autrum, Electrophysiological Analysis of the Visual Systems in Insects, *Exptl. Cell Res., Suppl.*, **5**: 426 (1958).

23. H. von Ludtke, Retinomotorik und Adaptionsvorgänge im Auge des Rückenschwimmers (*Notonecta glauca* L.), *Z. Vergleich. Physiol.*, **35**: 129 (1953).

24. V. B. Wigglesworth, *The Principles of Insect Physiology*, Methuen, London, 1950; K. D. Roeder, *Insect Physiology*, John Wiley and Sons, New York, 1953.

25. G. Hoyle, Functioning of the Insect Ocellar Nerve, *J. Exptl. Biol.*, **32**: 397 (1955).

26. P. Ruck, Dark Adaptation of Ocellus in *Periplaneta americana*: A Study of the Electrical Response to Illumination, *J. Insect Physiol.*, **2**: 189 (1958).

27. J. Loeb, *Forced Movements, Tropisms and Animal Conduct*, Lippincott, Philadelphia, 1918.

28. G. S. Fraenkel and D. L. Gunn, *The Orientation of Animals*, Monogr. Anim. Behav., Oxford, 1940, revised edition 1962.

29. J. L. Cloudsley-Thompson, *Animal Behavior*, Oliver and Boyd, Edinburgh, 1960.

30. S. O. Mast, *Light and the Behavior of Organisms*, John Wiley and Sons, New York and London, 1911.

31. W. von Buddenbrock, Die Lichtkompassbewegungen bei Insekten, insbesondere den Schmetterlingsraupen, S. B. Heidelberg. *Akad. Wiss. Math.-Natural* **8B**: 1 (1917).

32. F. Santschi, Le Mécanisme d'Orientation chez les Fourmis, *Rev. Suisse Zool.*, **19**: 117 (1911).

33. A. Forel, *Das Sinnesleben der Insekten*, Reinhardt, Munchen, 1910.

34. I. Beling, Über das Zeitgedächtnis der Bienen, *Z. Vergleich. Physiol.*, **9**: 259 (1929).

35. O. Wahl, Neue Untersuchungen über das Zeitgedächtnis der Bienen, *Z. Vergleich. Physiol.*, **16**: 529 (1932).

36. W. Grabensberger, Experimentelle Untersuchungen über das Zeitgedächtnis von Bienen und Wespen, *Z. Vergleich. Physiol.*, **20**: 388 (1934).

37. H. Kalmus, Über die Natur des Zeitgedächtnisses der Bienen, *Z. Vergleich. Physiol.*, **20**: 405 (1934).

38. G. Werner, Tänze und Zeitempfinden der Honigbiene in Abhängikeit vom Stoffwechsel, *Z. Vergleich. Physiol.*, **36**: 464 (1954).

39. M. Renner, Neue Versuche über den Zeitsinn der Honigbiene, *Z. Vergleich. Physiol.*, **40**: 85 (1957).

40. M. Renner, The Clock of the Bees, *Nat. Hist. Mag.*, **68**: 434 (1959).

41. M. Renner, Time-sense and Orientation in Bees, in *Biological Clocks*, Cold Spring Harbor Symp. Quant. Biol., **25**: 361 (1960).

42. K. von Frisch, Die Sonne als Kompass im Leben, *Experientia*, **6**: 210 (1950).

43. K. von Frisch and M. Lindauer, Himmel und Erde in Konkurrenz bei der Orientierung der Bienen, *Naturwiss.*, **41**: 245 (1954).

44. K. von Frisch, *Bees, Their Vision, Chemical Senses, and Language*, Cornell University Press, Ithaca, 1950.

45. M. Renner, Über ein weiteres Versetzungsexperiment zur Analyse des Zeitsinnes und der Sonnenorientierung der Honigbiene, *Z. Vergleich. Physiol.*, **42**: 449 (1959).

46. M. Lindauer, Time-compensated Sun Orientation in Bees, in *Biological Clocks*, Cold Spring Harbor Symp. Quant. Biol., **25**: 371 (1960).

47. L. Pardi, Innate Components in the Solar Orientation of *Littoral Amphipods*, in *Biological Clocks*, Cold Spring Harbor Symp. Quant. Biol., **25**: 395 (1960).

48. G. Birukow, Innate Types of Chronometry in Insect Orientation, in *Biological Clocks*, Cold Spring Harbor Symp. Quant. Biol., **25**: 403 (1960).

49. W. Braemer, A Critical Review of the Sun-Azimuth Hypothesis, in *Biological Clocks*, Cold Spring Harbor Symp. Quant. Biol., **25**: 413 (1960).

50. K. von Frisch, Die Polarisation des Himmelslichtes als orientierender Faktor bei den Tänzen der Bienen, *Experientia*, **5**: 142 (1949).

51. K. von Frisch, Die Richtungsorientierung der Bienen, *Verhandl. Deut. Zool. Ges. Freiburg*, pp. 58-72, 1952.

52. K. von Frisch, Die Tänze der Bienen, *Osterr. Zool. Z.*, **1**: 1 (1946).

53. K. von Frisch, *Aus dem Leben der Bienen*, Verlag-Springer, Wien, 1948.

54. W. H. Thorpe, *Learning and Instinct in Animals*, Methuen, London, 1956.

55. H. Kalmus, Sun Navigation of *Apis mellifera* L. in the Southern Hemisphere, *J. Exptl. Biol.*, **33**: 554 (1956).

56. R. Jander, 1957, Die optische Richtungsorientierung der roten Waldameise (*Formica rufa*) *Z. Vergleich. Physiol.*, **40**: 162 (1957).

57. A. D. Lees, *The Physiology of Diapause in Anthropods*, Cambridge University Press, London, 1955, and The Physiology and Biochemistry of Diapause, *Ann. Rev. Entomol.*, **1**: 1 (1956).

58. M. Kogure, The Influence of Light and Temperature on Certain Characters of the Silkworm, *Bombyx mori*, *J. Dept. Agr. Kyushu Univ.*, **4**: 1 (1933).

59. P. S. Corbet, Environmental Factors Influencing the Induction and Termination of Diapause in the Emperor Dragonfly, *Anax imperator* Leach (Odonata: Aeshnidae), *J. Exptl. Biol.*, **33**: 1 (1956).

60. J. de Wilde, C. S. Duntjer, and L. Mook, Physiology of Diapause in the Adult Colorado Beetle. I. The Photoperiod as a Controlling Factor, *J. Insect Physiol.*, **3**: 75 (1959).

61. O. H. Paris and C. E. Jenner, Photoperiodic Control of Diapause in the Pitcher-plant Midge, *Metriocnemus knabi*, in *Photoperiodism and Related Phenomena in Plants and Animals*, R. B. Withrow (Ed.), AAAS Publ. 55, p. 601, 1959.

62. A. D. Lees, Environmental Factors Controlling the Evocation and Termination of Diapause in the Fruit Tree Red Spider Mite *Metatetranychus ulmi* Koch (Acarina, Tetranychidae), *Ann. Appl. Biol.*, **40**: 449 (1953).

63. A. D. Lees, The Significance of Light and Dark Phases in the Photoperiodic Control of Diapause in *Metatetranychus ulmi* Koch, *Ann. Appl. Biol.*, **40**: 487 (1953).

64. A. D. Lees, Photoperiodism in Insects and Mites, in *Photoperiodism and Related Phenomena in Plants and Animals*, R. B. Withrow (Ed.), AAAS Publ. 55, p. 585, 1959.

65. K. F. Gayspitz, Light as a Factor Regulating the Cycle of Development of the Pine lasiocampid *Dendrolimus pini* L. (in Russian) *Doklady Acad. Nauk. SSSR*, **68**: 781 (1949).

66. D. S. Farner, Comparative Physiology — Photoperiodicity, *Ann. Rev. Physiol.*, **23**: 71 (1961).

67. F. C. Baker, The Effect of Photoperiodism on Resting, Treehold, Mosquito Larvae, *Can. Entomol.*, **67**: 149 (1935).

68. G. T. Harvey, A Relationship between Photoperiod and Cold-storage Treatment in the Spruce Budworm, *Science*, **128**: 1205 (1958).

69. V. B. Wigglesworth, The Physiology of Ecdysis in *Rhodnius prolixus* (Hemiptera). II. Factors Controlling Moulting and Metamorphosis, *Quart. J. Microscop. Sci.*, **77**: 191 (1934).

70. C. M. Williams, Physiology of Insect Diapause. IV. The Brain and Prothoracic Glands as an Endocrine System in the Cecropia Silkworm, *Biol. Bull.*, **103**: 120 (1952).

71. J. de Wilde and J. A. de Boer, Physiology of Diapause in the Adult Colorado Beetle. II. Diapause as a Case of Pseudoallatectomy, *J. Insect Physiol.*, **6**: 152 (1961).

72. A. D. Lees, The Role of Photoperiod and Temperature in the Determination of Parthenogenetic and Sexual Forms in the Aphid *Megour viciae* I and II, *J. Insect Physiol.*, **3**: 92 (1959); **4**: 154 (1960).

73. A. D. Lees, Some Aspects of Animal Photoperiodism, in *Biological Clocks*, Cold Spring Harbor Symp. Quant. Biol., **25**: 261 (1960).

74. J. S. Kennedy and C. O. Booth, Host Alternation in *Aphis fabae* Scop. II. Changes in the Aphids, *Ann. Appl. Biol.*, **41**: 88 (1954).

75. J. E. Harker, Animal Rhythms in the Animal Kingdom, *Biol. Rev. Cambridge Phil. Soc.*, **23**: 1 (1958).

76. B. P. Uvarov, Insects and Climate, *Trans. Entomol. Soc. London*, **79**: 1 (1931).

77. C. B. Williams, An Analysis of Four Year Captures of Insects in a Light Trap, *Trans. Roy. Entomol. Soc.*, **89**: 79 (1939).

78. A. J. Haddow, Studies of Biting-habits of African Mosquitoes, *Bull. Entomol. Res.,* **45**: 199 (1954).
79. A. H. R. Lumsden, The Crepuscular Biting Activity of Insects in the Forest Canopy in Bwamba, Uganda, *Bull. Entomol. Res.,* **42**: 721 (1952).
80. A. Tjonneland, The Flight Activity of Mayflies as Expressed in East African Species, *Univ. Bergen Arbok, Naturvitenskap., Rekke,* pp. 1-88, 1960.
81. P. S. Corbet and A. Tjonneland, The Flight Activity of Twelve Species of East African Trichoptera, *Univ. Bergen Arbok Naturvitenskap., Rekke,* p. 1-49, 1955.
82. L. S. Wolfe and D. G. Peterson, Diurnal Behaviour and Biting Habits of Black Flies (Diptera: Simmuliidae) in the Forests of Quebec, *Can. J. Zool.,* **38**: 498 (1960).
83. S. Taylor and H. Kalmus, Dawn and Dusk Flight of *Drosophila subobscura* Collin, *Nature,* **174**: 221 (1954).
84. P. S. Corbet and A. J. Haddow, Observations on Nocturnal Flight Activity in Some African Culicidae (Diptera), *Proc. Roy. Entomol. Soc. London,* **36A**: 113 (1961).
85. P. S. Corbet, Patterns of Circadian Rhythms in Insects, in *Biological Clocks,* Cold Spring Harbor Quant. Symp. Biol., **25**: 357 (1960).
86. V. R. D. Dyson-Hudson, The Daily Activity Rhythm of *Drosophila subobscura* and *D. obscura, Ecology,* **37**: 562 (1956).
87. R. B. Withrow (Ed.), *Biological Clocks,* Cold Spring Harbor Symp. Quant. Biol., **25**, 1960.
88. S. K. de F. Roberts, "Clock" Controlled Activity Rhythms in the Fruit Fly, *Science,* **124**: 172 (1956).
89. J. E. Harker, Diurnal Rhythms in *Periplaneta americana, Nature,* **173**: 689 (1954).
90. J. E. Harker, Factors Controlling the Diurnal Rhythm of Activity in *Periplaneta americana* L., *J. Exptl. Biol.,* **33**: 224 (1956).
91. J. E. Harker, Internal Factors Controlling the Subesophageal Ganglion Neurosecretory Cycle in *Periplaneta americana* L., *J. Exptl. Biol.,* **37**: 164 (1960).
92. J. E. Harker, Endocrine and Nervous Factors in Insect Circadian Rhythms, in *Biological Clocks,* Cold Spring Harbor Symp. Quant. Biol., **25**: 279 (1960).
93. S. Ozbas and E. S. Hodgson, Action of Insect Neurosecretion upon Central Nervous System *in vitro* and upon Behavior, *Proc. Natl. Acad. Sci.,* **44**: 825 (1958).
94. J. E. Harker, Experimental Production of Midgut Tumors in *Periplaneta americana* L., *J. Exptl. Biol.,* **35**: 251 (1958).
95. B. Scharrer, Experimental Tumors After Nerve Section in an Insect, *Proc. Soc. Exptl. Biol. Med.,* **60**: 184 (1945).
96. P. S. Corbet, A. J. Haddow, and J. D. Gillett, Observations on the Oviposition-Cycle of *Aedes aegypti* L., *Ann. Trop. Med. Parasitol.,* **54**: 156 (1960).
97. C. S. Pittendrigh, Circadian Rhythms and the Circadian Organization of Living Systems, Cold Spring Harbor Symp. Quant. Biol., **25**: 159 (1960).
98. C. S. Pittendrigh, Daily Rhythms as Coupled Oscillator Systems and Their Relation to Thermoperiodism and Photoperiodism, in *Photoperiodism and Related Phenomena in Plants and Animals,* R. B. Withrow (Ed.), AAAS Publ. 55, p. 475, 1959.
99. J. W. S. Pringle, On the Parallel Between Learning and Evolution, *Behaviour* **3**: 174 (1951).

CHAPTER 8

Organophosphorus Insecticides

The study of the reactions and metabolism of the organophosphates has enlarged our understanding of their action and selectivity more than in the case of any other class of insecticides. This study has been blessed with two circumstances: (1) a specific mode of action—namely, inhibition of the widely studied enzyme cholinesterase—which was discovered by students of chemical warfare agents before these compounds were widely used as insecticides; and (2) the potential for labeling with P^{32}, which in the 1950's was probably the most convenient radioisotope on account of its penetrating beta emission and the ease of obtaining high specific activities. In the 1960's, the existence of gas-flow chromatogram scanners and liquid scintillation counters has detracted from the importance of a strong beta emission, and the inconveniently short 14-day half-life of P^{32} has become an important factor.

Many hundreds of papers have been written about the metabolism of P^{32}-labeled organophosphates in insects, mammals, and plants. Fortunately, the existence of recent reviews[1,2] and books[3,4] makes it unnecessary to deal comprehensively with the topic. Instead, after some remarks on isotopic labeling, a general discussion will be given of penetration phenomena and of the principal metabolic pathways and their significance. Structures of the compounds to be discussed are given in Table 8.1.

1. Labeling

A discussion of this somewhat practical matter is worthwhile because, in the case of the organophosphates, most investigators have performed their own syntheses. This is mainly due to the fact that P^{32} has such a short half-life (14 days) that a synthesis is required for each experiment, shelf storage being impossible. Consequently, the cost of commercial synthesis is very high. It is also convenient to make such labile compounds on the premises.

A special feature of work with insecticide metabolism in insects is that usually not much biological material is available, a few grams being a good supply; and, furthermore, only a small quantity of compound per unit body weight can be applied if one wishes the insect to survive for a while. Thus, with a compound like dimethoate, whose LD_{50} to the housefly is 0.4 mg/kg,[5] only 2 µg can be applied to 5 g of flies if the effect of an LD_{50} dose is under

TABLE 8.1
Compounds Mentioned in Chapter 8

1. $(C_2H_5O)_2P(S)OCH_2COOC_2H_5$

    Acethion

2. 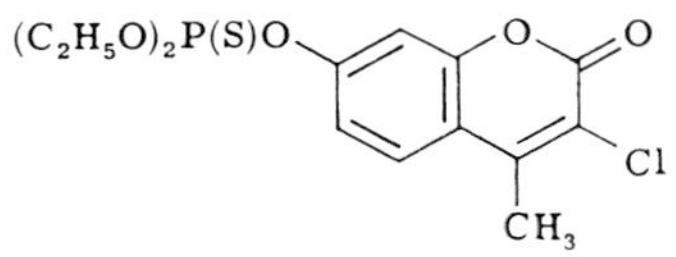 $(C_2H_5O)_2P(S)O$

    Co-Ral

3. $(CH_3O)_2P(O)OCH{=}CCl_2$

    DDVP

4. $(C_2H_5O)_2P(S)OC_2H_4SC_2H_5$

    Demeton (thiono isomer)

5. 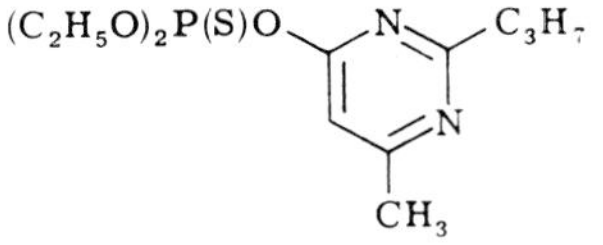 $(C_2H_5O)_2P(S)O$

    Diazinon

6. $(CH_3O)_2P(S)SCH_2CONHCH_3$

    Dimethoate

7. $(C_2H_5O)_2P(S)SC_2H_4SC_2H_5$

    Disyston

8.

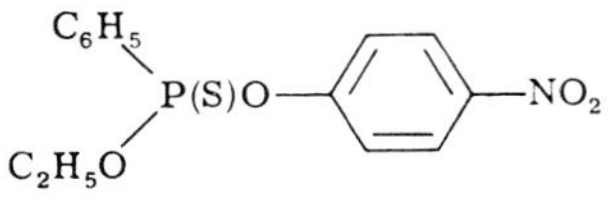

    EPN

9. $(CH_3O)_2P(S)SCHCOOC_2H_5$
    $\qquad\quad\; CH_2COOC_2H_5$

    Malathion

10. 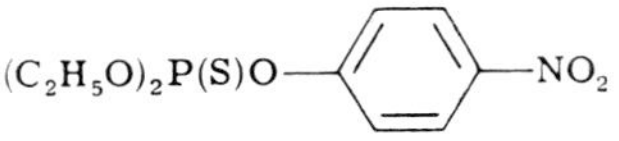 $(C_2H_5O)_2P(S)O$—⟨ ⟩—NO_2

    Parathion

11. $(CH_3O)_2P(O)OC{=}CHCOOCH_3$
    $\qquad\qquad\;\, CH_3$

    Phosdrin

12. 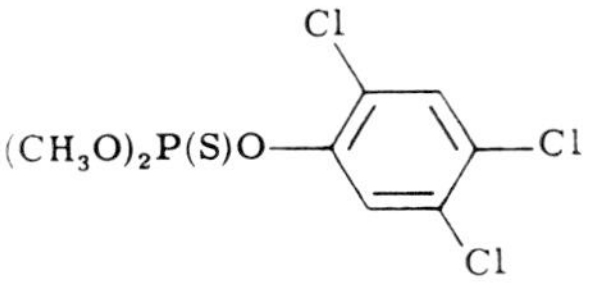 $(CH_3O)_2P(S)O$

    Ronnel

13.

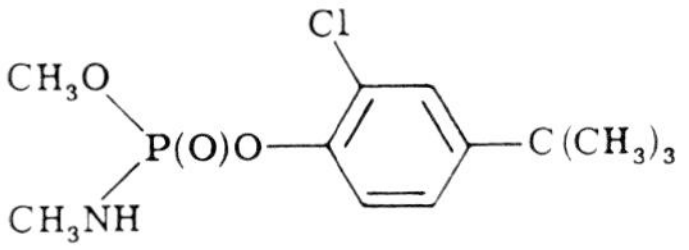

    Ruelene

14. $(C_2H_5O)_2P(S)SCH_2SC_2H_5$

    Thimet

examination. If one wishes to fractionate that portion which appears in particular insect tissues such as the nervous system, the quantities under study are minute, and high specific activity is imperative.

Early synthesis of P^{32}-labeled organophosphates used irradiated red phosphorus as a starting material, and specific activities were low, so that *in vivo* studies with insects were almost impossible. In 1958, Casida[6] described an extremely efficient exchange procedure in which P_2S_5 was heated with the cheap and highly active $H_3P^{32}O_4$. Also in 1958, Vigne and Tabeau[7] introduced an exchange procedure for $PSCl_3$ (and related compounds) and $H_3P^{32}O_4$. These procedures permitted the synthesis of compounds with high specific activity and commonly gave 20,000 counts/minute per microgram in an ordinary Geiger counter of 15% efficiency. This important advance made possible a host of *in vivo* studies with insects.

More recently, the use of C^{14}-labeled organophosphates has become of interest. Because of the long half-life of about 5500 years, it is impossible to get high specific activities. The activity per mole of carrier-free C^{14} and P^{32} is in the inverse ratio of their half-lives, so that P^{32} could be up to 142,000 times higher in activity than C^{14}. Nevertheless, the great stability of C^{14} is a convenience. A synthesis for phosphamidon-C^{14} was given in 1961,[8] and a metabolism study with DDVP-C^{14} was described in 1962 by Hodgson and Casida.[9] Undoubtedly, much more work with H^3 and C^{14} will be done in the coming years.

Given the right counting system, tritium offers a useful blend of safety, economy, and activity. Tritium in H_2^3O costs 14¢ per millicurie, compared with $1.10 for $H_3P^{32}O_4$, and $15 for $BaC^{14}O_3$. (These are about the cheapest possible starting materials.) Tritium is extremely safe because of its very weak beta emission and rapid turnover in the body, and 1 μg of fully tritiated parathion could, in theory, give 3.3×10^6 counts/minute in a counter with 15% efficiency, for the half-life is 12.5 years, a very convenient length of time.

In 1962 a new process was described for tritiating compounds with great ease and economy.[10] It uses H_2^3O with P_2O_5 and BF_3. An appropriate mix is simply stirred with the compound to be labeled for 6 hours at room temperature. Only the hydrogens of aromatic carbons exchange. Little degradation occurs, in contrast to the Wilzbach technique, in which exposure to carrier-free tritium is used, and which cannot be carried out in the ordinary laboratory. If the procedure is as simple as it appears to be, it could revolutionize metabolic studies, for the investigator could obtain pure compounds and tritiate them. We have recently shown[33] that this procedure is very effective for many insecticides, but not for most organophosphates.

In one case,[11] parathion labeled with S^{35} was used in a metabolic study. This was a most unfortunate choice, for the $P=S^{35}$ was, of course, desulfurated, with loss of the S^{35} from the parent molecule, and no label was left in the important metabolic product paraoxon.

2. Metabolism: Activating and Degrading

All the toxic organophosphates inhibit cholinesterase *in vivo*. About three-quarters of the common insecticidal ones do not affect the enzyme *in vitro* but undergo activation in the body. The best-known activation is desulfuration

$$(RO)_2P(S)OX \rightarrow (RO)_2P(O)OX$$

where R is usually C_2H_5 or CH_3, and X can vary enormously. This activation was first shown without use of radioisotopes, but since then it has been repeatedly demonstrated to occur with P^{32}-labeled compounds. Examples in mammals are malathion in the rat,[12] diazinon, dimethoate, parathion, and acethion in the mouse,[5] and Co-Ral in the cow.[13] Examples in insects are malathion in the American cockroach, housefly,[14] and *Culex tarsalis* mosquito.[15] Examples in plants are dimethoate in corn, peas, potatoes, and cotton.[16]

These studies have established as a reliable rule that compounds containing the P(S) group are invariably desulfurated in insects and mammals, and very likely in plants too. Yet, in several studies with P^{32} compounds where activation has been inferred on the basis of cholinesterase inhibition, it has been impossible to detect the product chromatographically. It is probable that this failure is due to the fact that degradation of all organophosphates, both parent and activation products, invariably occurs, and in these cases a small persistent level of activation product is maintained in the body by a steady activation and an equally steady degradation of the P(O) derivative. Examples are malathion in the dog[12] and ronnel in the cow and housefly.[17]

In compounds containing the thioether group —C—S—C, another kind of activation is possible, involving oxidation to the sulfoxide

$$
\begin{array}{c}
O \\
\parallel \\
-C-S-C-
\end{array}
$$

and sulfone

$$
\begin{array}{c}
O \\
\parallel \\
-C-S-C \\
\parallel \\
O
\end{array}
$$

both of which are more potent anticholinesterases than the parent compound. It happens that most of the thioethers contain also a P(S) group, and in such cases multiple activation pathways are clearly possible and, in fact, occur. However, formation of sulfoxide and sulfone is the prime activating reaction, particularly in plants, as has been shown with radioisotope studies for demeton,[18] Di-Syston, and Thimet[19] in many plants. It occurs also in the mouse.[20]

Degradation of organophosphates is, in almost all cases, hydrolytic. Typically, phosphatase action occurs, if we can use this term rather loosely to describe cleavage of either bond in the P—O—C or P—S—C sequence in the molecule. The most familiar case in compounds of the type $(RO)_2P(A)OX$ (where A can be S or O) is hydrolysis to $(RO)_2P(A)OH$. This has been shown as the major path in most cases, but there are important exceptions. Thus, ronnel is hydrolyzed primarily at the POX by houseflies but primarily at the POCH$_3$ by rats.[17] The latter type of hydrolysis, sometimes called "desalkylation," occurs also with methyl parathion in the American cockroach, in which insect 23% of the degradation followed this route,[21] and with malathion in the dog, with 21%.[12]

$$(CH_3O)_2P(S)SCHCOOC_2H_5 \qquad \longrightarrow \qquad \begin{array}{c} CH_3O \\ \diagdown \\ HO \diagup \end{array} P(S)SCHCOOC_2H_5$$

$$\underset{\text{Malathion}}{CH_2COOC_2H_5} \qquad\qquad \underset{\text{Desmethyl malathion}}{CH_2COOC_2H_5}$$

In plant metabolism of dimethoate, desalkylation is of special importance and accounts for 69% of internal metabolites in cotton and 64% in corn.[16]

When the organophosphate contains a carboxyester $C(O)OR$ group as in malathion or a carboxyamide $C(O)NR_2$ group as in dimethoate, hydrolysis is likely to occur here rather than at the phosphate bond. This effect is most pronounced in mammals: for instance, 68% of malathion cleavage in the mouse[14] and 74% of dimethoate cleavage in the steer[22] followed this route. Unfortunately, the rule is not absolute, for Phosdrin is hydrolyzed almost exclusively by phosphatase action in the cow[23] and pea plant.[24]

3. Alternative Metabolic Pathways

From what has been said already, it is evident that there is a good deal of variation in the way different species metabolize any given compound. These differences can be vitally important in determining toxicity of the compound. Furthermore, by selective blocking of one pathway, toxicity can be profoundly modified.

The most studied case is malathion. This can be metabolized by carboxyesterase action, i.e., hydrolysis of the COOC$_2$H$_5$ (I) or by two kinds of phosphatase action: hydrolysis of the PSC (II) or desalkylation (III). Most important of all, desulfuration of P(S) to P(O) occurs (IV), which produces the actual toxicant malaoxon. In mammals, carboxyesterase action is the major path and is very rapid, so that (IV) is of minor importance, and rather little malaoxon builds up in the body. In insects, carboxyesterase action is less

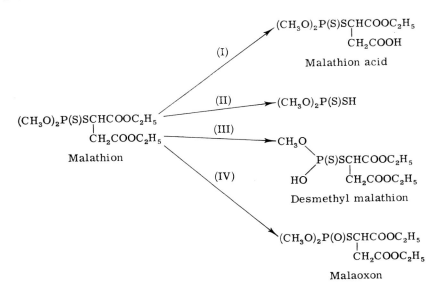

important than phosphatase action (Table 8.2), and both together are rather slow, so (IV) is important, and malaoxon accumulates.[14] A comparison of malaoxon accumulation in the American cockroach and mouse is shown in

TABLE 8.2
Extent of the Alternative Pathways for Malathion Hydrolysis[a]

	Per cent by phosphatase	Per cent by carboxyesterase
Whole mouse	21	68
Cow urine	20	80
Dog urine	30	67
Rat urine	24	59
American cockroach	42	28
German cockroach	42	23
Housefly	59	6

[a] Data of Krueger and O'Brien,[14] O'Brien et al.,[32] and Knaak and O'Brien.[12]

Fig. 8.1. The difference shown there probably accounts for the selective toxicity of malathion, which is 100 times more toxic to the American cockroach than to the mouse.

If one treats mammals with EPN, their sensitivity to malathion poisoning is vastly increased. This has been shown[12,25] to be due to a specific inhibition of the carboxyesterase pathway so that the mammal becomes biochemically like an insect in its ability to handle malathion and pays the penalty of becoming as susceptible as the insect to poisoning.

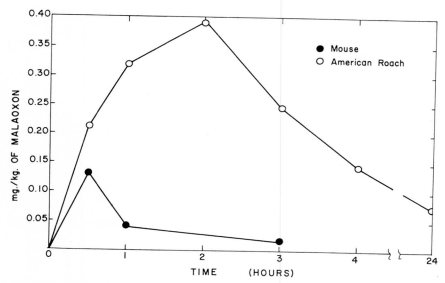

FIG. 8.1. Malaoxon levels in the whole body after injecting 30 μg of malathion-P^{32} per gram.

Matsumura[15] has used malathion-P^{32} to show that, when the *Culex tarsalis* mosquito develops specific resistance to malathion, it does so by greatly increasing its carboxyesterase level, thereby achieving a mammal-like ability to deal with malathion and, consequently, a mammal-like insensitivity to the compound.

Apparently minor structural changes can lead to important variations in contributions of alternate pathways. In resistant *Culex*,[15] malathion is hydrolyzed primarily by carboxyesterase, but malaoxon is hydrolyzed primarily by phosphatase action. An important consequence is that malathion toxicity is synergized by EPN (a carboxyesterase inhibitor), whereas malaoxon toxicity is synergized by fluoride (a phosphatase inhibitor).

The low mammalian toxicities of acethion, Diazinon, and dimethoate have also been attributed[5] to a balance of activating and degrading enzymes in the mammal which favors low levels of activation product compared with the insect. In the case of dimethoate, it has been shown[26] that the amount of degradation by liver (the main site of dimethoate degradation) by several vertebrates is inversely related to their susceptibility to dimethoate poisoning. This rapid degradation is attributable to carboxyamidase (I) rather than phosphatase (II), for the principal product in mammals, both *in vivo*[22] and *in vitro*,[26] is dimethoate acid.

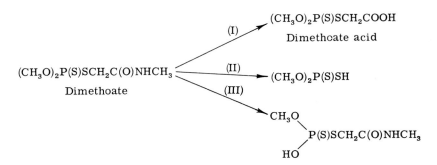

The existence of alternate metabolic pathways makes the task of examining metabolic routes an arduous one. For one thing, the relative contribution of the different routes may vary with the amount of insecticide administered. Surprisingly enough, this effect was not very extreme in a study on malathion

TABLE 8.3

CONCENTRATION DEPENDENCE OF CONTRIBUTION OF ALTERNATE METABOLIC PATHWAYS

(a) *In vivo*: Malathion Metabolites in Whole Insects after 4 hours[a]

Insect	Dose (mg/kg)	Per cent as phosphatase products	Per cent as carboxyesterase products
American cockroach	4	31	48
American cockroach	40	43	24
German cockroach	60	45	35
German cockroach	600	41	36
Housefly	15	68	10
Housefly	150	59	5

(b) *In vivo*: Ronnel Metabolites in Rat Urine[b]

Dose (mg/kg)	$R_2P(O)OH$[c]	$R_2P(S)OH$	$R(XO)P(O)OH$[d]	$R(XO)P(S)OH$
2	61	24	9	6
100	15	18	25	42

(c) *In vitro*: DDVP Metabolism by Rat Liver[e]

DDVP concentration	Per cent $POCH_3$ cleavage	Per cent $POCH{=}CCl_2$ cleavage
$2 \times 10^{-2}M$	5	95
$5 \times 10^{-4}M$	32	68

[a] From Krueger and O'Brien.[14]
[b] From Plapp and Casida.[21]
[c] R stands for CH_3O.
[d] X stands for 2,4,5-trichlorophenyl.
[e] From Hodgson and Casida.[9]

with insects *in vivo*, as shown in Table 8.3. However, in several other cases, the table shows that the dependence on dose or concentration was quite pronounced. The major cautionary note is that extrapolations from *in vitro* to *in vivo* can be dangerous, as it is very difficult to estimate the *in vivo* concentration within a tissue at any particular dose level. *In vitro* studies should be performed at various concentrations of parent material.

In the case of DDVP metabolism *in vitro*,[9] it was possible to "dissect out" the enzymic contributors to the different hydrolytic pathways in rat liver. The possible routes were POCH=CCl$_2$ hydrolysis (I) and desalkylation (II).

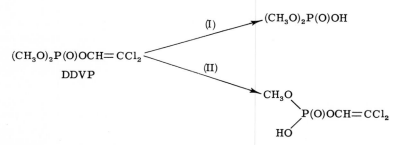

In mitochondria, only (I) occurred; in the soluble fraction, both (I) and (II). Only (I) was activated by Ca^{++} and Mn^{++}. The enzyme(s) for (I) could be precipitated at between 40% and 60% saturation of ammonium sulfate, whereas enzymes for (II) precipitated mainly between 60% and 80%.

Another "dissection" of such enzymes was recently achieved by Matsumura and Brown,[34] who used DEAE-cellulose chromatography to separate out the carboxyesterase in the resistant *Culex* referred to above. Manipulation of enzyme from such a tiny amount of highly heterogeneous starting material was, of course, only feasible because of the high sensitivity of the assay system, i.e., cleavage of malathion-P^{32} to a particular product (malathion acid) which could be chromatographically identified.

In spite of the great interest in malathion hydrolysis, no one has yet succeeded in determining whether malathion mono acid is (I) or (II), for, although identity between a synthetic malathion acid and the metabolite has been shown, the synthetic route is ambiguous and could lead to (I) or (II).

$(CH_3O)_2P(S)SCHCOOH$
$CH_2COOC_2H_5$

α-Acid (or β-ester)

(I)

$(CH_3O)_2P(S)SCHCOOC_2H_5$
CH_2COOH

β-Acid (or α-ester)

(II)

4. Penetration of the Cuticle

One of the most striking differences between insects and mammals is the nature of the integument. The skin of mammals is structurally so different from the cuticle of insects that one would imagine that many compounds could penetrate one far more readily than the other. Indeed, it is generally believed (on indirect grounds) that such a difference accounts for the selectivity of DDT. Yet, amazingly few direct measurements of rate of penetration of the insect cuticle have been made. For such studies, radioisotopes are invaluable.

A procedure which has been used is to apply a labeled organophosphate to a number of specimens of the living insect and at various times thereafter to rinse off individuals with solvent (usually acetone) and so measure the rate of loss from the surface. Very few authors have formulated their results in a way that throws light on the absorption process, and appropriate graphical treatment of their data can yield new information. For instance, if simple diffusion from the surface occurs, then the rate of diffusion should be proportional to the amount on the surface. Therefore, there should be linear relationships (1) between the dose applied and the amount taken up in a fixed time, and (2) between time and the logarithm of the fraction of dose remaining on the outside at that time. These relations follow from the exact analogy to the first-order kinetics of a chemical reaction, in which the rate at any given instant depends on the concentration of parent material at that instant.

$$-dx/dt = kx$$

Both of the above expectations, of course, assume that there is no "saturation" phenomenon, which could occur within the cuticle or simply on the cuticle, if, for instance, multimolecular layers of insecticide were applied to it. In fact, saturation is often noted in quite simple studies: with malathion, 30 minutes after application, the American cockroach absorbed 54% at 4 μg/g but only 22% at 40 μg/g. The same trend was evident for the German cockroach and the housefly.[14]

An extensive study of insecticide penetration through the cuticle was made by Matsumura[27] by using malathion-P^{32} with the American cockroach. Unfortunately, very low-specific-activity malathion was used (1 μg gave 32 counts/minute), and rather high quantities, such as 15 μg, were therefore applied. Penetration was a little different in living and dead insects (more detailed experiments confirmed the reality of the difference shown in Table 8.4) but was substantially increased by starvation or abrasion. However, acetone washing had little effect (Table 8.4). A kinetic analysis showed that, during the early stages, the rate of penetration was particularly fast, and an absorption process was inferred. It was shown that absorption occurred onto the hot-water-soluble fraction of cuticle, presumably endocuticular protein. Once this factor was taken into account, simple kinetics of diffusion were followed. For instance, over the greater part of the concentration range studied, absorption was a linear function of dose. Only at the very high dose of 120 μg and above did the absorption rate fall off.

TABLE 8.4

PENETRATION OF MALATHION THROUGH THE PRONOTUM OF THE AMERICAN COCKROACH[a]

Condition of insect	Dose (micrograms per roach)	Per cent penetration in 16 hours
Living	8.5	40.6
Dead	13.6	38.0
Living, water washed	11.4	48.9
Dead, acetone washed	13.2	39.4
Living, starved	11.0	55.7
Living, abraded	9.8	62.6

[a] From Matsumura.[27]

Autoradiography showed that penetration through spiracles was negligible, and, when malathion was picked up by the cockroach from a treated surface, the primary path was by legs and antennae.

Another recent study concerned Ruelene penetration in 19 insects and ticks.[28] Data are available for 16 of these species at 4 hours after application and show a variation of up to sixfold, which is perhaps rather less than one would anticipate. Ten out of 16 absorbed between 43 and 78%. Four gave especially low results: Gulf Coast tick *Amblyomma maculatum*, 14%; brown dog tick *Rhipicephalus sanguineus*, 19%; boll weevil *Anthonomus grandis*, 16%; and bed bug *Cimex lectularius*, 25%. Two gave especially high results: American cockroach, 77%; and honey bee, 88%. Except for the fact that the only two ticks examined gave low uptakes, there was no correlation with insect order or any obvious relation to cuticular type.

Differences in cuticular absorption could account for the development of resistance of insects to insecticides. However, there is not much evidence on this aspect, which is one that can be studied very well with radioisotopes. In one instance,[5] the penetration of Diazinon into a strain of houseflies 40-fold resistant to the insecticide was only 7% less than into susceptible houseflies. The experiment was done with both 4- and with 30-μg/g doses; results at 30 μg/g showed approximately first-order penetration, with a half-life of 50 minutes. The penetration difference was considered to be too small to account for the resistance.

Interspecific differences in toxicity could, in principle, be similarly explained. Malathion is ten times more toxic to American than to German cockroaches when applied topically but equitoxic when injected.[14] This suggested that penetration differences were involved. However, direct measurements with malathion-P[32] showed no substantial difference in loss of topically applied malathion from the surface. Two possibilities therefore exist: that the rate of disappearance from the surface does not measure the rate of appearance in the body proper, i.e., there is important holdup in the cuticle; or, alternatively, the intrinsic susceptibility to malathion may be the same, but the German cockroach may have an additional ability to degrade malathion only when it is delivered slowly into the body, as in topical application. The matter remains unresolved.

It is surprising how little has been done in the relation between structure and cuticle penetration. Nonisotopic work of Treherne[29] suggested a direct relation between molecular size and penetration rate of locust cuticle. However, he used excised cuticle, six out of his seven compounds were urea derivatives, and he had water on both sides of the cuticle. Consequently, the results are not directly relevant to insecticide application studies.

In our laboratory[30] we worked with the pronotum of the live American cockroach, and used six compounds varying 3000-fold in polarity. Penetration increased directly with polarity, although we had anticipated that liposoluble materials like paraoxon would go in much faster. This study was done with low concentrations (1 μg or less) applied in 1 μl of acetone which promptly evaporated. When application was made in a water droplet, little penetration occurred until the water evaporated. This demonstrated the radical difference between partitioning behavior, i.e., out of water into cuticle, and penetration of a solute placed directly on the cuticle. The latter we believe to be the more interesting problem, and we believe that Treherne's approach is unsuitable.

Within the somewhat limited range examined, uptake was linearly related to dose applied: dimethoate was used at between 0.4 and 2.5 μg per roach and $H_3P^{32}O_4$ was used at between 0.16 and 2.0 μg per roach.

At the one concentration (0.16 μg per roach) for which the matter was studied, a plot of the logarithm of residual compound vs. time showed very good conformation with first-order kinetics at first, with departure from linearity after 30 minutes for $H_3P^{32}O_4$ and after 40 minutes for dimethoate. Half-times for absorption were 16 minutes for $H_3P^{32}O_4$ and 28 minutes for dimethoate. When the data of Krueger and O'Brien[14] for malathion in the American cockroach were similarly plotted, rough half-times of 2 hours at 40 μg/g or 30 minutes for 4 μg/g were obtained. For the German cockroach, half-times of about 5 hours at 600 μg/g and 1 hour at 60 μg/g may be calculated.

The uptake from solutions of dimethoate and Co-Ral by larvae of the mosquitoes *Anopheles quadrimaculatus* and *Aedes taeniorhyncus* showed a linear relation between concentration and total uptake over a fourfold concentration range.[31] The difference between species was very small, even though these differ greatly in their permeability to DDT (see Chapter 9, Fig. 9.1). For dimethoate, the concentration-uptake curves passed through the origin, but for Co-Ral they were a little off, although not so drastically off as in the case of DDT (Fig. 9.1).

In summary, the limited results available indicate extremely rapid absorption of organophosphates by insects, with no evidence that the rates vary greatly among species or between resistant and susceptible strains. The next chapter will show a very different state of affairs for DDT.

REFERENCES

1. B. W. Arthur, Metabolism of Systemic and Other Recent Insecticides in Animals, *Radioisotopes and Radiation in Entomology*, p. 65, Intern. Atomic Energy Agency, Vienna, 1962.
2. J. E. Casida, Metabolism of Organophosphate Insecticides by Plants: a Review, *Radioisotopes and Radiation in Entomology*, p. 49, Intern. Atomic Energy Agency, Vienna, 1962.
3. R. D. O'Brien, *Toxic Phosphorus Esters*, 434 pp., Academic Press, New York, 1960.
4. D. F. Heath, *Organophosphorus Poisons*, 403 pp., Pergamon Press, New York, 1961.
5. H. R. Krueger, R. D. O'Brien, and W. C. Dauterman, Relationship between Metabolism and Differential Toxicity in Insects and Mice of Diazinon, Dimethoate, Parathion and Acethion, *J. Econ. Entomol.*, **53**: 25 (1961).
6. J. E. Casida, Phosphorus-32 Pentasulfide: Preparation by Isotopic Exchange and Conversion to Thiophosphoryl-32 Chloride and Phosphorus-32 Trichloride, *Acta Chem. Scand.*, **12**: 1691 (1958).
7. J. P. Vigne and R. L. Tabau, Preparation de Composes Halogenes du Phosphore Marques au ^{32}P, par une Reaction d'Echange, *Bull. Soc. Chim. (France)*, p. 1194, 1958.
8. R. Anliker, E. Beriger, and K. Schmid, Die Synthese von ^{14}C-markiertem Phosphamidon einem neuen systemischen Insektizid, *Experientia*, **17**: 492 (1961).
9. E. Hodgson and J. E. Casida, Mammalian Enzymes Involved in the Degradation of 2,2-Dichlorovinyl Dimethyl Phosphate, *J. Agr. Food Chem.*, **10**: 208 (1962).
10. P. M. Yavorsky and E. Gorin, New Reagent for Labeling Organic Compounds with Tritium, *J. Am. Chem. Soc.*, **84**: 1071 (1962).
11. J. A. Jensen, W. F. Durham, and G. W. Pearce, Studies on the Fate of Parathion in Rabbits, Using Radioactive Isotope Techniques, *Am. Med. Assoc. Arch. Ind. Health*, **6**: 326 (1952).
12. J. B. Knaak and R. D. O'Brien, Effect of EPN on *in Vivo* Metabolism of Malathion by the Rat and Dog, *J. Agr. Food. Chem.*, **8**: 198 (1960).
13. H. R. Krueger, J. E. Casida, and R. P. Niedermeier, Metabolism and Residues Associated with Dermal Application of Co-ral to Rats, a Goat, and a Cow, *J. Agr. Food Chem.*, **7**: 182 (1959).
14. H. R. Krueger and R. D. O'Brien, Relation between Metabolism and Differential Toxicity of Malathion in Insects and Mice, *J. Econ. Entomol.*, **52**: 1063 (1959).

15. F. Matsumura and A. W. A. Brown, Biochemistry of Malathion. Resistance in *Culex tarsalis, J. Econ. Entomol.*, **54**: 1176 (1961).

16. W. C. Dauterman, G. B. Viado, J. E. Casida, and R. D. O'Brien, Persistence of Dimethoate and Metabolites Following Foliar Application to Plants, *J. Agr. Food Chem.*, **8**: 115 (1960).

17. F. W. Plapp and J. E. Casida, Metabolic Fate of O,O-Dimethyl O-(2,4,5-trichlorophenyl) Phosphorothioate in Rats and a Cow, *J. Agr. Food Chem.*, **6**: 662 (1958).

18. R. L. Metcalf, R. B. March, T. R. Fukuto, and M. G. Maxon, The Nature and Significance of Systox Residues in Plant Materials, *J. Econ. Entomol.*, **48**: 364 (1955).

19. R. L. Metcalf, T. R. Fukuto, and R. B. March, Plant Metabolism of Dithio-Systox and Thimet, *J. Econ. Entomol.*, **50**: 338 (1957).

20. R. B. March, R. L. Metcalf, T. R. Fukuto, and M. G. Maxon, Metabolism of Systox in the White Mouse and American Cockroach, *J. Econ. Entomol.*, **48**: 355 (1955).

21. F. W. Plapp and J. E. Casida, Hydrolysis of the Alkyl-phosphate Bond in Certain Dialkyl Aryl Phosphorothioate Insecticides by Rats, Cockroaches and Alkali, *J. Econ. Entomol.*, **51**: 800 (1958).

22. W. C. Dauterman, J. E. Casida, J. B. Knaak, and T. Kowalczyk, Metabolism and Residues Associated with Oral Administration of Dimethoate to Rats and Three Lactating Cows, *J. Agr. Food Chem.*, **7**: 188 (1959).

23. J. E. Casida, P. E. Gatterdam, J. B. Knaak, R. D. Lance, and R. P. Niedermeier, Bovine Metabolism of Organophosphate Insecticides. Subacute Feeding Studies with O,O-Dimethyl 1-carbomethoxy-1-propen-2-yl Phosphate, *J. Agr. Food Chem.*, **6**: 658 (1958).

24. E. Y. Spencer and J. R. Robinson, Metabolism of the Systemic Insecticide O,O-Dimethyl 1-carbomethoxy-1-propen-2-yl Phosphate (Phosdrin) in the Pea Plant, *J. Agr. Food Chem.*, **8**: 293 (1960).

25. F. W. Seume and R. D. O'Brien, Metabolism of Malathion by Rat Tissue Preparations and Its Modification by EPN, *J. Agr. Food Chem.*, **8**: 36 (1960).

26. T. Uchida, R. D. O'Brien, and W. C. Dauterman, Metabolism of Dimethoate by Vertebrate Tissues. *J. Agr. Food Chem.* (in press).

27. F. Matsumura, The Permeability of Insect Cuticle, M.S. thesis, University of Alberta, Canada, 1959.

28. V. E. Brady and B. W. Arthur, Absorption and Metabolism of Ruelene by Arthropods, *J. Econ. Entomol.*, **55**: 833 (1962).

29. J. E. Treherne, The Diffusion of Non-electrolytes Through the Isolated Cuticle of *Schistocerca gregaria, J. Insect Physiol.*, **1**: 178 (1957).

30. W. Olson and R. D. O'Brien, The Relation Between Physical Properties and Penetration of Solutes into the Cockroach Cuticle, *J. Insect Physiol.* (in press).

31. C. H. Schmidt and D. E. Weidhaas, Absorption and Toxicity of Three Radioactive Insecticides in Larvae of Two Species of Mosquitoes, *J. Econ. Entomol.*, **51**: 640 (1958).

32. R. D. O'Brien, W. C. Dauterman, and R. P. Niedermeier, Metabolism of Orally Administered Malathion by a Lactating Cow, *J. Agr. Food Chem.*, **9**: 39 (1961).

33. B. D. Hilton and R. D. O'Brien, A simple technique for tritiation of aromatic insecticides, *J. Agr. Food Chem.* (in press).

34. F. Matsumura and A. W. A. Brown, Studies on Carboxyesterase in Malathion Resistant *Culex tarsalis, J. Econ. Entomol.*, **56**: 381 (1963).

CHAPTER 9

Chlorinated Hydrocarbons

This chapter is short because the use of radioisotopes in the study of chlorinated hydrocarbon metabolism has been limited. In part, this lack is attributable to the fact that much of the metabolic work was carried out before tracer techniques were in very general use. It is to be hoped that the simplified counting procedures which liquid scintillation counting has recently made possible for C^{14} and H^3 compounds will lead to renewed activity in this area.

Because of the lack of research, this chapter will, unlike Chapter 8, describe practically all that has been done with radioactive materials. It cannot, of course, deal with the far more extensive work with nonradioactive techniques.

1. DDT Metabolism

Many early studies on DDT metabolism did not use radioactive DDT. A drawback of nonradioactive methods is that, since one does not know which metabolites to look for, one cannot very well develop analytical methods for them. With isotopic procedures, unknown metabolites commonly force themselves on one's notice, and co-chromatography with potential metabolites can then be utilized. For instance, nonisotopic methods first revealed Kelthane as an important metabolite of DDT in the domestic fruit fly, *Drosophila melanogaster*.

Kelthane

Later isotopic work with this insect[1] showed that a second major metabolite in larvae was *p,p*-dichlorobenzophenone.

In adults, two other important metabolites were demonstrated chromatographically but not identified. They were both more polar than Kelthane. A striking strain difference was also demonstrated in this work: Kelthane, the major metabolite in strain Oregon Rc, was not a metabolite in strain Oregon R.

The place and mode of application of DDT to the housefly are important factors in determining transport and distribution.[2] Transport occurs by the hemolymph, and ligaturing therefore blocks transfer. There was evidence that mortality was controlled by the concentration of DDT in the head, for, with various application procedures, death and concentration in the head were correlated, and ligation of the cervicum ("neck") reduced toxicity markedly. This suggests the head as the site of action, but Kearns[3] cites evidence against this hypothesis, particularly an observation that decapitated flies show normal symptoms after DDT poisoning.

It is widely accepted that DDT-resistant houseflies owe most of their resistance to their ability to dehydrochlorinate DDT to DDE.

$$(ClC_6H_4)_2CH—CCl_3 \longrightarrow (ClC_6H_4)_2C{=}CCl_2$$

The proof rests primarily on nonisotopic studies. Later, Winteringham[4] showed that the *para*-dibromo[82] analog of DDT, $(Br^{82}C_6H_4)_2CH—CCl_3$, was metabolized by dehydrochlorination. Resistant houseflies metabolized 57% of a 0.6 μg dose in this way in 24 hours; susceptible flies did not metabolize it at all. Piperonyl cyclonene entirely inhibited this degradation.

There have been suggestions that houseflies metabolize DDT not only to DDE but to to other important metabolites insensitive to the Schechter-Haller colorimetric method for DDT and DDE. Such metabolites may constitute up to 61% of the dose.[5] However, Perry et al.[6] showed for resistant houseflies that recoveries of total radioactivity agreed well with recoveries of DDT plus DDE, so that large quantities of other metabolites probably did not occur. However, after long periods, significant quantities of water-soluble metabolite(s) appeared in the feces, and these could not be DDT or DDE. At 96 hours this material represented only 1.19% of the applied dose.

However, the results of Perry et al. are in flat contradiction to the earlier findings of Terriere and Schonbrod,[7] who found that a large fraction of the fecal metabolites was water soluble. The fraction varied with DDT dose; thus, in resistant flies a 0.24-μg dose yielded 89% of the fecal metabolites as water soluble, and for a 3-μg dose the figure was 70%. The fraction of the applied dose which was water soluble varied considerably, being 63% and 14%, respectively, in the above two cases.

The unknown water-soluble metabolite was not successfully chromatographed or identified, but it was certainly not one of the usual intermediates. On acid hydrolysis, much became solvent extractable, and it was therefore suspected that the unknown was a conjugate. However, it was not a glucoside or a glucuronide. There appeared to be no difference between susceptible and resistant strains in their ability to metabolize DDT to the unknown product. The unknown was nontoxic.

This study also showed that excretion was rather extensive. A dose of 0.125 μg of DDT was 96% excreted in a susceptible strain in 13 days. A dose of 24 μg was 63% excreted in 8 days. For resistant houseflies, these workers[7] reported much slower excretion: a 10-μg dose was excreted in feces to the extent of between 1 and 3% daily. In these resistant insects, the quantity excreted was actually lower with a high dose than with a low dose. Thus, with a 0.24-μg dose, 0.18 μg was excreted, whereas with a 3-μg dose, 0.05 μg was excreted.

In 1953, Butts et al.[8] reported that the American cockroach metabolized DDT-C^{14} to a water-soluble material which could be converted by refluxing with acid to an ether-soluble material. They suggested that a conjugation product was involved. The extent of metabolism was 43% in 2 days at 30–35°C, but only 7% at 25–30°C. They believed that the metabolism constituted a detoxification.

An extensive study on DDT-C^{14} metabolism by the American cockroach used both ring-labeled and ethane-2-C^{14}-labeled compounds.[9] Excretion was moderately rapid after an initial 2-day lag, so that 40% was excreted in the feces by 6 days. This excretion was about halved by 400 μg per roach of the synergist piperonyl cyclonene. For DDE the excretion rate was about half that for DDT, but the dose of DDE that was used was 2.5 times more than with DDT, so the rates are not truly comparable.

Distribution studies[9] after DDT revealed highest concentrations in foregut, hindgut, and feces, with most other components having a rather uniform distribution and nervous tissue having the lowest concentration of all. The feces contained only 5% of their activity as DDT, 5% as DDE, and 83% as two unknown, rather polar, metabolites. Small quantities of three other unknowns were also shown chromatographically. In general, the two kinds of labeled DDT gave the same pattern of metabolites, so the diphenylmethane nucleus must be present in all of them. It is clear that the conversion of DDT to DDE, the most important degradation in houseflies, is of minor importance in the American cockroach.

In the Madeira cockroach, *Leucophaea maderae*, two polar unknown metabolites were found plus a little DDE. At 22 days, one of the polar metabolites constituted 69% of the excreted radioactivity, with the other at 7%; DDT, 12%; DDE, 2%; and 1% of a third, apolar unknown.[10]

Larvae of the European cornborer, *Pyrausta nubilalis*, metabolized DDT primarily to DDE. Up to 43% of the internal radioactivity was as DDE 5 days after treatment with 180 μg/g.[10]

A comprehensive study[11] on the nature of DDT-C[14] metabolites in the rat showed that, in feces, DDA occurred complexed in an unknown way.

$$Cl-\langle\bigcirc\rangle-\underset{\underset{COOH}{|}}{\overset{H}{\underset{C}{|}}}-\langle\bigcirc\rangle-Cl$$

DDA

Acid hydrolysis restored the DDA, but alkaline hydrolysis did not, so the complex was probably not a glucuronide. Furthermore, tests for glucuronic acid were negative. An amide with (for instance) glycine was suggested, by analogy with formation of hippuric acid from benzoic acid and glycine. The DDT metabolites arrived in feces almost entirely via the bile. After 17 mg of DDT-C[14] per kilogram, 65% of the radioactivity was found in the bile by canulation of the bile duct. In the bile, substantial amounts of free DDA were found along with small amounts of DDT (8%) and DDE (3%).

A very different use of DDT-C[14] was made by Bowman et al.[12] The solubility of DDT has been variously reported as between 37 and 1000 ppb (parts per billion). By ultracentrifuging at 84,000 $\times$ g until no further material precipitated and by counting the DDT in the supernatant, a figure was established of 1.2 ppb as the maximum solubility at 25°C.

Another physical study dealt with the sorption of DDT by mud surfaces. This phenomenon is of major importance in determining the time for residual effectiveness on mud huts. Miles and Pearce[13] made mud cakes, dusted them with DDT-C[14] and kept them dry or at 47% or 94% relative humidity. They examined the loss of radioactivity with a Geiger tube placed over the cakes, and, because of the poor penetration of the C[14] beta particle, little more than surface activity would be measured. A steady decline was found: for the above three conditions, the loss after 10 days was 55, 43, and 10%, respectively. Colorimetric analysis confirmed the finding by showing that quite large amounts had penetrated into a layer between 1 and 2 mm from the surface. The amounts in this layer were 19, 9, and 2%, respectively, of the applied dose. Dry conditions are thus worst for residual effectiveness. Presumably, the reason lies in the effective polarity of the mud; under wet conditions it is more polar and therefore less permeable to hydrophobic materials.

2. DDT Absorption

Before discussing this topic, reference should be made to the general comments on p. 172. It is as true for chlorinated hydrocarbons as for organophosphates that the data have seldom been expressed in a way to permit conclusions as to mechanism.

There is a general belief that ". . . the apparently specific insecticidal properties of DDT are in reality due to very efficient absorption through the insect cuticle."[14] This belief, which one of us has played a part in disseminating,[15] is based upon the marked differences in toxicity by the cutaneous and intravenous routes found in mammals but not in most insects. However, the results to be described show that DDT penetrates rather slowly into insects, so that about one-half is absorbed in a day. The above belief may therefore be untenable.

The rate of penetration of topically applied DDT-C^{14} into houseflies was studied by Hoffman et al.[16] who found about 67% absorption the first day, with little difference between living and dead insects. Absorption was slow and continuous, being incomplete (at 75%) even at 9 days. An earlier paper by these authors with DDT-resistant flies[17] indicated that a maximum of 36% was absorbed at a dose of 15 µg per fly; with flies killed before application of DDT, only 2% was absorbed.

Another indication of a connection between resistance and absorption came from a study in which DDT-C^{14} was applied to the housefly leg, and the uptake after 24 hours was studied.[2] Fifty-two per cent was absorbed by a susceptible, and 3% by a resistant, strain of flies. This led to a 14-fold greater concentration of DDT in the heads of the susceptible insects. However, this difference is probably not the full cause of resistance, because the resistant flies were still relatively insensitive to DDT applied to the inside of the head.

The paradibromo analog of DDT was absorbed by houseflies far less rapidly than DDT itself. A dose of 2 µg per fly of bromo-DDT was absorbed in approximate accordance with first-order kinetics, with a half-life of 40 hours. (This figure is calculated from the data of Bridges.[18]) Nonisotopic data for DDT in the housefly, by using a dose of 2 µg per fly, showed approximately first-order penetration for the first 4 hours, with a half-life of about 3 hours (calculated from data of Sternburg et al.[19]). In the case of bromo-DDT, a 25 times larger dose was absorbed very slowly and not according to first-order kinetics; less than 10% was absorbed in 2 days.[18]

This nonisotopically derived figure of 3 hours appears grossly at odds with data quoted above. But, in fact, the departure from first-order absorption after 4 hours was such that, although the half-time during the rapid early phase was 3 hours, only 66% was absorbed in 24 hours, in good agreement with isotopic data.

Another reliable set of data[20] for resistant houseflies also showed a departure from strict first-order kinetics after 4 hours. An estimated half-time from the data is 18 hours at 21°C, which once again suggests that resistant insects absorb DDT slowly.

The uptake of DDT by mosquito larvae was studied in 1952.[21] Mixed

Aedes vexans and *Aedes sticticus* took up 1.7 µg each in 24 hours from a 0.0125 ppm solution. The effect was very temperature dependent and almost doubled on raising the temperature from 21°C to 32°C. Dead larvae absorbed two-thirds as much as living larvae.

In another study, uptake of DDT-C^{14} from water solution by two species of mosquito larvae showed excellent linearity in the relation between concentration and 24-hour uptake,[22] but the lines did not pass through the origin (Fig. 9.1). It is clear that the species vary greatly in uptake properties, but the difference would be undetected at low DDT concentrations. The failure to pass through the origin is unexpected: the implication is that,

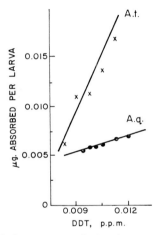

Fig. 9.1. Uptake of DDT from water solution by mosquito larvae: A.t. = *Aedes taeniorhynchus*; A.q. = *Anopheles quadrimaculatus*. Exposure time: 24 hours. (From Schmidt and Weidhaas.[22])

below 0.002 ppm, exceptionally high uptake rates prevailed. Such a phenomenon was not seen with the organophosphate, dimethoate. When the larvae were killed with carbon dioxide, absorption was reduced profoundly —by 88% for *Anopheles quadrimaculatus* and 75% for *Aedes taeniorhyncus*. One cannot say whether this reduction implies that DDT absorption is primarily by ingestion or that cuticular uptake is a vital process. There is obviously a severe discrepancy with the 1952 report described above.

Absorption of DDT by the American cockroach was examined by Robbins and Dahm.[9] Replotting of their data shows good first-order penetration throughout the 6-day period, with a half-life of 1 day; the dose was 40 µg per roach. The effect of 400 µg of the synergist piperonyl cyclonene, given along with the DDT, was examined at one time only (72 hours) after application: it reduced the control absorption of 72% to 57%. Of course, this small effect is in the opposite direction from what one would expect if the synergist owed its action to a penetration effect. Curiously enough, it also profoundly reduced excretion of DDT (69% in 6 days), which is also the opposite of expectation.

For the Madeira cockroach, *Leucophaea maderae*, replotting of the data of Lindquist and Dahm[10] shows excellent first-order kinetics of absorption, with a half-time of 7 days, a remarkable 7-fold difference from the American cockroach. In this case a correlation exists between sensitivity and absorption: the LD_{50} for the Madeira was over 42 µg/g, compared with 10 µg/g for the American cockroach.

Lindquist and Dahm[10] showed that the fifth-instar European corn borer (*Pyrausta nubilalis*) larvae took up DDT very slowly indeed: 15% in 5 days. They were also dramatically insensitive to DDT poisoning, with an LD_{50} of about 180 µg/g.

Little work has been done to explain the variation in susceptibilities found in any given strain of insects. One brief study[23] with DDT-C^{14} showed that, after exposure of houseflies to a surface film for a variety of exposure sequences, survivors contained about two-thirds as much radioactivity as dead flies. The implication was that variation in susceptibility was due in large part to variation, behavioral or physiological, in DDT uptake.

One of the curious features of DDT poisoning is its negative temperature coefficient: it is less toxic at higher temperatures. Yet, houseflies take up more DDT at increased temperatures. Roth and Lindquist[20] found that resistant houseflies absorbed 64% more of topically applied DDT at 32°C than at 21°C; yet, 41% died at 32°C, and 74% at 21°C. The increased uptake was not caused by hyperactivity at 32°C, for uptake rates at either temperature were not altered when flies were immobilized with CO_2.

3. "Benzene Hexachloride"

Early studies[24] with γ-benzene-hexachloride-C^{14} (γ-BHC, more properly called γ-hexachlorocylohexane) showed that about one-seventh of the insecticide was converted to water-soluble material by houseflies which had picked up a 4.4-µg dose over a 6-hour period. Resistant houseflies picked up somewhat less γ-BHC than susceptibles and, as a result, developed less internal insecticide. The differences were small, however, and dependent upon the method of application of compound: they were, for instance, negligible when exposure was to a film in a stoppered flask. The resistant insects degraded about twice as much of their dose to water-soluble metabolite(s). More extensive studies[25] showed that these two factors together reduced the internal γ-BHC level to one-quarter of that in susceptible flies 4 hours after exposure to vapor for 15 minutes.

Bradbury and Standen[26] showed that γ-BHC-C[14] was metabolized slowly in *Anopheles gambiae* mosquitoes. Only water-soluble metabolites were found and amounted to about 10% of the absorbed dose both at 1 hour and at 24 hours. *Anopheles gambiae* mosquitoes resistant to γ-BHC were somewhat less active than the susceptible strain in converting (thus, presumably, degrading) γ-BHC to water-soluble metabolites; they had about two-thirds the activity of the susceptibles. Furthermore, they took up substantially the same dose from a treated surface and absorbed the same fraction of what they took up.[26] Consequently, the causes of resistance remain unknown.

In the housefly[27] there were other, carbon tetrachloride-soluble metabolites: pentachlorocyclohexene, trichlorobenzene, and a "phenolic or acidic" substance. These components together never exceeded 3% of the dose. These results therefore conflict with the claim,[28] based on colorimetric studies, that pentachlorocyclohexene (I) is an important metabolite of γ-BHC in houseflies.

(I)

Carbon-14-labeled "benzene hexachloride" was also used by Bridges[29] to test the above claim. With the γ isomer, use of the isotope dilution technique revealed that only 1.5% of the compound was converted to (I), and the earlier (nonisotopic) results were explained as being due to nonspecificity of the colorimetric reaction.

Bridges has devoted a series of studies (e.g., Bridges[30,31]) to the topic of the fate of chlorinated hydrocarbon insecticides, especially benzene hexachloride, in foods. He has described the concentrations and compositions of residues to be expected as a result of insecticide treatments, particularly of cereals.

4. Cyclodienes

Conversion of aldrin to dieldrin and of isodrin to endrin both involve epoxidation. Epoxidation of both compounds occurs in houseflies[32] at similar and very rapid rates; with a dose of 2 µg per female fly, about 0.1 µg/hour was oxidized by one fly. The rates were identical for dieldrin-resistant and susceptible strains. Strangely enough, epoxides were also found on the outside, but only in the case of living insects. The amount after 8 hours was as great as 8% of the applied dose. Oxidation, either enzymic or nonenzymic, may therefore occur in or on the cuticle.

Aldrin   Dieldrin

Brooks[32] argues that epoxidation is not necessary to account for the toxicity of aldrin, for reduced aldrin cannot be epoxidized and yet is toxic. Furthermore, resistance of houseflies to aldrin is apparently not due to differences in epoxidation rate. There was no clear relation between rate of penetration of the cuticle and resistance. Excretion was negligible in the period studied. Presumably, the resistance is due to an intrinsic difference in sensitivity to the actual toxicant.

In the locust *Schistocerca gregaria*, aldrin is only slowly oxidized to dieldrin, as shown[33] by studies with aldrin-Cl[36]. Half of a 2-μg dose was oxidized in 7 days. An additional water-soluble metabolite was demonstrated but not identified and amounted to 4% at 7 days. Labeled dieldrin was not metabolized at all.

The thiolo analog of dieldrin was made with S[35].

It was shown[34] that this compound at a dose of 2 μg was 33% metabolized by both susceptible and dieldrin-resistant houseflies in 3 hours. Absorption and excretion were also virtually identical in both strains.

Recently, Heath[35] has examined dieldrin-Cl[36] metabolism in mice. After a dose of 12 mg/kg intravenously, brain levels rose promptly to about 16 μg/g and then declined linearly to give about 3 μg/g at 2 hours, a level which persisted thereafter. Other tissues achieved higher levels initially, but after 80 minutes all had declined rapidly except liver, which averaged 19 μg/g and even after 24 hours averaged 8 μg/g. Little was found in urine or feces. An exhaustive scheme for discovering metabolites failed to produce identifiable products but suggested that about one-third of the fecal output was water soluble, and so not dieldrin. Heath states that Vandekar has shown conclusively that rats excrete a metabolite in their bile.

References

1. D. B. Menzel, S. M. Smith, R. Miskus and W. M. Hoskins, The Metabolism of C^{14}-labeled DDT in the Larvae, Pupae and Adults of *Drosophila* melanogaster, *J. Econ. Entomol.*, **54**: 9 (1961).

2. E. J. Le Roux, The Adsorption, Distribution and Site of Action of DDT in DDT-Resistant and DDT-Susceptible House Flies Using Carbon^{14} Labeled DDT, *J. Econ. Entomol.*, **47**: 1058 (1954).

3. C. W. Kearns, The Mode of Action of Insecticides, *Ann. Rev. Entomol.*, **1**: 123 (1956).

4. F. P. W. Winteringham, P. M. Loveday, and A. Harrison, Resistance of Houseflies to DDT, *Nature*, **167**: 106 (1951).

5. A. S. Perry and W. M. Hoskins, The Detoxification of DDT by Resistant Houseflies and Inhibition of This Process by Piperonyl Cyclonene, *Science*, **111**: 600 (1950).

6. A. S. Perry, J. A. Jensen, and G. W. Pearce, Colorimetric and Radiometric Determination of DDT and its Metabolites in Resistant Houseflies, *J. Agr. Food Chem.*, **3**: 1008 (1955).

7. L. C. Terriere and R. D. Schonbrod, The Excretion of a Radioactive Metabolite by Houseflies Treated with Carbon-14 Labeled DDT, *J. Econ. Entomol.*, **48**: 736 (1955).

8. J. S. Butts, S. C. Chang, B. E. Christensen, and C. H. Wang, DDT Detoxification Products in American Cockroaches, *Science*, **117**: 699 (1953).

9. W. E. Robbins and P. A. Dahm, Absorption and Excretion, Distribution, and Metabolism of Carbon-14-labeled DDT by the American Cockroach, *J. Agr. Food Chem.*, **3**: 500 (1955).

10. D. A. Lindquist and P. A. Dahm, Metabolism of Radioactive DDT by the Madeira Roach and European Corn Borer, *J. Econ. Entomol.*, **49**: 579 (1956).

11. J. A. Jensen, C. Cueto, W. E. Dale, C. F. Rothe, G. W. Pearce, and A. M. Mattson, DDT Metabolites in Feces and Bile of Rats, *J. Agr. Food Chem.*, **5**: 919 (1957).

12. M. C. Bowman, F. Acree, and M. K. Corbett, Solubility of Carbon-14 DDT in Water, *J. Agr. Food Chem.*, **8**: 406 (1960).

13. J. W. Miles and G. W. Pearce, Rapid Measurement of Rate of Sorption of DDT by Mud Surfaces, *Science*, **126**: 169 (1957).

14. R. L. Metcalf, *Organic Insecticides*, Interscience Inc., p. 158, New York, 1955.

15. R. D. O'Brien, Selective Toxicity of Insecticides, *Advan. Pest Control Res.*, **4**: 75 (1961).

16. J. A. Hoffman, A. E. Roth, A. W. Lindquist, and J. S. Butts, Absorption of DDT in Houseflies over an Extended Period, *Science*, **115**: 312 (1952).

17. A. W. Lindquist, A. R. Roth, W. W. Yates, and R. A. Hoffman, Use of Radioactive Tracers in Studies of Penetration and Metabolism of DDT in Houseflies, *J. Econ. Entomol.*, **44**: 167 (1951).

18. P. M. Bridges, Absorption and Metabolism of (^{14}C) Allethrin by the Adult Housefly, *Musca domestica* L, *Biochem. J.*, **66**: 316 (1957).

19. J. Sternburg, C. W. Kearns, and W. N. Bruce, Absorption and Metabolism of DDT by Resistant and Susceptible House Flies, *J. Econ. Entomol.*, **43**: 214 (1950).

20. A. R. Roth and A. W. Lindquist, Effects of Temperature and the Activity of House Flies on Their Absorption of DDT, *J. Econ. Entomol.*, **46**: 127 (1953).

21. C. M. Gjullin, A. W. Lindquist, and J. S. Butts, Absorption of Radioactive DDT by Resistant and Non-resistant Mosquitoes, *Mosquito News*, **12**: 201 (1952).

22. C. H. Schmidt and D. E. Weidhaas, Absorption and Toxicity of Three Radioactive Insecticides in Larvae of Two Species of Mosquitoes, *J. Econ. Entomol.*, **51**: 640 (1958).

23. R. A. Hoffman, A. R. Roth, and A. W. Lindquist, Effect on House Flies of Intermittent Exposures to Small Amounts of DDT Residues, *J. Econ. Entomol.*, **44**: 734 (1951).

24. F. R. Bradbury and H. Standen, The Fate of Gamma-benzene-hexachloride in Normal and Resistant Houseflies. I, *J. Sci. Food Agr.*, **6**: 90 (1955).

25. F. R. Bradbury and H. Standen, The Fate of Gamma-benzene-hexachloride in Normal and Resistant Houseflies. II, *J. Sci. Food Agr.*, **7**: 389 (1956).

26. F. R. Bradbury and H. Standen, Benzene Hexachloride Metabolism in *Anopheles gambiae*, *Nature*, **178**: 1053 (1956).

27. F. R. Bradbury and H. Standen, The Fate of Gamma-benzene-hexachloride in Resistant and Susceptible Houseflies. III, *J. Sci. Food Agr.*, **9**: 203 (1958).

28. J. Sternburg and C. W. Kearns, Pentachlorocyclohexene, an Intermediate in the Metabolism of Lindane by House Flies, *J. Econ. Entomol.*, **49**: 548 (1956).

29. R. G. Bridges, Pentachlorocyclohexene as a Possible Intermediate Metabolite of Benzene Hexachloride in Houseflies, *Nature*, **184**: 1337 (1959).

30. R. G. Bridges, Fate of Labelled Insecticide Residues in Food Products. VII. The Fate of Gamma-benzene-hexachloride Residues in Flour During Baking, *J. Sci. Food Agr.*, **9**: 439 (1958).

31. R. G. Bridges, Fate of Labelled Insecticide Residues in Food Products. VI. Retention of Gamma-benzene-hexachloride by Wheat and Cheese, *J. Sci. Food Agr.*, **9**: 431 (1958).

32. G. T. Brooks, Mechanisms of Resistance of the Adult Housefly (*Musca domestica*) to 'Cyclodiene' Insecticides, *Nature*, **186**: 96 (1960).

33. A. J. Cohen and J. N. Smith, Fate of Aldrin and Dieldrin in Locusts, *Nature*, **189**: 600 (1961).

34. F. P. W. Winteringham and A. Harrison, Mechanisms of Resistance of Adult Houseflies to the Insecticide Dieldrin, *Nature*, **184**: 608 (1959).

35. D. F. Heath, Cl^{36}-dieldrin in Mice, in *Radioisotopes and Radiation in Entomology*, p. 83; Intern. Atomic Energy Agency, Vienna 1962.

CHAPTER 10

Miscellaneous Insecticides

1. Botanicals

Until the recent advent of tritiation techniques, the best available way for preparing botanically derived insecticides was by biosynthesis. Appropriate plants were grown in an atmosphere of $C^{14}O_2$ and later were worked up for their toxic components. Such procedures have been described for 14 nicotines by Ganz et al.,[1] for pyrethrins by Pellegrini[2] and Levy and Usubillaga,[3] and for rotenone by Luis and Munoz.[4]

The first study with radioactive pyrethrins was made in 1953 by Zeid et al.[5] using Pellegrini's material. Doses between 4 and 15 µg/g were used on the American cockroach. Four hours after intraspiracular injection, most of the activity (66%) was in the carcass, 20% was in the foregut, 7% in the hindgut, and other tissues contained very small amounts. Although nervous tissue contained very little of the dose, the concentration of pyrethrin in brain was high (0.22 mg/g) and second only to that in the foregut (0.66 mg/g).

The picture of metabolism that was presented was only qualitative. It would seem that most of the radioactivity in tissues was as the original esters in the mixed starting product, but that, in brain, only materials tentatively identified as hydrolysis products were present. Whether simple hydrolysis does occur is somewhat doubtful in the light of the work of Hopkins and Robbins described below.

Zeid et al. found that from 3 to 12% of the radioactivity was recoverable as expired CO_2. However, Winteringham et al.[6] pointed out that, since the pyrethrin preparation contained an amount of non-pyrethroid C^{14} which was greater than 12%, one cannot guarantee that the $C^{14}O_2$ was in fact derived from insecticidal material.

Winteringham et al. later described the metabolism of the same biosynthesized pyrethrin mixture and also of synthetic allethrin in houseflies.[6] In the case of topically applied material, absorption was of the order of 80% in 18 hours. If one assumes first-order penetration, the data suggest a half-time of about 6 hours for a dose of 1.5 µg/g. Absorption was little affected by prior killing of the insect, so, presumably, the effect was quite passive. Further evidence of passivity is that no selective absorption of any component of the mixture was found.

Metabolism of pyrethrins and allethrin was extensive: in 48 hours, up to 86% was recovered as nonpyrethroids. Except for one odd experiment, this degradation was greatly reduced in dead flies and also by treatment with 10 µg per fly of the synergist piperonyl cyclonene. The synergist was much less effective in blocking allethrin degradation. The nature of the degradation products was not established.

Bridges[7] made more detailed studies on the synthetic pyrethroid allethrin labeled with C^{14}. Little or no degradation was found with homogenates of housefly abdomens or thoraxes, but extensive degradation was found *in vivo*. In 5 hours, females degraded about 50% of the dose of 3.5 µg per fly, and males, about 20%. Treatment with 10 µg of the synergist piperonyl cyclonene markedly reduced degradation, e.g., to 19% in females.

Allethrin absorption by the housefly was compared with that of chlorinated hydrocarbons. Although very few experimental points were shown, low doses of allethrin (2 µg per fly) disappeared from the surface in accordance with first-order kinetics, i.e., replotting their data as log per cent remaining against time gives a roughly linear relation. The half-time was about 4.5 hours. At a higher dose (11 µg per fly), penetration was proportionately slower and was not first order. Presumably, the saturation condition was passed at this concentration (p. 172).

With DDT-resistant houseflies, Hopkins and Robbins[8] give figures for allethrin at 0.4 µg per fly which show first-order absorption for 12 hours with abrupt falling off thereafter. The half-time was 6.5 hours. Dead flies absorbed at a similar rate. The synergist piperonyl butoxide decreased absorption to a small extent, as in the case of DDT (p. 182). Excretion was rapid, and 44% was voided in 24 hours; it was somewhat inhibited by piperonyl butoxide which reduced this figure to 36%.

These authors found (as did Bridges) extensive degradation of allethrin, so that only traces of parent compound were present in the body of feces. One major metabolite was found but not identified; it was not the hydrolysis product, chrysanthemum carboxylic acid.

Piperonyl butoxide is not a botanical, but it is best known as a pyrethrin synergist. Schmidt and Dahm prepared piperonyl butoxide-C^{14} and observed its fate at a dose of 80 µg per insect in the Madeira roach.[9] If their absorption data are replotted, they are seen to follow approximately first-order kinetics, with a half-time on the order of 12 hours. Dead insects absorbed about half as much. Excretion roughly paralleled absorption but at about half the rate. Less than half the fecal radioactivity was due to piperonyl butoxide, the remainder being unidentified water-soluble products. Distribution experiments showed that the foregut contained more of the applied dose than any other tissue (2% after 2 days). Yet the brain and thoracic ganglia contained the highest concentration, about 15 µg/g, and foregut contained only 3 µg/g. This ability to concentrate in the brain may be very significant for the action of this compound.

Biosynthesized nicotine-C^{14} was used to study its metabolism in the rat and mouse.[10] In 16 hours, 94% of the 2 mg/kg dose was excreted in urine in the rat; for the mouse, 51% was excreted in urine in 6 hours. Feces were a minor outlet (2% in 6 hours for the mouse). Radioactivity in mouse tissues was measured and was high only in liver (3% of the dose after 6 hours). The nature of the metabolites was examined only in the rat urine, where 25% of the dose was as nicotine, and 69% was present as an unidentified metabolite that was not steam distillable.

2. Arsenates

One of the earliest uses of radioisotopes for insecticide study was in 1931 when Campbell and Lukens[11] used lead arsenate with radioactive lead ("thorium B") to examine excretion and solution. The dose was presented inside a leaf sandwich, kept together with starch paste. Both acid and basic lead arsenate were rapidly excreted by the silkworm *Bombyx mori*: a dose of 0.12 mg/kg was about 90% excreted in 5 hours. Of the excreted radioactivity, only about 5% was water soluble when basic lead arsenate was used, but the figure was 30% with acid lead arsenate. This difference might be an important cause of the greater toxicity of acid than of basic lead arsenate.

In 1941, radioactive arsenic was prepared by bombarding germanium in a cyclotron and was used as various salts (calcium, sodium, and lead) administered to *Bombyx*.[12] Doses of from 10 to 60 µg/g were injected into the foregut. Excretion was quite extensive, particularly between 1 and 6 hours after injection, with a sharp maximum at $3\frac{1}{2}$ hours. The extent of excretion by survivors was greatest for the lead salt, less for calcium, and least for the sodium salt (about 30%). Most of this "excretion" was undoubtedly voiding without absorption, hence the large extent for the insoluble forms. At death, the great majority of the arsenic remained in the gut. For example, after lead arsenate at a high dose (60 mg/kg), which was lethal, 55% was excreted, 33% was in the gut, 10% was regurgitated, and only 2% was in the rest of the body. However, with sodium arsenate, up to 10 times more was in the blood than with lead arsenate. There was little correlation between toxicity of the various arsenates and the concentrations of arsenic they produced in the tissues.

A study of $As_2{}^{76}O_3$ by Morrison and Oliver[13] in 1949 showed that, after injection of 10 µg into the hemocoele of larvae of the yellow mealworm *Tenebrio molitor*, the greater amount (average 64% at all times up to 20 hours) was in the "body wall"; most of the rest was in "body contents," by which was meant all but body wall and alimentary tract; and the alimentary tract therefore contained relatively little. However, in terms of concentration per unit weight of tissue, foregut was highest at first (1 hour), but by 20 hours the Malpighian tubules had the most. The other tissues were roughly equal at about one-third of the peak levels in these two tissues.

It is unfortunate that, in spite of great advances in our knowledge of the mechanism of arsenical poisoning in mammals, we know little more today about insect poisoning by this element than these early workers.

3. Fumigants

Little research has been done with radioactive fumigants. However, Bond[14] has described procedures for generating $HC^{14}N$ (from $KC^{14}N$ and phosphoric acid) by applying it to insects and measuring uptake with an ingenious micro-measuring device. A synthesis for methyl bromide-C^{14} has also been described.[15]

The labeled-pool technique was described in Chapter 5. Winteringham et al.[16] have utilized it to examine the action of the fumigant methyl bromide upon the housefly. The phosphate pool was labeled. The major finding was that the ATP levels and (under severe conditions) α-glycerophosphate were greatly reduced, as described on p. 103. However, this was apparently not caused by anoxia, for drowning the insects had far less effect on ATP. An anomaly is that, whereas the ATP effect was reversible after brief exposure to methyl bromide, the course of poisoning was not. This seems rather powerful evidence for a lack of connection between the two.

The authors attribute the ATP effect to a methylation reaction of the methyl bromide (perhaps directed to an SH group) which in some way inhibits phosphorylation. Evidence that inhibition is at the phosphorylation level is that brief exposure has no effect upon oxygen uptake, while it does reduce ATP.

4. Carbamates

No work has yet been published on the metabolism of radioactive carbamates. However, a synthesis for Sevin, 1-naphyl-N-methylcarbamate, has been described.[17]

REFERENCES

1. A. Ganz, F. E. Kelsey, and E. M. Geiling, Biosynthesis of Radioactive Nicotine, *Botan. Gaz.*, **113**: 195 (1951).
2. J. P. Pellegrini, A. C. Miller, and R. V. Sharpless, Biosynthesis of Radioactive Pyrethrins Using $C^{14}O_2$, *J. Econ. Entomol.*, **45**: 532 (1952).

3. L. W. Levy and A. Usubillaga, Experiments on Biosynthesis of Radioactive Pyre-thrins, *Inter-Am. Symp. Peaceful Appl. Nuclear Energy, Proc.*, **1**: 577 (1957).

4. L. W. Luis and R. A. Munoz, Biosynthesis of Radioactive Rotenone, *Inter-Am. Symp. Peaceful Appl. Nuclear Energy, Proc.*, **2**: 225 (1959).

5. M. M. I. Zeid, P. A. Dahm, R. E. Hein, and R. H. McFarland, Tissue Distribution, Excretion of $C^{14}O_2$ and Degradation of Radioactive Pyrethrins Administered to the American Cockroach, *J. Econ. Entomol.*, **46**: 324 (1953).

6. F. P. W. Winteringham, A. Harrison, and P. M. Bridges, Absorption and Metabolism of (^{14}C) Pyrethroids by the Adult Housefly, *Musca domestica* L, *Biochem. J.*, **61**: 359 (1955).

7. P. M. Bridges, Absorption and Metabolism of (^{14}C) Allethrin by the Adult House-fly, *Musca domestica* L, *Biochem. J.*, **66**: 316 (1957).

8. T. L. Hopkins and W. E. Robbins, The Absorption, Metabolism, and Excretion of C^{14}-Labeled Allethrin by Houseflies, *J. Econ. Entomol.*, **50**: 684 (1957).

9. C. H. Schmidt and P. A. Dahm, The Synthesis of C^{14}-Labeled Piperonyl Butoxide and Its Fate in the Madeira Roach, *J. Econ. Entomol.*, **49**: 729 (1956).

10. A. Ganz, F. E. Kelsey, and E. M. Geiling, Excretion and Tissue Distribution Studies on Radioactive Nicotine, *J. Pharmacol.*, **103**: 209 (1951).

11. F. L. Campbell and C. Lukens, A Radioactive Indicator Method for Estimating the Solubility of Acid Lead Arsenate within the Alimentary Tract of the Silkworm, *J. Econ. Entomol.*, **24**: 88 (1931).

12. L. B. Norton and R. Hansberry, Radioactive Tracer Methods for Detection of the Disposition of Arsenic in the Silkworm, *J. Econ. Entomol.*, **34**: 431 (1941).

13. F. O. Morrison and W. F. Oliver, The Distribution of Radioactive Arsenic in the Organs of Poisoned Insect Larvae, *Can. J. Res.* (D), **27**: 265 (1949).

14. E. J. Bond and F. Call, Apparatus for Treating Insects with Radioactive Fumigants, *J. Econ. Entomol.*, **54**: 808 (1961).

15. W. W. Foreman, A. Murray, and A. R. Ronzio, Microsynthesis with Tracer Ele-ments II. Methyldi-(beta-chloroethyl)-amine Hydrochloride (Nitrogen Mustard) and Methyl Bromide Labelled with C^{14}, *J. Org. Chem.*, **15**: 119 (1950).

16. F. P. W. Winteringham, G. C. Hellyer, and M. A. McKay, Effects of Methyl Bromide on Phosphorus Metabolism in the Adult Housefly, *Musca domestica* L, *Biochem. J.*, **69**: 640 (1958).

17. W. J. Skraba and F. G. Young, Radioactive Sevin (1-Naphthyl-1-carbon-14-*N*-methylcarbamate), a Convenient Synthesis, *J. Agr. Food Chem.*, **7**: 612 (1959).

AUTHOR INDEX

Numbers in parentheses are reference numbers and are included to assist in locating references when the author's name is not mentioned in the text. Numbers in italics refer to pages on which the references are listed.

A

Acree, F., 180 (12), *186*
Adamson, D. M., 45 (70), *53*
Agarwal, H. C., 91, *110*
Alexander, P., 23 (51), 39 (51), *52*
Alibert, J., 66 (62), *69*
Allen, D., 102, 103, *112*
Amand, G. S., 45 (69), *53*
Amy, R. L., 33, 43, 49 (26), *51*
Anderson, J. R., 57 (14), *67*
Anliker, R., 165 (8), *175*
Arifov, V. A., 79 (34), *81*
Arnason, A. P., 57 (14), *67*
Arnason, T. J., 49 (80), *54*, 122 (15), *129*
Arthur, B. W., 163 (1), 173 (28), *175, 176*
Artmeladze, I. D., 79 (34), *81*
Auerbach, S. I., 46 (74), 47 (75), *53*

B

Babers, F. H., 56 (4), 58 (23), *67*, 106 (65), *113*, 124 (22, 28), *130*
Bacq, Z. M., 23 (51), 39 (51), *52*
Baker, F. C., 150 (67), *160*
Baker, V. H., 24 (85), *54*, 74 (17, 20), 77 (17, 20, 27), 78 (17, 20), *80, 81*
Baldwin, E., 103 (59), *112*
Baldwin, W. F., 28 (17, 18, 19), 29, 30 (18), 31, 32 (23), 33 (23), 35 (23), 39, (20, 49), 40 (53), 41 (53, 54), *51, 52*
Ball, H. J., 137 (19), *158*
Balock, C. W., 76 (23), *80*
Banks, C. J., 59 (28), 66 (58), *68, 69*
Barnes, M. M., 59, *68*
Barnov, V. A., 79 (34), *81*
Bar-Zeev, M., 62 (43), *68*
Baxter, R. C., 33 (24), 37, *51*
Beck, S. D., 90 (15), 91 (20), *110*
Beecher, H. K., 39 (45), *52*
Beling, I., 143, *159*
Bergonie, J., 24 (2), *50*

Beriger, E., 165 (8), *175*
Beroza, M., 3 (19), *22*
Bheemeswar, B., 109, *113*
Biellman, G., 31 (21), *51*
Birukow, G., 145 (48), *159*
Bjorling, K., 59 (32), 62 (32), *68*
Blair, H. A., 38 (40), *52*
Bletchley, J. D., 75 (22), *80*
Bloch, K., 88, 89 (14), 90 (16), *110*
Block, R. J., 92 (23), 93 (25), 95 (30), *110, 111*
Blumenthal, R., 45 (67), *53*
Bodenstein, D., *21*
Bodine, J. H., 26 (9), *50*
Bond, E. J., 192, *193*
Booth, C. O., 152 (74), *160*
Bostian, C. H., 36 (34), *51*
Bourgin, R. C., 42 (16), *50*
Boxer, G. E., 104 (61), *113*
Bowen, V. T., 121 (10, 11, 13), 123 (10), *129*
Bowman, M. C., 180, *186*
Bradbury, F. R., 183 (24, 25), 184 (26, 27), *187*
Brady, V. E., 173 (28), *176*
Braemer, W., 145 (49), *159*
Brian, M. V., 59 (29), *68*
Bricteux-Grégoire, S., 99 (39, 40), 100 (44), 101 (52), *111, 112*
Bridges, P. M., 102 (57), *112*, 181 (18), *186*, 189 (6), 190, *193*
Bridges, R. G., 184, *187*
Brogle, R. C., 74 (16), 78 (16), 79 (16), *80*
Brooks, G. T., 184 (32), 185, *187*
Brown, A. W. A., 166 (15), *176*
Brownell, L. E., 77 (26), 78 (29, 30), *81*
Bruce, W. N., 181 (19), *186*
Bueding, E., 19 (16), *27*
Bugher, J. C., 57 (11), *67*
Bull, J. O., 75, *81*
Bulmer, J. J., 77 (26), *81*

195

F

Fang, S. C., 102, 103, *112*
Farber, E., 19 (16), *22*
Farinacci, C. J., 57 (8), *67*
Farner, D. S., 150 (66), *160*
Fay, R. W., 58 (18, 19), 60 (18), 62 (19), *67*
Fernandez-Moran, H., 135 (5, 10), *157, 158*
Fisher, R. C., 75 (22), *80*
Flemion, F., 65 (54, 55), *69*
Florkin, M., 97 (34), 98 (34), 99 (39), 100 (44), 101 (52), *111, 112*
Folkers, K., 89, *113*
Forel, A., 143 (33), *159*
Foreman, W. W., 192 (15), *193*
Forgash, A. J., 108 (71, 72), *113*
Forseberg, A., 34 (25), *51*
Fraenkel, G., 89 (14), *110*
Fraenkel, G. S., 140 (28), 141 (28), 142 (28), 143 (28), *158*
Fredeen, F. J. H., 57 (14), *67*
Frederickson, C. F., 58 (27), *68*
Frontali, N., 108, *113*
Fukai, H., 98 (35), 100 (35), *111*
Fukuda, T., 97, 98 (36), 99 (37, 38, 41, 43), 100 (45, 46), *111, 112*
Fukuhara, H., 87 (8), *110*
Fukuto, T. R., 166 (18, 19, 20), *176*

G

Gahan, J. B., 73 (14), *80*
Ganz, A., 189, 191 (10), *192, 193*
Gatterdam, P. E., 166 (23), *176*
Gayspitz, K. F., 150 (65), *160*
Geiling, E. M., 189 (1), 191 (10), *192, 193*
Giese, A. C., 88 (9), *110*
Gillett, J. D., 155 (96), *161*
Gilmour, D., 83 (1), 92 (1), *109*
Gjullin, C. M., 181 (21), *187*
Glass, B., 39 (46), *52*
Godwin, P. A., 58 (25), *68*, 76 (24), *81*
Goldblith, S. A., 74 (16), 78 (16), 79 (16), *80*
Goldsmith, T. H., 135 (6), 136 (14), 137, 138 (6), *157, 158*
Gorin, E., 165 (10), *175*
Grabensberger, W., 143 (36), *159*

Green, B. C., 60 (36), *68*
Grosch, D. S., 24 (65, 82, 88), 33 (62), 41 (55), 42 (55), 43 (62), 44, 45 (65), 49 (62), *52, 53, 54*
Grundmann, A. W., 62 (44), *68*
Grundy, A. V., 74 (16), 78 (16), 79 (16), *80*
Gumansky, G. A., 79 (34), *81*
Gunn, D. L., 140 (28), 141 (28), 142 (28), 143 (28), *158*
Gupta, P. D., 135 (3), 138 (3), *157*

H

Haas, V. A., 122 (17), *129*
Haddow, A. J., 154 (78, 84), 155 (96), *161*
Hahn, P. F., 122 (17), *129*
Haines, T. H., 92, 93 (25), *111*
Hall, N. S., 65 (51), *69*
Hamilton, M. A., 64, *69*
Handler, E. L., 85 (4), *110*
Hansberry, R., 191 (12), *193*
Harker, J. E., 17 (12), *21*, 153 (75), 154 (75), 155, 156, 157 (94), *160, 161*
Harrington, N. G., 48 (79), *53*
Harrison, A., 102 (55), *112*, 178 (4), 185 (34), *186, 187*, 189 (6), *193*
Hartwell, W. V., 56 (6), *67*
Harvey, G. T., 150 (68), *160*
Hassett, C. C., 23 (87), *54*, 57 (15), *67*, 74 (19), 77 (19), *80*, 122 (16), *129*
Hayaski, T., 97 (34), 98 (34), 99 (37, 38), *111*
Heath, D. F., 163 (4), *175*, 185, *187*
Heidenthal, G., 23 (84), *54*
Hein, R. E., 189 (5), *193*
Hellyer, G. C., 102 (57), 103 (58), *112*, 192 (16), *193*
Henry, S. M., 92, 93 (25, 26, 27), 95 (30), *111*
Henshaw, C. T., 25 (5), 26 (5), *50*
Henshaw, P. S., 25, 26, 49, *50*
Herbert, C. M., 57 (8), *67*
Herr, E. B., 39 (47, 52), 40 (52), *52*
Heslop, J. P., 104 (62), 105, *113*
Hilchey, J. D., 45 (65), *53*, 92 (22), 93 (26, 27), *110, 111*
Hodgson, E., 165 (9), 170, 171 (9), *175*
Hodgson, E. S., 157 (93), *161*

P

Packard, C., 23, 25, 32, 34 (1), *50*
Pappius, H. M., 128 (39), *130*
Pardi, L., 145 (47)
Paris, O. H., 147 (61), 150 (61), *160*
Pashinsky, S. Z., 79 (34), *81*
Patton, R. L., 119, *129*
Pearce, G. W., 165 (11), *175*, 178 (6), 180
  (11), *186*
Pellegrini, J. P., 189, *192*
Pendleton, R. C., 62 (44), *68*
Peng, C. T., 56 (6), *67*
Perry, A. S., 178 (5), *186*
Perry, M. M., 135 (11), *158*
Peterson, D. G., 154 (82), *161*
Philpott, D. E., 135 (6), 138 (6), *157*
Pimentel, D., 58 (19), 62 (19), *67*
Pirenne, M. H., 133 (1), *157*
Pittendrigh, C. S., 155, *161*
Plaine, H. L., 39 (46), *52*
Plapp, F. W., 166 (17, 21), 170, *176*
Pontin, A. J., 63 (46), *69*
Poulson, D. F., 121 (13), *129*
Price, G. M., 104, *113*
Pringle, J. W. S., 156, *161*
Proctor, B. E., 74 (16), 78 (16), 79 (16),
  80
Provost, M. W., 61 (40), *68*

Q

Quan, S. F., 56 (6), *67*
Quarterman, K. D., 56 (7), 57 (12), 60
  (7, 37), *67, 68*
Quastler, H., 42 (16), *50*

R

Radeleff, R. D., 57 (16), 59 (16), *67*, 124
  (27), *130*
Ramsay, J. A., 120, *129*
Ray, J., 73 (15), *80*
Ray, J. W., 104 (62), 105, *113*
Read, M. S., 78 (32), *81*
Rempel, J. G., 57 (14), *67*
Renner, M., 143 (39), 144 (40, 41), *159*
Ribbands, C. R., 66 (60), *69*
Rings, R. W., 56, *67*
Roan, C. C., 56 (4), 57 (17), 58 (23), *67*,
  106 (65), *113*, 124 (22), *130*

Robbins, W. E., 88 (11), 90 (11), 91 (17,
  18, 19), *110*, 179 (9), 182, *186*, 190,
  193
Robertson, J. D., 135 (9), *158*
Robinson, J. R., 166 (24), *176*
Rodriguez, J. G., 65 (52), *69*, 124 (26),
  130
Roeder, K. D., 125 (30), 126, *130*
Rogers, R. W., 34, 35 (27), 47 (76, 77),
  48 (27), *51, 53*
Rogers, W. I., 45 (65), *53*
Ronzio, A. R., 192 (15), *193*
Roth, A. R., 57 (9), *67*, 181 (16, 17, 20),
  183 (23), *186, 187*
Rothe, C. F., 180 (11), *186*
Rubin, M. A., 36 (37), 38 (37), *51*
Ruck, P., 139 (26), *158*

S

Sacher, G. A., 38, *52*
Sacktor, B., 19 (17), *22*
Saenger, E. L., 57 (8), *67*
Salthouse, T. N., 27 (17, 18), 29, 30 (18),
  39 (20, 49), *51, 52*
Sanborn, R. C., 95 (28), *111*
Santschi, F., 143, *158*
Sato, J., 101 (51), *112*
Scharrer, B., 157 (95), *161*
Scheer, B. T., 17 (10), *21*
Schmialek, P., 16 (6, 7), *21*
Schmidt, C. H., 62 (43), *68*, 71 (5), 72
  (5), *80*, 175 (31), *176*, 182 (22), *187*,
  190 (9), *193*
Schmid, K., 165 (8), *175*
Schonbrod, R. D., 178, 179 (7), *186*
Schoof, H. F., 59 (34), 61 (34, 38, 39, 41),
  68
Scott, C. M., 26 (10), *50*
Scott, K. G., 56 (6), *67*
Seume, F. W., 168 (25), *176*
Sharpless, R. V., 189 (2), *192*
Shchenkov, S, N., 79 (34), *81*
Shirmura, K., 98 (35), 99 (42), 100 (35,
  47, 48, 49), 101 (50), *111, 112*
Sievert, R., 34 (25), *51*
Silva, G. M., 84, 85, *109*
Sirlin, J. L., 59 (33), *68*

SUBJECT INDEX

A

Absorption, 115-121
Acanthoscelides obtectus, 74
Acetate pool, *see* Labeled-pool technique
Acethion, 164, 166, 169
Acetylcholinesterase, 17
Acronycta rumicis, 147
Action spectra, 131-132
Advantages of insects for experiments, 19-20, 23, 31
Aedes aegypti, 57, 107, 122, 175
Aedes communis, 66
Aedes quadrimaculatus, 182
Aedes sticticus, 182
Aedes taeniorhyncus, 61, 175, 182
Aedes triseriatus, 150
Aedes vexans, 182
Aging, 37-38
Alanine utilization, 100, 101
Aldrin metabolism, 184-185
Allethrin,
    absorption, 190
    metabolism, 189-190
Almond moth, *see Ephestia cautella*
Alpha radiation, 34, 47
Alpha-glycerophosphate, 103, 104, 105
Alternative metabolic pathways, 167
    concentration dependence, 170-171
Amblyomma americana, 57
Amblyomma maculatum, 173
American cockroach, *see Periplaneta americana*
Ametabola, 4
Amino acid absorption, 117-120
Amino acid metabolism, 92-102, 105
    see also Essential amino acids and individual amino acids
γ-Aminobutyrate, 105, 108
Anagasta kühniella, 11, 15, 38, 39, 40, 42, 73, 75, 141
Anasa tristis, 107, 129
Anatomy of insects, 6-8
Anax imperator, 147-9
Anax junius,
    eyes, structure of, 138

Angoumois grain moth, *see Sitotraga cerealella*
Anobium punctatum, 75
Anopheles gambiae, 184
Anopheles quadrimaculatus, 73, 175
Anorexia from radiation, 44
Anthereae pernyi,
    diapause in, 147-8, 150
Anthonomus grandis, 56, 173
Ants,
    role as aphid nurses, 66
Aphids,
    polymorphism in, 150-2
Aphis fabae, 66, 152
Apis mellifera, 23, 66, 108, 136, 173
Apterygota, 4
Arctia caja, 59
Arginine phosphate, 104, 105
Armigerea obturbans, 63
Arsenates, 191-192
Arsenic oxide, uptake, 191
Arthropodin, 12
Australian cockroach, *see Periplaneta australasiae*
Autoradiography, 173

B

Banded woolybear, *see Isia isabella*
Barathra brassicae, 148
Barium, 121, 123
Bean aphid, *see Aphis fabae*
Bean weevil, *see Acanthoscelides obtectus*
Bed bug, *see Cimex lectularius*
Beetle roach, *see Diploptera punctata*
Beneficial effects of radiation, 43-44
"Benzene hexachloride", 183-184
    in foods, 184
    metabolism and resistance, 183-184
    uptake, 183
Bergonie-Tribondeau "law", 24
Biological clocks, 155
Biosynthesis of botanicals, 189
Black blow fly, *see Phormia regina*
Blatella germanica, 90, 92, 95, 121, 124, 137, 168, 170, 174
Blatta orientalis, 92

203

selectivity, 172, 181
solubility, 180
uptake from solution, 181-182
DDT resistance,
absorption and, 181
dehydrochlorination, 178
glutathione synthesis, 95
P³² incorporation, 106
thiol involvement, 95
DDVP, 164, 165, 170, 171
Death-watch beetle, *see Xestobium rufoviolosum*
Definition of insects, 1
Deformations after irradiation, 27
Demeton, 164
Dendroctonus pseudotsugae, 102-103
Dendrolimus pini, 150
Dermestes maculatus, 89
Desalkylation, 167, 171
Desert locust, *see Schistocerca gregaria*
Desheathing, 126, 127
Desulfuration, 166
Diapause, 15, 146-151
control of, 16-17
cytochrome c in, 17
definition, 146
hormones and, 150-1
photoperiod, induction of, 147
photoperiod, termination of, 150
protein synthesis during, 101
Diazinon, 164, 166, 169, 173
p,p-Dichlorobenzophenone, 177
Dieldrin metabolism, 185-186
Differential grasshopper, *see Melanoplus differentialis*
Digestion, 115-121
Dimethoate, 163-164, 166, 169-70, 174, 175, 182
Diploptera punctata, 92
Disease vectors, 61, 64-65
Dispersal of insects, 60-63
Distribution in insects, of DDT, 179
Disyston, 164, 166
Diurnal rhythms,
see Rhythms
Domestic fruit fly, *see Drosophila melanogaster*
Dorsal light reaction, 143
Dose and penetration rate, 174

Dose-effect relationships, 31-33
Douglas-fir beetle, *see Dendroctonus pseudotsugae*
Drosophila azteca, 39
Drosophila gibberosa, 106
Drosophila melanogaster, 11, 23, 25, 26, 27, 32, 33, 34, 36, 37, 38, 39, 41, 42, 43, 49, 59, 62, 87, 122, 123, 124, 137, 177
Drosophila repleta, 62, 121
Drosophila robusta, 155-6
Drosophila subobscura, 155
Drowning, 104
Dyes, for double tagging of insects, 58

E

Ecdysis, 9
Ecdysone, 15
Ectohormones, *see* Pheromones
Eggs of insects, 9, 11
Elemental turnover, 123-124
Embden-Meyerhof pathway, 83-85
Endocuticle, 12
Endogenous irradiation, 49-50
Endopterygota, 4
Ephestia cautella, 75, 76
Epicuticle, 12
Epidermal cells,
ecdysone, effects on, 15
Epilachna varivestis, 92
EPN, 164, 168
Epoxidation, 184-185
Ergosterol, 90
Eristalis tenax,
light, behavior to, 141
Essential amino acids, 96-97
Euchaetias egle, 107
European cornborer, *see Pyrausta nubilalis*
Eurycotis floridana, 92
Evolution and diversification of insects, 3, 4
Exopterygota, 4

F

Farnesol, 16, 18
Fat absorption, 118-119
Fat metabolism, 88
Feeding studies, 63-66
Fibroin, *see* Silk production
Firebrat, *see Thermobia domestica*
Fixation of CO_2, 87
Flat grain beetle, *see Laemophloeus pusillus*

Flight muscles,
  glycolysis in, 19
Florida cockroach, *see Eurycotis floridana*
Florida harvester ant, *see Pogonomyrmex badius*
Flour mite, *see Tyroglyphus farinae*
Food transfer between insects, 66
Formate metabolism, 108-109
Formica rufa, 146
Formica sanguina puberula, 62
Fractionation of radiation, 35, 76
Fructose absorption, 117
  excretion, 120
Fumigants, 192
Fumigation, comparison with irradiation, 79
Furniture beetle, *see Anobium punctatum*

G

Galleria melonella, 15, 121
Gamma-aminobutyrate, 105, 108
Ganglion, ion permeability, 126
Gay harlequin, *see Euchaetias egle*
Genome number, 36-37
Geotrupes silvaticus,
  time sense of, 145
German cockroach, *see Blatella germanica*
Glucose,
  conversion to trehalose, 85, 87, 117, 128
  excretion, 120
  penetration of nerve cord, 128
  uptake in gut, 115-117
  uptake by Malpighian tubules, 120
  utilization, 83-86
Glutamate, 108
Glycine absorption, 117-118
  utilization, 98-99, 100, 101, 108
Glycolysis, 19
Granary weevil, *see Sitophilus granarius*
Graptolitha molesta, 147-8
Greater wax moth, *see Galleria melonella*
Green meadow locust, *see Chortophaga viridifasciata*
Green peach aphid, *see Myzus persicae*
Growth,
  effect of light on, 137
  neuroendocrine control, 13-18
Gulf coast tick, *see Amblyomma maculatum*
Gut absorption, *see Absorption*

H

H³, *see Tritium*
Harlequin bug, *see Murgantia histrionica*
Harrisina brillians, 147
Heat sensitivity, 40-41
Hemimetabola, 4
Hexachlorocyclohexane, *see "Benzene hexachloride"*
Hide beetle, *see Dermestes maculatus*
Hippelates collusor, 137
Holometabola, 4
Honey bee, *see Apis mellifera*
Honey transfer between insects, 66
Hormones,
  control of rhythm, 156
  diapause and, 150-1
  nervous system and, 150-1
House fly, *see Musca domestica*
Hyalophora cecropia, 15, 97, 101, 150

I

Indian-meal moth, *see Plodia interpunctella*
Injury, effect on protein synthesis, 101
Inorganics, uptake of, 121-123
Insects,
  anatomy of, 6-8
  behavior, chemical factors controlling, 3
  classification, 4-5
  color vision in, 135-8
  definition, 1
  determination of adult characters, 11
  diapause in, 146-51
  dominance of, 1-4
  egg structure, 9
  eggs, types of, 11
  embryonic development, 9-11
  evolution and diversification, 3, 4
  experimentation with, 19-20, 23, 31
  fertilization, 9
  hormones and nervous system, 150-1
  immature forms, 4
  integument of, 12-13
  light, effects on, 131-157
  light, responses of, 139-146
  metamorphosis, 4, 11
  nervous system, 3, 7-8, 13-14
  nervous system and hormones, 150-1
  neuroendocrine systems in, 13-18

T

Tagging insects,
  advantages of radioisotopes, 55
  comparison of radioisotopes, 56
  methods, 57-60
  toxicity problem, 56-57, 58
Tagging large animals, 59
Tagging parasites, 62-63
Tagging plants, 59, 62, 64, 65
Talitrus saltator, 145
Tarnished plant bug, *see Lygus lineolaris*
Taxis,
  definition, 140
Tectocuticle, 12
Temperature and DDT uptake, 183
Tenebrio molitor, 16, 40, 92, 119, 121, 129, 191
Termite, *see Calotermes flavicollis*
Tetrahydrobiopterins, 137-8
Tetranychus telarius, 65, 84, 124, 147
Thermobia domestica, 122
Thimet, 164, 166
Thioethers, 166
Thiol compounds and DDT resistance, 95
Thiolo-dieldrin, 185
Thiouracil, 107
Thyroxine, 106-107
Time sense, 144
Tissue cultures, 48
Tonofibrillae, 12
Toxicity of irradiated food, 78
Transamination, 99
Trehalose, 19
  formation, 85, 87
Tribolium castaneum, 45, 75
Tribolium confusum, 23, 24, 43, 44, 74, 75, 76
Tricarboxylic acid cycle, 86
Tritium, labeling with, 165
Trogoderma granarium, 35, 75
Trogoderma sternale, 47
Trogoderma versicolor, 107

Tropism,
  definition, 140
Tsetse fly, 73
Two-spotted spider mite, *see Tetranychus telarius*
Tyroglyphus farinae, 44
Tyrosine, 106

U

Ultraviolet radiation, 47
Uptake of insecticides from solution, 175, 181
Urea excretion, 120
Uric acid formation, 109

V

Vanessa urticae, 142
Velia currens, 145
Ventriculus, absorption from, 116
Vespa crabro, 121
Vespa maculata, 121
Virus vectors, 64-65
Visual pigment,
  absorption spectrum of, 137
Vitamin A_1, 136-7
Vitellophages, 9-10

W

Water intake, 65
White-pine weevil, *see Pissodes strobi*
Wilzbach technique, 165
Wireworm, *see Melanotus communis*

X

Xestobium rufoviolosum, 75

Y

Yellow-fever mosquito, *see Aedes aegypti*
Yellow mealworm, *see Tenebrio molitor*
Yttrium, 123

Z

"Zeitgedächtnis," 143-6